P9-DIW-759

Test Bank

Raymond X. Williams
Howard University

to accompany

CHEMISTRY
Matter and Its Changes
Third Edition

James E. Brady
St. John's University, New York

Joel W. Russell
Oakland University, Michigan

John R. Holum
Augsburg College (Emeritus), Minnesota

John Wiley & Sons, Inc.
New York / Chichester / Weinheim / Brisbane / Singapore / Toronto

To order books or for customer service call 1-800-CALL-WILEY (225-5945).

Copyright © 2000 by John Wiley & Sons, Inc.

Excerpts from this work may be reproduced by instructors for distribution on a not-for-profit basis for testing or instructional purposes only to students enrolled in courses for which the textbook has been adopted. *Any other reproduction or translation of this work beyond that permitted by Sections 107 or 108 of the 1976 United States Copyright Act without the permission of the copyright owner is unlawful. Requests for permission or further information should be addressed to the Permissions Department, John Wiley & Sons, Inc., 605 Third Avenue, New York, NY 10158-0012.*

ISBN 0-471-35859-2

Printed in the United States of America

10 9 8 7 6 5 4 3 2 1

Printed and bound by Victor Graphics, Inc.

CONTENTS

Chapter 1   Fundamentals of Chemical Change

Multiple Choice

1.   A characteristic which distinguishes between a true science and a pseudoscience is:

      a. one deals with quantitative information only, while the other deals with qualitative information only
      b. one deals with natural phenomena, while the other deals with artificial phenomena
!   c. one deals with reproducible observations, while the other does not
      d. one deals with scientific facts, while the other deals with empirical facts
      e. one is developed in academic research laboratories, while the other is developed in non-academic laboratories

2.   A broad generalization based on many observations of relations between various pieces of observed data associated with natural phenomena that is broadly applicable to such data is called

      a. the scientific method
!   b. a scientific law
      c. a scientific theory
      d. a hypothesis
      e. an empirical fact

3.   A theoretical model developed to explain relations between various pieces of observed data associated with natural phenomena is called

      a. the scientific method
      b. a scientific law
      c. a scientific theory
!   d. a hypothesis
      e. an empirical fact

4.   Complete the following sentence. A scientific law is:

!   a. a statement describing a reproducible relationship between phenomena
      b. a tentative explanation for a set of observations that can be tested by further experimentation
      c. a tested explanation that explains a body of facts and relations
      d. a model used to visualize the invisible
      e. an absolutely correct explanation of a scientific principle to which no exception can be found

5. Which one of the following does not involve a chemical change?

    a. a fish that is left for some time in an unrefrigerated place decomposes
    b. apple juice which is left in an open bottle ferments
    c. a loaf of bread rises and its volume expands when it is baked in an oven
    ! d. when a lake starts to freeze in winter, ice is formed on the surface
    e. when sugar is fermented under certain conditions, alcohol is produced

6. Which one of the following is a physical change?

    a. when ignited with a match in open air, paper burns
    ! b. in cold weather, water condenses on the inside surface of single pane windows
    c. when treated with bleach, some dyed fabrics change color
    d. when heated strongly, sugar turns dark brown
    e. grape juice left in an open unrefrigerated container turns sour

7. Which one of the following is a chemical change?

    ! a. when blood is washed with 3% hydrogen peroxide solution, it changes color
    b. when water is boiled, it forms steam
    c. when a solid stick of butter is heated, it becomes a liquid
    d. when blue paint is mixed with yellow paint, a green color is obtained
    f. when a bar of gold metal is pounded with a hammer, it flattens out

8. Which one of the following properties is a chemical property?

    ! a. combustibility
    b. volatility
    c. viscosity
    d. malleability
    e. ductility

9. Which one of the following is an extensive property of matter?

    a. density
    b. specific gravity
    c. electrical conductivity
    d. refractive index
    ! e. mass

10. Which one of the following is an SI base unit?

    a. dyne
    b. newton
    c. milliliter
    ! d. ampere
    e. joule

11. The kilo is
    a. a unit of mass
    b. a unit employed in medical terminology
  ! c. a decimal multiplier in the metric system
    d. a unit of speed
    e. a volume unit employed by the DEA (drug enforcement agency)

12. The SI base units of temperature and mass respectively are

    a. degree and gram
  ! b. kelvin and kilogram
    c. celsius and milligram
    d. °K and kilogram
    e. kelvin and gram

13. The device used for measuring mass accurately is

  ! a. analytical balance
    b. ballistic galvanometer
    c. scale
    d. buret
    e. dynamometer

14. Which one of the following is not a unit of surface area?

  ! a. gigabyte
    b. acre
    c. square mile
    d. dm^2
    e. square yard

15. The boiling point of barium is 725 °C. Determine the equivalent value in °F

    a. 435 °F
  ! b. 1337 °F
    c. 1247 °F
    d. 1362 °F
    e. 1273 °F

16. The melting point of antimony is listed in one handbook as 630.74 °C. Determine the equivalent value in °F

    a. 382.41 °F
    b. 1103.3 °F
    c. 1077.7 °F
  ! d. 1167.3 °F
    e. 1192.9 °F

17. On a day in the summer of 1992, the temperature fell from 98 °F to 75° F in just three hours. The temperature drop expressed in celsius degrees (C°) was

   ! a. 13 C°
      b. 41 C°
      c. 45 C°
      d.   9 C°
      e. 75 C°

18. On a day in the summer of 1976, the temperature fell from 95 °F to 75 ° F in just three hours. The temperature drop expressed in celsius degrees (C°) was

   ! a. 11 C°
      b. 13 C°
      c. 18 C°
      d. 20 C°
      e. -12 C°

19. The melting point of antimony was listed in one handbook as 1167.3 °F. Expressed in kelvins this temperature would be

      a. 357.6 K
      b. 496.8 K
      c. 583.7 K
      d. 894.2 K
   ! e. 903.9 K

20. The melting point of lead acetate, a white solid, is 280 °C. Determine the melting point of this compound in units of °F

      a. 446 °F
      b. 472 °F
      c. 504 °F
   ! d. 536 °F
      e. 562 °F

21. The boiling point of chlorine is -34.6 °C. This temperature expressed in kelvins is

      a. -30.3 K
      b. 177.4 K
   ! c. 238.6 K
      d. 243.0 K
      e. 307.6 K

22. A special alloy melts at 601 °C. What is this temperature in °F?

        a.   302 °F
        b.   365 °F
        c. 1050 °F
        d. 1082 °F
 ! e. 1114 °F

23. The boiling point of carbonyl selenide is –21.7 °C. What is this temperature in °F?

 ! a. - 7.1 °F
      b. - 44.1 °F
      c. - 96.7 °F
      d.   0.00 °F
      e. +18.5 °F

24. The highest temperature recorded in the athletic field house when the cooling units were being replaced and upgraded was 122.0 °F. Express this in °C.

 ! a.   50.0 °C
      b.   64.4 °C
      c.   67.8 °C
      d. 162.0 °C
      e. 219.6 °C

25. An electronic scale used in the mailroom is calibrated (and displays) in tenths of a kilogram from 1 to 140 kg. Determine how many significant figures should be used to express the mass of anyone using the scale whose mass is between 80.2 and 83.5 kg.

 ! a. 3
     b. 5
     c. 4
     d. 2
     e. 1

26. Which response gives the correct number of significant figures for all three of the following measurements?   #1) 7.103 cm   #2) 0.00005 inch   #3) 1.3400×10^{-4} dm^3

     a. 3, 5, and 4
     b. 3, 1, and 3
     c. 4, 1, and 3
 ! d. 4, 1, and 5
     e. 4, 5, and 5

27. After evaluating the expression,

$$\frac{13.726 + 0.027}{8.221}$$

how many significant figures should be displayed in the result?

     a. 1
     b. 2
     c. 3
!   d. 4
     e. 5

28. How many significant figures should there be in result of the operation, 8.5201 + 1.93?

     a. 1
     b. 2
     c. 3
!   d. 4
     e. 5

29. When the expression, 412.272 + 0.00031 - 1.00797 + 0.000024 + 12.8, is evaluated, the result should be expressed as

     a. 424
     b. 424.0
!   c. 424.1
     d. 424.06
     e. 424.064364

30. When the expression, 16.0200 + 0.00048 - 11.184 - 221.1, is evaluated, the result should be expressed as

!   a. -216.3
     b. -216.26
     c. -216.2635
     d. -216.26352
     e. -2.2×10^2

31. One radio station operates on an assigned frequency of 96.3 megahertz while another one operates on an assigned frequency of 1280 kilohertz. What is the ratio of the larger to the smaller value?

     a. 13.3
     b. 13.29
!   c. 75.2
     d. 75.23
     e. 13.2918

32. When a student evaluates the expression,

$$\frac{0.04616 \times 0.082057 \times 293.30}{0.654}$$

the result should be expressed as

    a. 1.69
! b. 1.70
    c. 1.699
    d. 1.6987
    e. 1.69870

33. When a student evaluates the expression

$$\frac{4.268 \times 0.082057 \times 373.15}{\frac{744.6}{760.0} \times 2.688}$$

the result should be expressed as

    a. 49.623
    b. 49.631
! c. 49.62
    d. 49.63
    e. 49.623202

34. One radio station operates on an assigned frequency of 88.1 megahertz while another one operates on an assigned frequency of 1460 kilohertz. What is the ratio of the larger to the smaller value?

    a. 16.5
    b. 16.57
    c. 16.57208
! d. 60.3
    e. 60.342

35. The SI prefixes giga and micro represent, respectively:

! a. 10^9 and 10^{-6}
    b. 10^{-9} and 10^{-6}
    c. 10^6 and 10^{-3}
    d. 10^3 and 10^{-3}
    e. 10^{-9} and 10^{-3}

36. The SI prefixes mega and nano represent, respectively:

      a. 10^9 and 10^{-6}
      b. 10^{-6} and 10^9
 ! c. 10^6 and 10^{-9}
      d. 10^6 and 10^9
      e. 10^{-6} and 10^{-9}

37. A distance of 18×10^{-3} meters is numerically equivalent to

      a. 1.8 micrometers
      b. 1.8 millimeters
      c. 0.18 meters
 ! d. 1.8 centimeters
      e. 18 kilometers

38. The diameter of an atom was determined and a value of 2.35×10^{-8} cm was obtained. How many nanometers is this?

      a. 2.35×10^1 nm
      b. 2.35×10^{-19} nm
      c. 2.35×10^{-15} nm
 ! d. 2.35×10^{-1} nm
      e. 2.35×10^{-10} nm

39. How many micrometers are there in 3.672 km?

      a. 3.672×10^6
      b. 2.723×10^{-7}
      c. 2.723×10^{-4}
 ! d. 3.672×10^9
      e. 3.672×10^3

40. How many mm (millimeters) are there in 6.3 km?

      a. 6.3×10^{-5} mm
      b. 6300 mm
      c. 6.3×10^4 mm
      d. 6.3×10^5 mm
 ! e. 6.3×10^6 mm

41. How many cm^3 are there in 0.00424 dm^3?

      a. 0.0424 cm^3
      b. 0.424 cm^3
 ! c. 4.24 cm^3
      d. 0.00000424 cm^3
      e. 424 cm^3

42. How many cubic inches are in 1.00 dm³? 1 in = 2.54 cm.

   ! a. 61.0 in³
      b. 155 in³
      c. 394 in³
      d. 1.64×10^4 in³
      e. 383×10^2 in³

43. The average distance from the earth to the sun is 9.30×10^7 miles. Light travels at a speed of 3.00×10^8 meters per second. If the sun were to be suddenly extinguished, how long would it take for the effect to be visible here on the earth?

      a. 8.31 seconds
      b. 5.38 minutes
      c. 0.499 seconds
   ! d. 8.31 minutes
      e. 0.310 seconds

44. Which one of the following represents the smallest distance?

   ! a. 4.5 mm
      b. 0.20 inch
      c. 0.83 cm
      d. 0.73 m
      e. 0.30 yard

45. How many square meters are there in a rectangular piece of carpet which measures 12.0 feet by 22.0 feet? 1 m = 39.37 in, 1 ft = 12 in.

   ! a. 24.5 m²
      b. 28.4 m²
      c. 866 m²
      d. 80.5 m²
      e. 966 m²

46. How many square meters of floor space are there in a room which has 225.0 square yards of floor space? 1 m = 39.37 in, 1 yard = 36 in.

   ! a. 188.1 square meters
      b. 269.0 square meters
      c. 246.0 square meters
      d. 205.7 square meters
      e. 172.0 square meters

47. If a car has an EPA mileage rating of 30 miles per gallon, what is this rating in km L^{-1}? 1 liter = 1 dm^3, 1 gallon = 3.785 liter, 1 mile = 1.609 meter.

    ! a. 13 km L^{-1}
    b. 200 km L^{-1}
    c. 180 km L^{-1}
    d. 70 km L^{-1}
    e. 11 km L^{-1}

48. The number, 0.0030600, is properly expressed in scientific notation as

    a. 3.0600×10^{-2}
    b. 0.30600×10^{-2}
    c. 0.306×10^{-2}
    d. 3.06×10^{-3}
    ! e. 3.0600×10^{-3}

49. The number, 0.02100, is properly expressed in scientific notation as

    a. 0.21×10^{-1}
    b. 2.1×10^{-2}
    ! c. 2.100×10^{-2}
    d. 21.0×10^{-3}
    e. 2.10×10^{-2}

50. An empty volumetric flask, weighing 60.42 grams, weighed 309.60 grams when filled with water. After emptying the water and drying the flask, it was filled with ethylene glycol. It now weighed 338.72 grams. What is the specific gravity of the ethylene glycol?

    a. 0.8048
    b. 0.9140
    c. 1.094
    ! d. 1.1169
    e. 1.2424

51. An empty volumetric flask, weighing 27.16 grams, has a volume of 100.4 cm^3. How much would it weigh when it filled with bromine (a liquid element) which has a density of 3.1028 g cm^{-3}?

    a. 59.51 g
    b. 284.4 g
    c. 311.5 g
    ! d. 338.7 g
    e. 395.8 g

52. How many cm^3 of water will overflow from a full container of water if a 52.5 gram sample of nickel (density = 8.90 g cm^{-3}) is carefully placed in the container so there is no splashing, just overflowing?

       a. 467 cm^3
       b. 0.170 cm^3
!   c. 5.90 cm^3
       d. 43.6 cm^3
       e. 61.4 cm^3

53. How many cm^3 of water will overflow from a full container of water if a 66.7 gram sample of vanadium (density = 6.11 g cm^{-3}) is carefully placed in the container so there is no splashing, just overflowing?

       a. 11.9 cm^3
       b. 9.92 cm^3
       c. 60.6 cm^3
!   d. 10.9 cm^3
       e. 0.0916 cm^3

54. A sample of zinc metal (density = 7.14 g cm^{-3}) was submerged in a graduated cylinder containing water. The water level rose from 162.5 cm^3 to 186.0 cm^3 when the sample was submerged. How many grams did the sample weigh?

!   a. 168 g
       b. 22.7 g
       c. 26.1 g
       d. 48.8 g
       e. 3.29 g

55. A sample of an alloy (density = 9.62 g cm^{-3}) was submerged in a graduated cylinder containing water. The water level rose from 166.5 cm^3 to 182.0 cm^3 when the sample was submerged. How many grams did the sample weigh?

       a. 0.621 g
       b. 175 g
       c. 18.9 g
       d. 17.8 g
!   e. 149 g

56. A compound, once named "Isooctane" and used as a fuel in gasoline engines because it had an antiknock octane rating of 100, has a density of 0.6919 g cm^{-3}. How many pounds would 20.4 gallons of this fuel (a typical full tank) weigh? 1 gallon = 3785 cm^3 = 4 quart; 1 pound = 453.6 g

       a. 77.2 pounds
       b. 246 pounds
!   c. 118 pounds
       d. 24.2 pounds
       e. 50.6 pounds

57. Mercury, which has a density of 13.595 g cm^{-3}, is usually stored in iron vessels for shipment. Typically, these vessels have a capacity of 2.60 liters. How many pounds of mercury would a filled container hold? 1 pound = 0.4536 kg, 1 liter = 1 dm^3.

   ! a. 77.9 pounds
      b. 86.7 pounds
      c. 11.5 pounds
      d. 16.0 pounds
      e. 42.6 pounds

58. Iron has a density of 7.86 g cm^{-3}. How many pounds does a block of iron with a volume of 1.65 cubic feet weigh? 1 pound = 0.4536 kg.

   ! a. 810 pounds
      b. 0.871 pounds
      c. 871 pounds
      d. 491 pounds
      e. 3.01 pounds

59. Gold has a density of 19.3 g cm^{-3}. How many pounds does a gold sphere

$$volume = \frac{4}{3}(\pi r^3)$$

weigh if it has a diameter of 5.20 inches? 1 pound = 0.4536 kg.

      a. 16.3 pounds
      b. 19.7 pounds
   ! c. 51.3 pounds
      d. 63.7 pounds
      e. 411 pounds

60. A spherical cannon ball which has a volume given by

$$volume = \frac{4}{3}(\pi r^3)$$

is made of an iron alloy and has a diameter of 9.55 inches and a density of 7.89 g cm^{-3}. How many pounds does this cannon ball weigh? 1 pound = 0.4536 kg.

      a. 59.0 pounds
   ! b. 130 pounds
      c. 41.4 pounds
      d. 124 pounds
      e. 21.0 pounds

61. Iridium has a density of 22.65 g cm^{-3}. The vice president for research and development has an iridium figurine on his desk which weighs 11.50 pounds. What is its volume, in cubic inches? 1 pound = 0.4536 kg, 1 inch = 2.54 cm exactly.

      a. 5.533 cubic inches
      b. 9.410 cubic inches
!   c. 14.05 cubic inches
      d. 35.70 cubic inches
      e. 90.67 cubic inches

62. The metric equivalent of the popular 55 gallon drum has a volume of 0.200 cubic meters. One such drum was filled with a colorless liquid, Sukanol, which has a density of 1.168 g cm^{-3}. How many kg should this quantity of Sukanol weigh? 1 inch = 2.54 cm, exactly.

      a. 24.3 kg
!   b. 234 kg
      c. 243 kg
      d. 2.34 x 10^5 kg
      e. 500 kg

63. A coastal patrol boat which weighed 35.6 metric tons (1 metric ton = 1000 kg) was traveling at a speed of 15.0 knots (1 knot = 1.852 km hr^{-1}) when, due to navigational error, it collided with a very bulky submerged object. For the record (and the court of inquiry) how much kinetic energy did the boat possess prior to the impact?

      a. 1.37 x 10^{13} joules
!   b. 1.06 x 10^3 kilojoules
      c. 1.06 newtons
      d. 13.7 megajoules
      e. 17.8 kilojoules

64. A flatbed truck loaded with cinder blocks had a gross weight of 65.2 tons at the last weigh station. It lost its brakes and went off a curve on the interstate highway at a speed of 76.5 miles per hour, crashing into a bridge abutment. Calculate the kinetic energy possessed by the truck, in megajoules, prior to the impact. 1 pound = 0.4536 kg = 5.000 x 10^{-4} ton, 1 mile = 1.609 km.

      a. 0.191 megajoules
      b. 13.4 megajoules
!   c. 34.6 megajoules
      d. 64.9 megajoules
      e. 168 megajoules

65. The density of iron is 7.86 g cm^{-3}. What is the mass (in kg) of 20.00 cubic inches of iron? 1 inch = 2.54 cm, exactly.

      a. 6.46 x 10^{-3} kg
      b. 4.17 x 10^{-2} kg
      c. 0.393 kg
      d. 2.54 kg
  ! e. 2.58 kg

Fill in the Blanks

66. How many significant figures does the number 30.340 contain? _____ (! 5)

67. What will be the cost, in dollars, of gasoline for a 3170 mile trip in a car pulling a trailer that delivers 13.30 miles per gallon, if the average price of gas is $1.449 cents per gallon? _____
(! $345.36--$345.40)

68. What will be the cost of gasoline for a 4710 mile automobile trip if the car delivers 27.35 miles per gallon of gasoline, and the average price of gas is $1.249 per gallon? _____ (! $215.10)

69. A kilometer is _____ times as long as a centimeter. (! 10^{+5})

70. Carbon tetrachloride, a colorless liquid, has a density of 1.5867 g cm^{-3} at 25.0 °C and a freezing point of -22.9 °C, while water has a density of 0.99704 g cm^{-3} at 25.0 °C and a freezing point of 0.00 °C What is the specific gravity of carbon tetrachloride? _____ (! 1.5914)

71. A 201 g sample weighs _____ mg. (! 2.01 x 10^5 mg)

72. A spot on a microchip which is 7500 nm (nanometers) in diameter is _____ pm (picometers) in diameter. (! 7.500 x 10^6 pm)

73. An object weighing 450 kg, expressed in megagrams (Mg), is _____ Mg. (! 0.450 Mg)

74. Many home freezers maintain a temperature of 0.0 °F. Express this temperature in °C. _____
(! -17.8 °C)

75. How many significant digits are there in the number 1.050 x 10^9? _____ (! 4)

76. Express the result of the operation, 8.520 + 2.7, to the proper number of significant digits.
_____ (! 11.2)

True and False

77. Chemistry is a physical science which deals with the forces which affect matter, and the relative strengths of these forces. (! F)

78. The chemical makeup of ice is somewhat different from that of water. (! F)

79. Scientific theories which do not require testing by observation are called hypotheses. (! F)

80. A sample of each of the seven base units in the SI system of measurement is kept by the French Academy of Sciences in a special temperature controlled room. (! F)

81. The international standard meter is preserved on a platinum alloy bar kept at the National Institute of Standards and Technology (NIST) in Gaithersburg, Maryland near Washington, DC. (! F)

82. The international standard 1-kilogram mass sample is kept at the United Nations Office of Standards in New York City. (! F)

83. A large crowd attending a bicentennial celebration in a metropolitan area was described as 450,000 in the morning newspaper the next day. A chemistry student stated that, mindful of the purpose of using scientific notation, this should be correctly expressed in scientific notation as 4.50000×10^5. Does the number expressed this way truly represent the crowd estimate, true or false? (! F)

84. Any number known accurately to six or more significant digits is defined as an exact number. (! F)

85. In determining the number of significant digits in the result of a calculation, exact numbers are considered as having a value to six significant digits. (! F)

86. The ambiguity in the precision of a number being expressed can be eliminated by proper use of scientific notation. (! T)

87. The result of the following operation, 8.52010×7.9, should be expressed as 67.3088. (! F)

88. A 15 km distance run is a shorter run than a 10 mile distance run. (! T)

89. A 5.00 pound bag of sugar weighs more than a 2.50 kg bag of sugar. (! F)

90. A piece of carpet which measures 44.0 square yards is smaller that a piece of carpet which measures 44.0 square meters. (! T)

91. A liter of carbon tetrachloride is a smaller quantity than a quart of the same substance. (! F)

92. An increase of one kelvin in temperature is a smaller change than an increase of one degree Fahrenheit. (! F)

93. Since the large ocean going container vessel (200,000 tons) was drifting at just 1.5 miles per hour on the tide when it struck the bridge pylon, it possessed less kinetic energy than the 4500 pound speedboat which struck the same pylon last year while going 48.5 miles per hour. 1 pound = 0.4536 kg = 5.000×10^{-4} ton, 1 mile = 1.609 km. (! F)

94. Intensive properties of matter depend on only one property, color. (! F)

95. Specific gravity equals (mass/volume) divided by time. (! F)

Critical Thinking

96. Given this data from lab, for mass and then the volume of water displaced in a graduated cylinder by introduction of a metal sample to the cylinder.

$$\text{Mass of weighing cup} = 0.452 \text{ g.}$$
$$\text{Mass of weighing cup} + \text{metal sample} = 72.943 \text{ g.}$$
$$\text{Volume of water in cylinder} = 15.2 \text{ cm}^3.$$

Introduction of the metal sample causes the water above the submerged metal sample to rise to the 19.0 cm^3 mark. What is the density of the metal?

      a. 2.15 g cm^{-3}
      b. 3.84 g cm^{-3}
      c. 4.80 g cm^{-3}
 ! d. 19.0 g cm^{-3}
      e. 19.2 g cm^{-3}

97. A spherical cannonball made of an iron alloy has a specific gravity of 7.88, and weighs 22.12 pounds. It has a diameter of 13.46 cm. On the other hand, spent uranium (from processing which removes the commercially important rare isotope) has a specific gravity of 19.05. How many pounds would a uranium cannonball of the same dimensions as the iron cannonball weigh? _____ (! 53.5 pounds)

98. A spherical cannonball made of an iron alloy has a density of 7.86 g cm^{-3}, and weighs 22.12 pounds. On the other hand, spent uranium (from processing which removes the commercially important rare isotope) has a density of 19.05 g cm^{-3}. What would be the diameter, in cm, of a uranium round shot which has exactly twice the weight as the iron ball described above? 1 pound = 0.4536 kg. _____ (! 12.62 cm)

99. Some students in the AP chemistry class have come up with an idea they would like to have tested which involves collaboration with two or three DOD facilities. They want to test two small muzzle loading cannon like the ones used in the 18th century. One would be using spherical cannonballs made of iron, while the other using spherical cannonballs made of spent uranium. Both cannon will be using cannonballs with a diameter of 5.000 inches. If uranium has a density of 19.05 g cm^{-3}, what would be the mass, in pounds, of the uranium cannonballs? 1 pound = 453.6 g, 1 inch = 2.54 cm exactly. _____ (! 45.04 pounds)

100. If 1 meter = 39.37 inch and 1 foot = 12.00 inch, calculate a conversion factor to four significant digits, which will convert cubic feet into cubic meters directly. 1 ft^3 = _____ m^3? (! 0.2832)

101. A young high school student has invented a new temperature scale, the Zuban scale (his last name, of course). In common with the Kelvin, Celsius, and Fahrenheit scales, it is a linear scale. According to Zuban,

   1) the boiling point of water which is 100.00 °C = 373.15 K = 0.00 °Z
   2) the boiling point of sulfur which is 444.60 °C = 717.75 K = 250.00 °Z
   3) the melting point of silver which is 960.15 °C = 1233.30 K = 624.02 °Z

Calculate the value of absolute zero on the Zuban Scale. _____ (! -270.71 °Z)

102. Iron has a density of 7.86 g cm^{-3}. As part of their exam, students in the junior class at a boarding school were to weigh a metal sphere, measure its diameter and calculate its density. Some of the seniors sneaked into the lab the weekend before, took the iron sphere, took it downtown, and had the interior partially hollowed and the surface repaired so it wouldn't be noticed and replaced it in the cabinet late on Sunday. The junior students who had this iron sphere for their "unknown" obtained 9.30 cm for the diameter and 2.44 kg for the mass. What value should they have reported for the mass of the sphere if it had not been tampered with, and what was the volume of the hollowed out space in the interior of the sphere? _____ (! 3.31 kg and 111 cm^3)

103. Kevin, a ninth grade whiz kid, has invented a new temperature scale, the Vitellan scale (his last name, of course). In common with the Kelvin, Celsius, and Fahrenheit scales, it is a linear scale. According to Kevin,

   1) the melting point of benzene which is 5.53 °C = 0.00 °V
   2) the boiling point of benzene which is 80.10 °C = 100.00 °V
   3) the melting point of lead which is 327.50 °C = 431.77 °V

Calculate the value for the melting point of mercury (-38.86 °C) on the Vitellan scale. _____ (! -59.53 °V)

Chemicals in Our World 1: Ascorbic Acid—Limes, Scurvy, and the Scientific Method

104. A disease caused by a vitamin deficiency is

   a. malaria
   b. dengue fever
   c. yellow fever
   d. cholera
   ! e. scurvy

105. A vitamin present in citrus fruit which is important in the human diet

   a. vitamin A
   ! b. ascorbic acid
   c. glycine
   d. vitamin K
   e. niacin

Chapter 2 The Periodic Table and Some Properties of the Elements

Multiple Choice

1. The two major types of pure substances are

    ! a. compounds and elements
       b. compounds and solutions
       c. elements and mixtures
       d. mixtures and solutions
       e. solutions and elements

2. All of the following properties of a sample of a pure substance can be used for identification except its

       a. density
       b. freezing point temperature
    ! c. mass
       d. melting point temperature
       e. solubility in 100 g of water (g solute/100 g water at 25 $^{\circ}$C)

3. A chemical reaction must be used to separate

       a. air into oxygen, nitrogen, and other components
    ! b. a compound into its elements
       c. gases from liquids
       d. a mixture into its components
       e. solids from liquids

4. Distillation can readily be used to separate

       a. the elements in a compound
       b. a heterogeneous mixture of two solids
       c. a homogeneous solution of two solids
       d. iron filings from sugar and salt crystals
    ! e. a liquid solvent from a dissolved solid

5. The symbol "Si" is used to represent the element:

       a. silver
    ! b. silicon
       c. sodium
       d. sulfur
       e. silicium

6. An example of a chemical compound is

        a. gun metal
        b. brass
        c. bronze
        d. granite
  ! e. table salt

7. Which element below occurs in nature as a gas composed of diatomic molecules at ordinary temperatures and pressures?

        a. boron
        b. silver
        c. neon
  ! d. nitrogen
        e. sulfur

8. Which element below is a liquid which conducts electricity very well at ordinary temperatures and pressures?

        a. bromine
        b. copper
        c. argon
  ! d. mercury
        e. cadmium

9. Which one of the statements below is true?

        a. When two atoms combine, they do so in definite proportions by weight
        b. When two different compounds combine to form an element, they do so in definite proportions by weight
  ! c. When two different elements combine to form a compound, they do so in definite proportions by weight
        d. When two molecules combine, they do so in definite proportions by weight
        e. When two different elements combine to form a mixture, they do so in definite proportions by weight

10. The relative number of atoms of each element in a particular compound,

        a. is always 1:1
        b. is the same as the density ratio
        c. is the same as the weight ratio
  ! d. is definite and constant
        e. cannot be determined experimentally

11. The smallest unit of a compound that still maintains the proper atomic ratios for that compound is the

      a. atom
      b. electron
! c. molecule
      d. nucleon
      e. nucleus

12. Naturally occurring boganium, Bo, has the following composition.
$$^{47}Bo, 46.972 \text{ a.m.u.}, 69.472\%$$
$$^{49}Bo, 48.961 \text{ a.m.u.}, 21.667\%$$
$$^{50}Bo, 49.954 \text{ a.m.u.}, 8.8610\%$$
What is the average atomic weight of naturally occurring boganium?

! a. 47.667
      b. 47.699
      c. 48.629
      d. 48.667
      e. 48.961

13. Naturally occurring engrium, En, has the following composition.
$$^{147}En, 146.9672 \text{ a.m.u.}, 64.792\%$$
$$^{149}En, 148.9638 \text{ a.m.u.}, 26.117\%$$
$$^{150}En, 149.9592 \text{ a.m.u.}, 9.0910\%$$
What is the average atomic weight of naturally occurring engrium?

      a. 49.254
! b. 147.76
      c. 148.63
      d. 148.67
      e. 147.80

14. Naturally occurring vitellium, Vi, has the following composition.
$$^{188}Vi, 187.9122 \text{ a.m.u.}, 10.861\%$$
$$^{191}Vi, 190.9047 \text{ a.m.u.}, 12.428\%$$
$$^{193}Vi, 192.8938 \text{ a.m.u.}, 76.711\%$$
What is the average atomic weight of naturally occurring vitellium?

      a. 64.035
      b. 190.57
      c. 190.67
      d. 192.08
! e. 192.11

15. Naturally occurring zubanium, Zb, has the following composition.

^{148}Zb, 147.9554 a.m.u., 10.563%
^{151}Zb, 150.9496 a.m.u., 70.811%
^{153}Zb, 152.9461 a.m.u., 18.626%

What is the average atomic weight of naturally occurring zubanium?

    a. 50.335
    b. 150.62
    c. 150.67
!   d. 151.01
    e. 151.08

16. Which one of the statements below is reasonably accurate?

!   a. a cation is formed by removal of an electron(s) from an atom
    b. a cation is a positively charged electron
    c. a cation is a positively charged neutron
    d. a cation is a negatively charged neutron
    e. a cation is a negatively charged proton

17. Which one of the following contributes to the charge but does NOT contribute significantly to the mass of an atom?

!   a. electrons
    b. nuclei
    c. photons
    d. neutrons
    e. protons

18. Uranium exists in nature in the form of several isotopes; the different isotopes have different

    a. atomic numbers
    b. charges
    c. numbers of electrons
!   d. numbers of neutrons
    e. numbers of protons

19. Which answer below best describes all atoms of a given isotope of a particular element?

    a. they possess the same mass, only
    b. they possess the same chemical properties and the same mass, but nothing else in common
    c. they possess the same atomic number and the same mass, but have nothing else in common
    d. they possess the same number of electrons, the same atomic number, the same mass, but nothing else in common
!   e. they possess the same number of electrons, the same atomic number, the same mass, and the same chemical properties

20. Which answer below best describes all atoms of a particular element?

    a. they possess the same number of electrons, the same atomic number, the same mass, but nothing else in common

    b. they possess the same mass and the same chemical properties, but nothing else in common

!   c. they possess the same number of electrons, the same atomic number, the same chemical properties, but not necessarily the same mass

    d. they possess the same chemical properties and the same mass, but nothing else in common

    e. they possess the same atomic number and the same mass, but have nothing else in common

21. The species shown below which has 24 neutrons is

    a. ^{52}Cr
    b. $^{56}Fe^{2+}$
    c. ^{24}Mg
! d. ^{45}Sc
    e. ^{51}V

22. The species shown below which has 24 protons is

! a. ^{52}Cr
    b. $^{56}Fe^{2+}$
    c. ^{24}Mg
    d. ^{45}Sc
    e. ^{51}V

23. Both $^{85}Rb^{+}$ and $^{80}Br^{-}$ have the same

! a. number of electrons
    b. mass
    c. number of neutrons
    d. atomic mass number
    e. number of protons

24. Consider the atoms of ^{26}Mg and ^{27}Al. Both of these species have the same

    a. number of electrons
    b. mass
! c. number of neutrons
    d. atomic mass number
    e. number of protons

25. Consider the atoms of ^{59}Co and ^{60}Co. Both of these atoms have the same

       a. number of electrons
       b. number of neutrons
       c. atomic mass number
       d. number of photons
 ! e. number of protons

26. Consider the atoms of ^{65}Cu and ^{65}Zn. Both of these atoms have the same

       a. number of electrons
       b. mass
       c. number of neutrons
 ! d. atomic mass number
       e. number of protons

27. The fluoride ion possesses

       a. 8 electrons
       b. 9 electrons
 ! c. 10 electrons
       d. 16 electrons
       e. 18 electrons

28. Compare the ^{23}Na atom and the ^{23}Na$^+$ ion. In what respect do these species differ?

 ! a. number of electrons
       b. number of neutrons
       c. atomic mass number
       d. number of photons
       e. number of protons

29. Compare the ^{26}Mg^{2+} ion and the ^{27}Al^{3+} ion. In what respect do these species differ?

       a. number of electrons **and** number of protons
       b. number of neutrons **and** number of protons
 ! c. atomic mass number **and** number of protons
       d. number of neutrons **and** number of electrons
       e. atomic mass number **and** number of electrons

30. A neutral iodine atom has an atomic mass number = 131. Which description below fits this atom?

       a. 39 protons, 78 neutrons, 39 electrons
 ! b. 53 protons, 78 neutrons, 53 electrons
       c. 53 protons, 78 neutrons, 54 electrons
       d. 53 protons, 131 neutrons, 53 electrons
       e. 53 protons, 131 neutrons, 54 electrons

31. Which description below fits the $^{65}Cu^{2+}$ ion?

      a. 29 protons, 65 neutrons, 29 electrons
      b. 29 protons, 36 neutrons, 34 electrons
      c. 29 protons, 36 neutrons, 31 electrons
! d. 29 protons, 36 neutrons, 27 electrons
      e. 31 protons, 34 neutrons, 29 electrons

32. Which description below fits the $^{112}Cd^{2+}$ ion?

      a. 48 protons, 64 neutrons, 48 electrons
      b. 48 protons, 62 neutrons, 48 electrons
! c. 48 protons, 64 neutrons, 46 electrons
      d. 48 protons, 62 neutrons, 46 electrons
      e. 50 protons, 64 neutrons, 48 electrons

33. Which one of the following properties is exhibited by solid sodium chloride?

      a. it is highly combustible
      b. it is a very good conductor of electricity
! c. it is very brittle
      d. it is very malleable
      e. it is very ductile

34. What is the correct formula for an ionic compound formed between magnesium and chlorine?

      a. $MgCl$
! b. $MgCl_2$
      c. Mg_2Cl
      d. Mg_2Cl_7
      e. Mg_7Cl_2

35. A compound containing a cation and a polyatomic oxyanion has the formula $CaFnO_4$. The polyatomic oxyanion in this compound has a parent acid. What is the formula of the parent acid?

      a. HFn
      b. H_2Fn
      c. $HFnO_4$
      d. H_2FnO_2
! e. H_2FnO_4

36. A compound containing a cation and a polyatomic oxyanion has the formula $CaFnO_4$. What is the charge on the polyatomic anion in this compound?

     a. +2
     b. +1
     c. 0
     d. -1
 ! e. -2

37. A compound containing a cation and a polyatomic oxyanion has the formula $Ca(ZbO_3)_2$. The polyatomic oxyanion in this compound has a parent acid. What is the formula of the parent acid?

     a. HZb
     b. H_2Zb
 ! c. $HZbO_3$
     d. H_2ZbO_3
     e. H_2ZbO_4

38. A compound containing a cation and a polyatomic oxyanion has the formula $Ca(ZbO_3)_2$. What is the charge on the polyatomic oxyanion in this compound?

     a. +2
     b. +1
     c. 0
 ! d. -1
     e. -2

39. Calcium karnellate, $Ca(KnO_3)_2$, contains a polyatomic anion which has a parent acid. Based upon the nomenclature system, how should that acid be named?

     a. hydrokarnellic acid
     b. hypokarnellous acid
     c. karnellous acid
 ! d. karnellic acid
     e. perkarnellic acid

40. Which one of the acids named below is the one which probably does not have ANY oxygen in it?

 ! a. hydrokarmic acid
     b. hypokarmic acid
     c. karmic acid
     d. karmous acid
     e. perkarmic acid

41. Which set of elements below are all in the same period?

        a. Ba, Pb, As, Sn
        b. Fr, U, Am, Ca
        c. K, Na, Li, Cs
   !   d. Na, Al, P, Ar
        e. Nd, Dy, Pu, Os

42. Which one of the pairs below contains elements from the same period?

   !   a. silver, tin
        b. silver, sulfur
        c. sodium, manganese
        d. copper, tin
        e. sodium, cerium

43. Which one of the pairs below contains elements from the same period?

        a. iron, barium
        b. potassium, gold
        c. potassium, barium
   !   d. potassium, iron
        e. tin, bromine

44. Which one of the pairs below contains elements from the same group?

        a. tin, zirconium
        b. potassium, sulfur
   !   c. potassium, cesium
        d. potassium, nitrogen
        e. carbon, silver

45. Which one of the pairs below contains elements from the same group?

        a. manganese, barium
        b. lithium, fluorine
        c. xerium, radium
        d. copper, iron
   !   e. zinc, mercury

46. Sodium and cesium are an example of two elements which belong to the same

        a. class
        b. generation
        c. grade
   !   d. group
        e. period

47. Silver and antimony are an example of two elements which belong to the same

        a. class
        b. generation
        c. grade
        d. group
   ! e. period

48. Which set of elements below includes only known elements which are metals?

        a. lead, bismuth, bromine, magnesium
        b. mobanium, nevadium, zeon, bromium, silanium
        c. nitrogen, silicon, sulfur, arsenic
   ! d. uranium, americium, praseodymium, zinc
        e. zinc, radon, barium, tin

49. Which set of elements below includes mostly non-metals?

        a. barium, calcium, strontium
        b. lanthanum, lutecium, rhodium
   ! c. oxygen, selenium, tellurium
        d. silicon, zinc, strontium
        e. sodium, lithium, nitrogen

50. What is the charge on all the simple ions of metals of group IA?

   ! a. +1
        b. +2
        c. -1
        d. -2
        e. +4

51. The set below featuring one alkali, one alkaline earth, one halogen, and one lanthanide is . . .

        a. cesium, barium, bromine, erbium, samarium
   ! b. francium, beryllium, iodine, terbium, berkelium
        c. lithium, manganese, fluorine, lanthanum, vanadium
        d. potassium, radium, iodine, lutetium, platinum
        e. rubidium, strontium, chlorine, thorium, plutonium

52. Which set below includes TWO and only two actinide elements?

        a. gallium, germanium, iron, barium, tellurium
        b. lithium, sodium, potassium, rubidium, francium
        c. magnesium, gallium, fluronium, missourium, neptunium
        d. radium, polonium, actinium, platinum, selenium
   ! e. uranium, francium, gallium, plutonium, titanium

53. Which set below includes only alkali metal elements?

      a. gallium, germanium, iron, barium, tellurium
!   b. lithium, sodium, potassium, rubidium, francium
      c. magnesium, gallium, fluronium, missourium, neptunium
      d. radium, polonium, actinium, platinum, selenium
      e. uranium, francium, gallium, plutonium, titanium

54. Which set below does not include at least one transition metal element?

      a. gallium, germanium, iron, barium, tellurium
      b. lithium, radium, magnesium, palladium, boron
!   c. magnesium, gallium, aluminum, missourium, neptunium
      d. radium, polonium, actinium, platinum, selenium
      e. uranium, francium, gallium, plutonium, titanium

55. Which of the sets below includes the largest number of elements?

      a. alkali metals
      b. alkaline earth elements
      c. halogens
!   d. lanthanides
      e. noble gases

56. Which set below represents elements which are often found in nature as uncombined elements?

      a. magnesium, vanadium, hydrogen, tin, chlorine
!   b. neon, gold, platinum, silver, carbon
      c. uranium, iron, argon, silver, manganese
      d. sodium, sulfur, lithium, barium, helium
      e. calcium, chromium, copper, phosphorus, zinc

57. The present form of the periodic table evolved from the pioneering work, in this area, of . . .

      a. John Dalton
!   b. Dmitri Mendelyev
      c. Isaac Newton
      d. J. J. Thomson
      e. Ernest Rutherford

58. What is the correct name for the compound IBr_3?

      a. bromic iodide
      b. iodine bromate
!   c. iodine tribromide
      d. iodine tribromine
      e. monoiodine tribromite

59. What is the correct name for the compound S_2Cl_2?

        a. disulfur chlorate
    ! b. disulfur dichloride
        c. disulfur dichlorine
        d. sulfur(I) chloride
        e. sulfur(II) chlorine(II)

60. What is the correct name for the compound $HI(g)$?

        a. hydriodic acid
        b. hydrogen monoiodide
    ! c. hydrogen iodide
        d. iodic acid
        e. monohydrogen monoiodide

61. An alkaline earth element, which we will call X, unites with a halogen, which we will call Q. What would be the correct formula of the resulting compound?

        a. XQ
    ! b. XQ_2
        c. XQ_4
        d. X_2Q
        e. X_4Q

62. Aluminum unites with a second element, which we will call E, to form a definite compound whose formula is AlE_3. Element E is most probably

        a. an actinide element
        b. an alkali metal
        c. a chalcogen
    ! d. a halogen
        e. a transition element

63. What is the correct name for the compound $HI(g)$?

        a. hydriodic acid
        b. hydrogen monoiodide
    ! c. hydrogen iodide
        d. iodic acid
        e. monohydrogen monoiodide

64. What is the correct name for the compound V_2O_5? (Remember, for transition metals . . .)

    a. divanadium pentoxide
    b. vanadic oxide
! c. vanadium(V) oxide
    d. vanadium(V) pentoxide
    e. vanadous oxide

65. What is the correct name for the compound $NaCl_3$?

    a. sodium chlorate
    b. sodium chlorite
    c. sodium perchloride
    d. sodium trichloride
! e. there is no such compound

66. What is the correct name for the compound $CuBr_2$? (Remember, for transition metals . . .)

    a. copper(I) bromide(II)
! b. copper(II) bromide
    c. copper(II) bromite
    d. copper dibromide
    e. cuprous bromide

67. What is the correct name for the compound $HCN(g)$?

    a. hydrocarbonitride
    b. hydrocyanic acid
    c. hydrogen carbonitride
    d. hydrogen cyanate
! e. hydrogen cyanide

68. What is the correct name for the compound Na_2O?

    a. disodium oxide
! b. sodium oxide
    c. sodium(I) oxide
    d. sodium peroxide
    e. sodium superoxide

69. A typographical error on an exam produced the formula, P_4Se_7, in one of the questions. How would you name this compound?

    a. tetraphosphorus hexaselenide
! b. tetraphosphorus heptaselenide
    c. phosphorus heptaselenite
    d. phosphorus(IV) selenide
    e. phosphorus(VII) selenide

70. Which one of the following is a correct name for the compound $FeBr_3$?

        a. ferrous bromide
!   b. iron(III) bromide
        c. iron bromite
        d. iron tribromide
        e. iron tribromine

71. Which one of the following is the correct formula for the compound ferrous sulfate?

!   a. $FeSO_4$
        b. $Fe(SO_4)_2$
        c. Fe_2SO_4
        d. $Fe_2(SO_4)_3$
        e. $Fe_3(SO_4)_2$

72. Which one of the following is a correct name for the compound Hg_2Cl_2?

        a. dimercury dichloride
        b. mercuric chloride
!   c. mercury(I) chloride
        d. mercury(II) dichloride
        e. there is no correct name, the formula should be $HgCl$

73. Which one of the following is a correct formula for mercury(I) phosphate?

        a. $HgPO_3$
        b. $HgPO_4$
        c. Hg_3PO_4
        d. Hg_2PO_3
!   e. $(Hg_2)_3(PO_4)_2$

74. Which one of the following is a correct name for the compound CoF_3?

        a. cobalt fluoride
        b. cobalt trifluoride
!   c. cobaltic fluoride
        d. cobaltic trifluoride
        e. cobaltous fluoride

75. A correct name for the compound, SnF_4, would be

        a. stannic tetrafluoride
        b. stannous fluoride
        c. stannous(IV) fluoride
!   d. tin(IV) fluoride
        e. tin tetrafluoride

76. A correct formula for stannous nitrate would be

        a. $Sn(NO_2)_2$
!   b. $Sn(NO_3)_2$
        c. $Sn(NO_3)_3$
        d. $Sn(NO_3)_4$
        e. Sn_2NO_3

77. What is the correct formula for the compound, magnesic chlorate?

        a. $MgClO_3$
        b. $Mg(ClO_3)_2$
        c. Mg_2ClO_3
        d. $MgO(ClO_3)_2$
!   e. there is no such compound

78. What is the correct name for the compound $BaSeO_3$?

        a. barium selenate
        b. barium selenide
!   c. barium selenite
        d. barium selenium trioxide
        e. barium selenoxate

79. What is the correct name for the compound $Na_2Cr_2O_7$?

        a. sodium chromium(VII)-ate
!   b. sodium dichromate
        c. sodium dichromium heptaoxide
        d. sodium heptaoxochromate
        e. sodium perchromate

80. The compound $Na_2S_2O_3$ is used extensively in photographic film processing. What is its chemical name?

        a. sodium bisulfite
        b. sodium disulfur trioxide
        c. sodium oxosulfate(IV)
!   d. sodium thiosulfate
        e. sodium trioxosulfite

81. What is the correct name for the compound $H_2Cr_2O_7$?

        a. bichromic acid
        b. chromic acid
!   c. dichromic acid
        d. hydrogen dichromate
        e. hydrogen dichromium heptaoxide

82. If the NtO_4^{2-} ion is called nortonate, what is the correct name for the compound H_2NtO_4?

    a. dihydrogen nortonium tetraoxide
    b. dihydrogen nortonate
    c. hydrogen nortonate
!   d. nortonic acid
    e. nortonous acid

83. What is the correct name for the compound Cu_2SO_3?

!   a. copper(I) sulfite
    b. copper(II) sulfite
    c. copper thiosulfate
    d. cuprous sulfate
    e. dicopper sulfur trioxide

84. What is the correct name for the $C_2H_3O_2^-$ ion?

!   a. acetate ion
    b. hydrocarbonate ion
    c. monocarbonate ion
    d. oxalate ion
    e. sucrose ion

85. What is the correct name for H_3PO_2?

    a. hydrogen hypophosphite
    b. hydrogen phosphite
!   c. hypophosphorus acid
    d. phosphoric acid
    e. trihydrogen phosphorus dioxide

86. Which one of the following is a correct name for the $HCrO_4^-$ ion?

!   a. bichromate ion
    b. dichromate ion
    c. hydrogen chromium tetraoxide ion
    d. monochromate ion
    e. monochromic acid

87. Which one of the following is a correct name for the compound $KHCr_2O_7$?

    a. potassium bichromite
    b. potassium bichromate
    c. potassium dichromic acid
    d. potassium monohydrogen chromite
!   e. potassium monohydrogen dichromate

88. What is the correct name for the compound $BaHSeO_4$?

    a. barium selenic acid
    b. barium hydrogen selenium tetraoxide
    c. barium monohydrogen selenite
    d. barium monohydrogen selenoxate
!   e. there is no compound with that formula

89. What is the correct name for the compound $LiHPO_4$?

    a. lithium monohydrogen phosphate
    b. lithium hydrogen phosphoric acid
    c. lithium hydrogen phosphorus tetraoxide
    d. lithium monohydrogen phosphite
!   e. there is no compound with that formula

90. What is the correct name for the compound Li_2HPO_4?

!   a. lithium monohydrogen phosphate
    b. there is no compound with that formula
    c. dilithium monohydrogen phosphate
    d. lithium hydrogen phosphorus tetraoxide
    e. lithium phosphoric acid

91. What is the correct name for the compound $CuHSO_4$?

!   a. copper(I) bisulfate
    b. copper(II) bisulfate acid
    c. copper hydrogen sulfur tetraoxide
    d. copper hydrogen sulfate
    e. copper sulfuric acid

92. What is the correct formula for the oxalate ion?

    a. CO_3^{2-}
    b. $C_4O_2^{2-}$
    c. $C_4O_4^{2-}$
!   d. $C_2O_4^{2-}$
    e. $C_2H_3O_2^{-}$

93. If the NtO_4^{2-} ion is called nortonate, what is the correct name for the compound $CsHNtO_4$?

    a. cesium monohydrogen nortonite
    b. cesium nortonic acid
!   c. cesium binortonate
    d. cesium hydrogen nortonium tetraoxide
    e. based on the information given, this compound couldn't exist with the formula as given

94. One of the compounds below has the formula written incorrectly. Which one?

    a. $Al(H_2PO_4)_3$
    b. $Al(HCO_3)_3$
    c. $Ba(H_2AsO_4)_2$
    d. $Ca(HCO_3)_2$
    ! e. $KHPO_4$

95. One of the compounds below has the formula written incorrectly. Which one?

    ! a. $Al(H_2CO_3)_3$
    b. $Al(H_2PO_4)_3$
    c. $Ba(HCO_3)_2$
    d. $Ca(H_2AsO_4)_2$
    e. KH_2PO_4

96. The correct name for the compound $Al(SO_4)_3$ is:

    ! a. there is no compound with that formula--it must be incorrectly written
    b. aluminum sulfate
    c. aluminum trisulfate
    d. aluminum(III) sulfate
    e. aluminum sulfite

97. Which one of the following chemical substances represents a correct formula for an acid salt?

    a. $NaHCl$
    b. $CaHCl$
    ! c. $Ba(HSO_3)_2$
    d. $Ca(HCl)_2$
    e. $CaSO_4$

98. Which one of the following is not a polyprotic acid?

    a. arsenic acid
    b. sulfuric acid
    ! c. nitric acid
    d. carbonic acid
    e. phosphorous acid

Fill in the Blanks

99. What is the correct name for the compound CH_4? _____ (! methane)

100. What is the correct name for the compound $H_3N(g)$? _____ (! ammonia

101. How many atoms are there in one formula unit of $[NH_4]_4[Fe(CN)_6]$? _____ (! 33)

102. How many atoms are there in one formula unit of $NH_4Al(SO_4)_2 \cdot 24H_2O$? _____ (! 88)

103. How many atoms are there in one formula unit of $Al_2(SO_4)_3 \cdot 18H_2O$? _____ (! 71)

104. What is the charge on all the simple ions of metals of Group IIA? _____ (! +2)

105. What is the correct formula for the sulfide ion? _____ (! S^{2-})

106. The correct formula for lithium phosphate is _____ (! Li_3PO_4)

107. The correct formula for barium selenite is _____ (! $BaSeO_3$)

108. The correct formula for barium iodite is _____ (! $Ba(IO_2)_2$)

109. What is the correct formula for the compound, chromium (III) dihydrogen phosphate? _____
(! $Cr(H_2PO_4)_3$)

110. What is the formula for calcium bicarbonate? _____ (! $Ca(HCO_3)_2$)

True and False

111. A correct name for the compound P_4Se_{10} is phosphorus(IV) selenium. (! F)

112. The correct name for the compound $CrBr_2$, is chromic bromide. (! F)

113. The correct name for the compound $RbClO_4$, is rubidium(I) perchlorate. (! F)

114. The compound $HBrO_3$, is named hydrogen bromate acid. (! F)

115. The correct name for the $CrO_4{}^{2-}$ ion is perchromate. (! F)

116. A correct name for the compound $Ni(OBr)_2$ is nickel(II) hypobromite. (! T)

117. The correct name for the compound $ZnBr_2$, is zirconium bromide. (! F)

118. The correct name for the compound $Mn(ClO_4)_2$, is magnesium chlorate. (! F)

119. The compound N_2O_4, is named nitrate tetraoxide. (! F)

120. The correct name for $K_2Cr_2O_7$ is potassium dichromium heptaoxide. (! F)

Critical Thinking

121. Vitellium arsenate has the formula, $Vi_3(AsO_4)_2$, while sodium nortonate has the formula, Na_2NtO_4. Which of the following would be the expected formula for vitellium nortonate?

  ! a. $ViNtO_4$
     b. Vi_2NtO_4
     c. $Vi(NtO_4)_2$
     d. $Vi_2(NtO_4)_3$
     e. $Vi_3(NtO_4)_2$

122. Engrium sulfate has the formula, $En_2(SO_4)_3$, sodium nortonite has the formula Na_2NtO_3, and engrium arsenite has the formula, $EnAsO_3$. Based on these names and formulas, what would you expect for the formula of engrium nortonate?

     a. $EnNtO_4$
     b. En_2NtO_4
     c. $En(NtO_4)_2$
  ! d. $En_2(NtO_4)_3$
     e. $En_3(NtO_4)_2$

123. Two elements, Qr and E, combine to form an ionic compound whose formula is QrE_2. Qr also combines with element Z for form an ionic compound, Qr_3Z_2. Based on this information, what is a reasonable value for the charge on E?

     a. +1
  ! b. - 1
     c. +2
     d. - 2
     e. - 3

124. Kevin Vitellan, a high school whiz in chemistry, thinks aluminum would be a far better element than carbon to serve as the basis of the atomic weight scale. Naturally occurring aluminum consists of only one isotope, it is abundant, and can be obtained in a very high state of purity. The atomic mass of this isotope, ^{27}Al, is listed as 26.98154 amu. Kevin would redefine it to a value of 27.0000 amu. Given these current values for atomic weights of a few elements as they occur in nature— carbon: 12.011 amu   oxygen: 15.9994 amu   calcium: 40.078 amu, what would be the value listed for the atomic weight of oxygen in Kevin Vitellan's new table of atomic weights? _____
(! 16.010)

125. Joe Smith, a student in the AP chemistry class, thinks that Vitellan's idea of letting the element aluminum be the basis of the atomic weight scale should merit serious consideration. The element is known to consist of only one isotope, it is abundant, and can be obtained in a very high state of purity. The atomic mass of this isotope, ^{27}Al, is listed as 26.98154 amu. Kevin would redefine it to a value of 27.0000 amu. Given these current values for atomic weights of a few elements as they occur in nature—carbon: 12.011 amu   oxygen: 15.9994 amu   calcium: 40.078 amu, what would be the value listed for the formula weight of calcium carbonate based on Kevin Vitellan's new table of atomic weights? _____   (! 100.16)

126. The compound, Cr_2O_3, contains chromium and oxygen combined in a ratio of 2.167 grams of chromium to 1.000 gram of oxygen. Another compound containing chromium and oxygen gave a different analysis and properties—a 2.500 g sample of this second compound contains 1.300 grams of chromium. This works out to a different ratio. What is the formula for this compound? _____ (! CrO_3)

127. A compound which has the formula, V_2O_3, contains vanadium and oxygen combined in a ratio of 2.123 grams of vanadium to 1.000 gram of oxygen. A 2.500 gram sample of a different compound containing the same two elements was analyzed and found to contain 1.400 grams of vanadium. What is the formula for this second compound? _____ (! V_2O_5)

128. Naturally occurring silver consists of two isotopes
$$^{107}Ag, 106.905092 \text{ u} \qquad ^{109}Ag, 108.904757 \text{ u}$$
The atomic weight of naturally occurring silver is listed in the Handbook as 107.868 u. From this data, calculate the percent of the ^{107}Ag isotope in naturally occurring silver. _____ (! 51.846 or 51.847)

129. Naturally occurring silver consists of two isotopes
$$^{107}Ag, 106.905092 \text{ u} \qquad ^{109}Ag, 108.904757 \text{ u}$$
A meteorite (or more properly, an extra-terrestrial object) which was retrieved from the ocean floor by one of the Explorer vessels contained a high percentage of silver. Oddly however, even though the silver contained the same two isotopes as our natural silver, the average atomic weight of the silver in this object, as verified by several reputable scientific laboratories in the United States and abroad, gave a value of 108.548 u! From this data, calculate the percent of the ^{107}Ag isotope in the object retrieved from the ocean floor. _____ (! 17.840 or 17.841)

130. Naturally occurring indium consists of two isotopes
$$^{113}In, 112.904061 \text{ u} \qquad ^{115}In, 114.903880 \text{ u}$$
A meteorite (or more properly, an extra-terrestrial object) which was retrieved from the ocean floor by one of the Explorer vessels contained a high percentage of indium. Oddly however, even though the indium contained the same two isotopes as our natural indium, the average atomic weight of the indium in this object, as verified by several reputable scientific laboratories in the United States and abroad, gave a value of 113.458 u! From this data, calculate the percent of the ^{113}In isotope in the object retrieved from the ocean floor. _____ (! 72.300 or 72.301)

131. Naturally occurring indium consists of two isotopes
$$^{113}In, 112.904061 \text{ u} \qquad ^{115}In, 114.903880 \text{ u}$$
The atomic weight of naturally occurring indium is listed in the Handbook as 114.818 u. From this data, calculate the percent of the ^{115}In isotope in naturally occurring indium. _____ (! 95.705 or 95.706)

Chapter 3   Stoichiometry: Quantitative Chemical Relationships

Multiple Choice

1.   How many moles of ^{12}C are there in a 3.50 g sample of this substance?

        a. 0.286 moles
!   b. 0.292 moles
        c. 1.00 moles
        d. 3.43 moles
        e. 3.50 moles

2.   The atomic weight of aluminum is 26.982. How many moles of Al are there in a 4.55 g sample of aluminum?

!   a. 0.169 moles
        b. 0.220 moles
        c. 1.33 moles
        d. 4.55 moles
        e. 5.93 moles

3.   The atomic weight of helium is 4.0026. What is the mass of a helium sample which contains 0.427 moles of He gas?

        a. 0.427 g
        b. 0.107 g
!   c. 1.71 g
        d. 2.57 g
        e. 9.37 g

4.   The atomic weight of boron is 10.811. What is the mass of a boron sample which contains 0.585 moles of B atoms?

        a. 0.00541 g
        b. 1.80 g
        c. 3.52 g
!   d. 6.32 g
        e. 18.5 g

5.   If the atomic weight of gold is 196.9665, then 0.150 mol Au ⇔ ___ g Au?

        a. 7.62×10^{-4} g
!   b. 29.5 g
        c. 29.54498 g
        d. 7.61551×10^{-4} g
        e. 0.903 g

6. How many atoms of ^{12}C are there in a 3.50 gram sample of this particular isotope?

       a. 1.72×10^{23}
 ! b. 1.76×10^{23}
       c. 2.07×10^{24}
       d. 2.11×10^{24}
       e. 8.01×10^{23}

7. The atomic weight of aluminum is 26.982. How many aluminum atoms are there in a 4.55 g sample of aluminum?

 ! a. 1.02×10^{23}
       b. 1.32×10^{23}
       c. 2.74×10^{24}
       d. 3.57×10^{24}
       e. 8.01×10^{23}

8. The atomic weight of neon is 20.1797. What is the mass, in grams, of a neon sample which contains 1.00×10^{20} neon atoms?

       a. 1.66×10^{-4} g
       b. 2.02×10^{-19} g
       c. 298 g
 ! d. 3.35×10^{-3} g
       e. 8.33×10^{-6} g

9. How many atoms are there in one formula unit of $(NH_4)_4Fe(CN)_6$?

       a. 15
       b. 25
       c. 28
 ! d. 33
       e. 35

10. How many atoms are there in one formula unit of $NiSO_4 \cdot 7H_2O$?

       a. 9
       b. 14
 ! c. 27
       d. 28
       e. 33

11. The formula mass of $(NH_4)_2SO_4$ is

    a. 84.12
    b. 116.12
    c. 118.13
!   d. 132.14
    e. 221.53

12. The formula mass of $Co(NH_3)_6(ClO_4)_3$ is

    a. 318.53
    b. 389.43
    c. 402.57
!   d. 459.47
    e. 754.13

13. The formula mass of $Ni(H_2O)_6Cl_2$ is

    a. 157.69
    b. 193.00
    c. 227.61
!   d. 237.69
    e. 296.83

14. A sample of $C_{12}H_{22}O_{11}$, contains 0.4662 moles of carbon atoms. How many moles of hydrogen atoms (H) are there in the sample?

    a. 0.2543 moles
    b. 0.4662 moles
    c. 10.26 moles
!   d. 0.8547 moles
    e. 0.9324 moles

15. A sample of $K_3Fe(CN)_6$ contains 1.084×10^{24} carbon atoms. How many potassium atoms are there in the same sample?

    a. 1.084×10^{24} atoms
    b. 3.252×10^{24} atoms
    c. 2.168×10^{24} atoms
    d. 3.613×10^{23} atoms
!   e. 5.420×10^{23} atoms

16. A sample of $C_7H_5N_3O_4$, contains 0.4662 moles of carbon atoms. How many nitrogen atoms are there in the sample?

    a. 2.807×10^{23} atoms
! b. 1.203×10^{23} atoms
    c. 4.101×10^{23} atoms
    d. 1.998×10^{22} atoms
    e. 6.551×10^{23} atoms

17. A sample of $(N_2H_5)_2C_3H_4O_4$ contains 1.084×10^{24} carbon atoms. How many moles of hydrogen atoms are there in the same sample?

    a. 4.200 moles
    b. 4.725 moles
    c. 7.000 moles
! d. 8.400 moles
    e. 2.400 moles

18. How many moles of carbon atoms are combined with 11.2 moles of hydrogen atoms in a sample of the compound, C_3H_8?

    a. 3.00
    b. 5.60
! c. 4.20
    d. 6.02×10^{23}
    e. 29.9

19. A sample of phosphorus trifluoride, PF_3, contains 1.400 moles of the substance. How many atoms are there in the sample?

    a. 4
    b. 5.6
    c. 8.431×10^{23}
    d. 2.409×10^{24}
! e. 3.372×10^{24}

20. A sample of arabinose, $C_5H_{10}O_5$, contains 0.6000 moles of the substance. How many carbon atoms are there in the sample?

    a. 3
    b. 5
    c. 3.613×10^{23}
! d. 1.807×10^{24}
    e. 3.011×10^{24}

21. A sample of sulfolane, $C_4H_8O_2S$, contains 5.00×10^{24} atoms. How many moles of sulfolane are there in the sample

     a. 0.120 moles
! b. 0.554 moles
     c. 1.81 moles
     d. 8.30 moles
     e. 3.33×10^{23} moles

22. The mass of 5.20 moles of glucose, $C_6H_{12}O_6$, is correctly expressed as

     a. 1.56×10^{-21} g
     b. 31.2 g
     c. 34.7 g
! d. 937 g
     e. 6.43×10^{20} g

23. How many molecules of carbon dioxide are there in 154.0 grams of carbon dioxide?

     a. 3.499
! b. 2.107×10^{24}
     c. 4.214×10^{24}
     d. 9.274×10^{25}
     e. 4.081×10^{27}

24. A sample of trifluoromethanesulfonic acid, CHF_3O_3S, contains 4.62×10^{23} oxygen atoms. How many moles of CHF_3O_3S are there in the sample?

! a. 0.256 moles
     b. 2.30 moles
     c. 0.259 moles
     d. 0.767 moles
     e. 1.53×10^{23} moles

25. Which one of the following contains the greatest number of carbon atoms?

! a. 0.250 moles of glucose, $C_6H_{12}O_6$
     b. 1.20 moles of carbon dioxide, CO_2
     c. 0.500 moles of CaC_2
     d. 0.450 moles of $Al_2(CO_3)_3$
     e. 0.350 moles of $C_4H_8O_2S$

26. A gas sample contains 16.0 g of CH_4, 16.0 g of O_2, 16.0 g of SO_2, and 33.0 g of CO_2. The total number of moles, of *everything*, is:

      a. 2.25
!   b. 2.50
      c. 2.75
      d. 3.00
      e. 4.00

27. What is the percent, by weight, of calcium in $Ca(OCl)_2$, to the proper number of significant digits? Use the atomic weights provided which come from your text!

!   a. 28.030
      b. 28.571
      c. 31.562
      d. 43.787
      e. 44.493

28. What is the percent, by weight, of boron in $Al(BF_4)_3$, to the proper number of significant digits? Use the atomic weights provided which come from your text!

      a. 9.501 %
      b. 9.385 %
      c. 10.152 %
!   d. 11.285 %
      e. 23.713 %

29. What is the percent, by weight, of chromium in K_2CrO_4, to the proper number of significant digits? Use the atomic weights provided which come from your text!

!   a. 26.776 %
      b. 31.763 %
      c. 40.268 %
      d. 42.241 %
      e. 51.996 %

30. What is the percent, by weight, of oxygen in $NiSO_4 \cdot 7H_2O$?

      a. 14.846
      b. 39.875
      c. 43.273
      d. 49.531
!   e. 62.661

31. A 7.300 gram sample of aluminum combined quantitatively with some selenium to form a definite compound. The compound weighed 39.35 grams. What is the empirical formula for this compound?

       a. AlSe
       b. Al_2Se
       c. $AlSe_2$
  ! d. Al_2Se_3
       e. Al_3Se_2

32. Magnetite is a binary compound containing only iron and oxygen. The percent, by weight, of iron is 72.360 %. What is the empirical formula of magnetite?

       a. FeO
       b. FeO_2
  ! c. Fe_3O_4
       d. Fe_2O_3
       e. Fe_2O_5

33. A compound contains sodium, boron, and oxygen. The experimental analysis gave values of 53.976 % sodium and 8.461 % boron, by weight, the remainder is oxygen. What is the empirical formula of the compound?

       a. $NaBO_2$
  ! b. Na_3BO_3
       c. Na_3BO_2
       d. NaB_3O
       e. $Na_3B_3O_8$

34. A compound contains potassium, nitrogen, and oxygen. The experimental analysis gave values of 45.942 % potassium and 16.458 % nitrogen, by weight, the remainder is oxygen. What is the empirical formula of the compound?

  ! a. KNO_2
       b. KNO_3
       c. $K_2N_2O_5$
       d. KN_3O_8
       e. K_2N_2O

35. A compound used in a polymer research project contains carbon, hydrogen, and nitrogen. The assay values are: carbon, 58.774%; hydrogen, 13.810%; nitrogen, 27.416%. Determine the empirical formula of this compound.

       a. C_3H_7N
       b. C_2H_7N
       c. C_2H_8N
  ! d. $C_5H_{14}N_2$
       e. $C_7H_{16}N_4$

36. A well characterized compound contains potassium, sulfur, and oxygen. The assay values are: potassium, 49.410%; sulfur, 20.261%. Determine the empirical formula of this compound.

    ! a. K_2SO_3
       b. K_2SO_4
       c. $K_2S_2O_4$
       d. $K_2S_2O_3$
       e. $K_3S_2O_8$

37. A new compound contains nitrogen, hydrogen, boron, and fluorine. The assay values are: nitrogen, 13.360%; hydrogen, 3.8455%; boron, 10.312%. Determine its empirical formula.

       a. NH_3BF_3
       b. NH_4B_3F
       c. N_4HB_4F
    ! d. NH_4BF_4
       e. NH_3BF_4

38. A freshly prepared compound contains potassium, hydrogen, phosphorus, and oxygen. The assay values are: potassium, 44.895%; hydrogen, 0.5787%; phosphorus, 17.783%; Determine the empirical formula of this compound.

       a. $K_2H_4P_4O$
    ! b. K_2HPO_4
       c. $K_2H_2PO_4$
       d. $K_2HP_2O_5$
       e. KH_2PO_4

39. A 4.626 gram sample of a hydrocarbon, upon combustion in a combustion analysis apparatus, yielded 6.484 grams of carbon dioxide. The percent, by weight, of carbon in the hydrocarbon is therefore:

    ! a. 38.25 %
       b. 19.47 %
       c. 71.35 %
       d. 40.16 %
       e. 42.16 %

40. A 6.789 gram sample of a hydrocarbon, upon combustion in a combustion analysis apparatus, yielded 9.883 grams of carbon dioxide. The percent, by weight, of carbon in the hydrocarbon is therefore:

       a. 18.75 %
    ! b. 39.73 %
       c. 68.69 %
       d. 45.57 %
       e. 34.44 %

41. A 4.626 gram sample of a hydrocarbon, upon combustion in a combustion analysis apparatus, yielded 6.527 grams of water. The percent, by weight, of hydrogen in the hydrocarbon is therefore:

    a. 14.11 %
! b. 15.79 %
    c. 41.09 %
    d. 66.22 %
    e. 85.89 %

42. A 6.789 gram sample of a hydrocarbon, upon combustion in a combustion analysis apparatus, yielded 6.527 grams of water. The percent, by weight, of hydrogen in the hydrocarbon is therefore:

    a. 9.615 %
! b. 10.76 %
    c. 28.00 %
    d. 38.72 %
    e. 58.53 %

43. A 6.789 gram sample of a compound was analyzed for nitrogen in a nitrogen analysis apparatus. In the procedure, all the nitrogen present was completely converted to ammonia (NH_3). 1.637 grams of ammonia were obtained. The percent, by weight, of nitrogen in the compound is therefore:

    a. 35.57 %
    b. 24.11 %
    c. 75.89 %
    d. 31.77 %
! e. 19.83 %

44. A 4.927 gram sample of a compound was analyzed for nitrogen in a nitrogen analysis apparatus. In the procedure, all the nitrogen present was completely converted to ammonia (NH_3). 1.369 grams of ammonia were obtained. The percent, by weight, of nitrogen in the compound is therefore:

    a. 27.79 %
    b. 38.48 %
! c. 22.85 %
    d. 61.52 %
    e. 36.71 %

45. In a quantitative analysis study, 4.624 grams of a hydrocarbon (which contains carbon and hydrogen only) sample yielded 13.84 g of CO_2 and 7.556 g of H_2O in a combustion analysis apparatus. Determine the empirical formula of the hydrocarbon.

    a. CH_3
    b. C_2H_5
! c. C_3H_8
    d. $C_{10}H_{26}$
    e. $C_{10}H_{27}$

46. In a quantitative analysis study, 4.624 grams of a compound containing carbon, hydrogen and oxygen only yielded 6.557 g of CO_2 and 4.026 g of H_2O in a combustion analysis apparatus. Determine the empirical formula of the compound.

     a. CH_2O
! b. CH_3O
     c. CH_4O
     d. C_2H_4O
     e. C_4H_2O

47. Which one of the following is definitely not an empirical formula?

     a. $C_{12}H_{16}O_3$
     b. $C_{12}H_{22}O_{11}$
     c. $C_3H_8O_2$
     d. $C_4H_{12}N_2O$
! e. $C_6H_{12}O_4$

48. A compound has an empirical formula CH_2O. An independent analysis gave a value of 150.13 for its molar mass. What is the correct molecular formula?

! a. $C_5H_{10}O_5$
     b. $C_6H_{12}O_6$
     c. $C_{11}H_2O$
     d. $C_6H_6O_8$
     e. $C_9H_{10}O_2$

49. A compound has an empirical formula C_2H_4O. An independent analysis gave a value of 132 for its molar mass. What is the correct molecular formula?

     a. $C_4H_4O_5$
     b. $C_{10}H_{12}$
     c. C_7O_3
! d. $C_6H_{12}O_3$
     e. $C_4H_8O_5$

50. When the chemical equation, $AsF_3 + CCl_4 \rightarrow AsCl_3 + CCl_2F_2$, is correctly balanced, the sum of the smallest set of integer coefficients will be

     a. 4
     b. 5
! c. 10
     d. 14
     e. 20

51. When the chemical equation,
$$BaCl_2 + K_3PO_4 \rightarrow KCl + Ba_3(PO_4)_2(s)$$
is correctly balanced, the sum of the smallest set of integer coefficients will be

    a. 7
    b. 8
    c. 10
! d. 12
    e. 16

52. When the remaining coefficients in the chemical equation,
$$1\ C_{10}H_8 + 6\ CrO_3 + \underline{\quad}H_2SO_4 \rightarrow 1\ C_8H_6O_4 + 2\ CO_2 + 3\ Cr_2(SO_4)_3 + \underline{\quad}H_2O$$
are calculated, the coefficient for the H_2O will be

    a. 13
    b. 5
    c. 3
    d. 20
! e. 10

53. When the remaining coefficients in the chemical equation,
$$1\ C_{10}H_8 + 9\ MnO_2 + \underline{\quad}H_2SO_4 \rightarrow 1\ C_8H_6O_4 + 2\ CO_2 + \underline{\quad}MnSO_4 + \underline{\quad}H_2O$$
are calculated, the coefficient for the H_2SO_4 will be

! a. 9
    b. 13
    c. 8
    d. 12
    e. 10

54. When the coefficients in the chemical equation,
$$K_2Cr_2O_7 + BaCl_2 + H_2O \rightarrow BaCrO_4 + KCl + HCl$$
are calculated, the sum of the smallest set of integer coefficients will be

    a. 8
! b. 10
    c. 13
    d. 16
    e. 18

55. When $BaCl_2$ reacts with Na_3PO_4, $Ba_3(PO_4)_2$ and $NaCl$ are formed. How many moles of Ba_3PO_4 are formed for each mole of $BaCl_2$ that is consumed?

    a. 3
    b. 1
! c. 0.3333
    d. 2.3333
    e. 1.5

56. The left side of a balanced chemical equation is shown below,

$$K_2Cr_2O_7 + 4\,H_2SO_4 + 3\,SeO_2 \rightarrow \ldots$$

If 0.600 moles of $K_2Cr_2O_7$, 2.800 moles of H_2SO_4 and 1.500 moles of SeO_2 are brought together and allowed to react, then

    a. H_2SO_4 is the limiting reagent
    b. $K_2Cr_2O_7$ is the limiting reagent
    c. there are 1.300 moles of H_2SO_4 in excess
! d. there are 0.100 moles of $K_2Cr_2O_7$ in excess
    e. there are 0.300 moles of SeO_2 in excess

57. Given the balanced chemical equation, $C_3H_8 + 5\,O_2 \rightarrow 3\,CO_2 + 4\,H_2O$. If 0.3818 moles of C_3H_8 and 1.718 moles of O_2 are allowed to react, and this is the only reaction which occurs, theoretically how many moles of water should be produced?

    a. 1.336 moles
! b. 1.374 moles
    c. 1.527 moles
    d. 1.718 moles
    e. 3.426 moles

58. Given the balanced chemical equation, $C_4H_4 + 5\,O_2 \rightarrow 4\,CO_2 + 2\,H_2O$. If 0.3618 moles of C_4H_4 are allowed to react with 1.818 moles of O_2, and this is the only reaction which occurs, what is the maximum quantity of carbon dioxide that could be produced?

! a. 1.447 moles
    b. 1.454 moles
    c. 1.456 moles
    d. 2.180 moles
    e. 0.3978 moles

59. Given the chemical reaction, $C_4H_8 + O_2 \rightarrow CO_2 + H_2O$. If 0.3218 moles of C_4H_8 are allowed to react with 2.000 moles of O_2, what would be the theoretical yield of water, in moles?

    a. 1.333 moles
    b. 1.609 moles
    c. 0.6436 moles
! d. 1.287 moles
    e. 2.574 moles

60. Given the chemical reaction, $AsF_3 + C_2Cl_6 \rightarrow AsCl_3 + C_2Cl_2F_4$, if 1.3618 moles of AsF_3 are allowed to react with 1.000 mole of C_2Cl_6, what would be the theoretical yield of $AsCl_3$, in moles?

    a. 0.3618 moles
    b. 0.7343 moles
    c. 0.7500 moles
! d. 1.3333 moles
    e. 1.3618 moles

50

61. Given the balanced chemical equation, $C_4H_4 + 5 O_2 \rightarrow 4 CO_2 + 2 H_2O$. If 0.3618 moles of C_4H_4 are allowed to react with 1.818 moles of O_2, and this is the only reaction which occurs, what is the maximum quantity of water that could be produced?

    a. 11.02 g
  ! b. 13.04 g
    c. 13.20 g
    d. 19.64 g
    e. 65.50 g

62. Given the chemical reaction, $AsF_3 + C_2Cl_6 \rightarrow AsCl_3 + C_2Cl_2F_4$, if 1.3618 moles of AsF_3 are allowed to react with 1.000 moles of C_2Cl_6, what would be the theoretical yield of $C_2Cl_2F_4$, in grams?

    a. 128.1 grams
    b. 134.1 grams
  ! c. 170.9 grams
    d. 174.6 grams
    e. 185.5 grams

63. Thermal decomposition of $KClO_3(s)$ yields $KCl(s)$ and $O_2(g)$. When 4.289 grams of $KClO_3$ (0.03500 moles) undergo this reaction, how many grams of oxygen are produced?

    a. 1.120 grams
    b. 0.5601 grams
    c. 2.240 grams
  ! d. 1.680 grams
    e. 4.288 grams

64. When aluminum metal reacts with $HCl(aq)$, $AlCl_3(aq)$, and hydrogen gas are produced. If 4.288 grams of Al(0.1590 moles) undergo this reaction with an excess of hydrochloric acid, how many grams of hydrogen gas should be produced? (Write the equation first!)

    a. 0.1603 grams
    b. 0.4770 grams
    c. 6.048 grams
    d. 1.388 grams
  ! e. 0.4808 grams

65. PI_3 (MW = 411.69 g mol^{-1}) and water (MW = 18.015 g mol^{-1}) react to form H_3PO_3 (MW = 81.996 g mol^{-1}) and HI(MW = 127.91 g mol^{-1}). If 0.5000 moles of phosphorus triiodide and 2.500 moles of water are used, what is the theoretical yield of hydrogen iodide?

    a. 63.96 g of hydrogen iodide should be produced
    b. 205.8 g of hydrogen iodide should be produced
  ! c. 191.9 g of hydrogen iodide should be produced
    d. 319.8 g of hydrogen iodide should be produced
    e. 383.7 g of hydrogen iodide should be produced

66. Phosphorus tribromide (PBr_3, MW = 270.69 g mol^{-1}) and water (MW = 18.015 g mol^{-1}) react to form phosphorous acid (H_3PO_3, MW = 81.996 g mol^{-1}) and hydrogen bromide (MW = 80.912 g mol^{-1}). If 0.5000 moles of phosphorus tribromide react with 2.000 moles of water and 98.048 grams of hydrogen bromide were obtained, what was the percent yield from the reaction?

    a. 72.16 %
    b. 97.22 %
    c. 78.62 %
    d. 85.93 %
!   e. 80.79 %

67. 150.0 grams of AsF_3 was reacted with 180.0 g of CCl_4 to produce $AsCl_3$ and CCl_2F_2. The theoretical yield of CCl_2F_2 produced, in moles, should be

    a. 0.7802 moles
    b. 0.5685 moles
    c. 1.274 moles
!   d. 1.170 moles
    e. 1.705 moles

68. In certain cases, calcium hydroxide and sulfuric acid react to produce calcium bisulfate and water. When 0.0720 moles of sulfuric acid are reacted with 0.0240 moles of calcium hydroxide, how much calcium bisulfate, $Ca(HSO_4)_2$, is produced?

    a. 0.0120 moles
!   b. 0.0240 moles
    c. 0.0360 moles
    d. 0.0480 moles
    e. 0.0720 moles

69. 150.0 grams of AsF_3 was reacted with 180.0 g of CCl_4 to produce $AsCl_3$ and CCl_2F_2. The yield of CCl_2F_2, in grams, should be

!   a. 141.5 grams
    b. 206.2 grams
    c. 137.5 grams
    d. 104.4 grams
    e. 152.6 grams

70. A 0.150 molar solution of sodium chloride in water should be prepared in

    a. a beaker
    b. an erlenmeyer flask
    c. a volumetric pipet
!   d. a volumetric flask
    e. a florence (round bottom) flask

71. A solution is sitting undisturbed on a side shelf in the laboratory. A small crystal of the same solute of which the solution is made was gently dropped into the quiet solution. Suddenly, a mass of crystals formed and settled to the bottom of the container. The solution is, or must have been

    a. dilute
    b. concentrated
    c. unsaturated
    d. saturated
    ! e. supersaturated

72. What is the molar concentration of a solution prepared by dissolving 0.100 moles of potassium nitrate in enough water to prepare 400 mL of the solution?

    a. 2.50×10^{-4} molar
    b. 0.0400 molar
    ! c. 0.250 molar
    d. 4.00 molar
    e. 40.0 molar

73. A solution is made by taking 54.62 grams of K_2CrO_4 in enough water to make 250.0 mL of solution. The molarity of the solution is therefore:

    a. 0.0002813 molar
    b. 0.001125 molar
    c. 0.2813 molar
    ! d. 1.125 molar
    e. 1.409 molar

74. Sodium acetate, $NaC_2H_3O_2$, has a formula weight of 82.034. What is the molar concentration of a solution prepared by dissolving 4.10 grams of sodium acetate in enough water to prepare 250 mL of the solution?

    ! a. 0.200 molar
    b. 1.025 molar
    c. 1.345 molar
    d. 5.00 molar
    e. 16.4 molar

75. Potassium nitrate, KNO_3, has a formula weight of 101.10. What is the molar concentration of a solution prepared by dissolving 7.58 grams of potassium nitrate in enough water to prepare 250 mL of the solution?

    a. 0.0937 molar
    ! b. 0.300 molar
    c. 1.895 molar
    d. 3.065 molar
    e. 3.34 molar

76. A mixture was obtained by mixing the following: 50.0 mL of 0.200 molar NaCl, 25.0 mL of 0.300 molar $BaCl_2$ and 125 mL of 0.150 molar NH_4Cl. The total number of grams of the element, chlorine, in the mixture is

    a. 0.133 grams
    b. 0.428 grams
    c. 0.665 grams
    d. 0.1.47 grams
 ! e. 1.55 grams

77. How many mL of 3.25 molar $(NH_4)_2SO_4(aq)$ would be used, if it must contain 8.60 g of $(NH_4)_2SO_4$ which is to be used up in a chemical reaction?

    a. 2.65 ml
 ! b. 20.0 ml
    c. 50.0 ml
    d. 265 ml
    e. 378 ml

78. How many grams of $NiSO_4 \cdot 7H_2O$ would be required to prepare 500 mL of a solution that is 0.300 molar in $NiSO_4(aq)$?

    a. 0.534 grams
    b. 14.3 grams
    c. 23.2 grams
 ! d. 42.1 grams
    e. 52.2 grams

79. How many grams of $Fe(NO_3)_3 \cdot 9H_2O$ would be required to prepare 250 mL of a solution that is 0.100 molar in $Fe(NO_3)_3(aq)$?

    a. 6.05 grams
 ! b. 10.1 grams
    c. 14.3 grams
    d. 20.2 grams
    e. 52.2 grams

80. 66.7 mL of 18.0 molar sulfuric acid solution was dissolved in enough water to make 500 mL of solution. The molarity of the diluted mixture is

 ! a. 2.40 molar
    b. 0.135 molar
    c. 36.0 molar
    d. 9.00 molar
    e. 0.00741 molar

81. 66.7 mL of 18.0 molar sulfuric acid solution was added to 233.3 mL of 1.50 molar sulfuric acid, and enough water added to make 500 mL of solution. The final molarity of the diluted mixture is

    a. 0.135 molar
    b. 0.318 molar
    c. 1.55 molar
    d. 2.40 molar
! e. 3.10 molar

82. When 25.0 mL of sulfuric acid solution was completely neutralized in a titration with 0.050 molar NaOH solution, it took 18.3 mL of the NaOH(aq) to complete the job. The reaction is:
$$NaOH(aq) + H_2SO_4(aq) \rightarrow Na_2SO_4(aq) + H_2O(l)$$
What was the molarity of the sulfuric acid solution?

    a. 0.0100
    b. 0.0148
! c. 0.0183
    d. 0.0325
    e. 0.0366

83. A student wants to know how many mL of 0.300 molar sulfuric acid is to be added to 50.0 mL of 0.250 molar barium hydroxide solution to neutralize it completely. The reaction is:
$$Ba(OH)_2(aq) + H_2SO_4(aq) \rightarrow BaSO_4(s) + H_2O(l)$$

    a. 20.8 ml
    b. 30.0 ml
! c. 41.7 ml
    d. 60.0 ml
    e. 110 ml

84. How many grams of lead(II) iodate, $Pb(IO_3)_2$, (formula weight = 557.0) are precipitated when 320 mL of 0.285 M $Pb(NO_3)_2(aq)$ are mixed with 386 mL of 0.512 M $NaIO_3(aq)$ solution? The reaction is: $Pb(NO_3)_2(aq) + NaIO_3(aq) \rightarrow Pb(IO_3)_2(s) + NaNO_3(aq)$

    a. 25.4 g
    b. 39.8 g
    c. 48.3 g
! d. 50.8 g
    e. 55.0 g

85. How many mL of 0.200 molar $Na_2SO_4(aq)$ solution are required to completely react with 3.23 grams of $BaCl_2$ (formula weight = 208.2) to form products as shown below?

$$BaCl_2(s) + Na_2SO_4(aq) \rightarrow BaSO_4(s) + NaCl(aq)$$

    a. 0.0155 ml
    b. 0.0776 ml
    c. 15.5 ml
    d. 31.0 ml
!   e. 77.6 ml

86. How many mL of 0.446 molar $KMnO_4(aq)$ are required to react with 50.0 mL of 0.200 molar $H_2C_2O_4(aq)$ in the presence of excess $H_2SO_4(aq)$? The reaction is:

$2 KMnO_4(aq) + 5 H_2C_2O_4(aq) + 3 H_2SO_4(aq) \rightarrow$
$$2 MnSO_4(aq) + 10 CO_2(g) + 8 H_2O + K_2SO_4(aq)$$

!   a. 8.97 ml
    b. 17.9 ml
    c. 44.8 ml
    d. 55.8 ml
    e. 112 ml

87. 45.00 mL of an aqueous H_2SO_4 solution required 32.0 mL of 0.200 molar $NaOH(aq)$ to neutralize it completely. The reaction is:

$$NaOH(aq) + H_2SO_4(aq) \rightarrow Na_2SO_4(aq) + H_2O(l)$$

The molarity of the H_2SO_4 solution is therefore:

!   a. 0.0711 molar
    b. 0.142 molar
    c. 0.200 molar
    d. 0.281 molar
    e. 0.284 molar

88. A 2.710 g sample contains some $CaCl_2$, which is inert to $HCl(aq)$ and also some CaO, which reacts: $CaO(s) + HCl(aq) \rightarrow CaCl_2 (aq) + H_2O(l)$. It took 32.05 mL of 2.445 molar $HCl(aq)$ to react completely with all the CaO in the sample. The percent, by weight, of CaO in the sample is

    a. 35.15 %
    b. 61.67 %
    c. 77.62 %
!   d. 81.08 %
    e. 84.17 %

89. How many mL of 0.200 molar NaOH(aq) solution are required to neutralize 1.858 g of $KHC_8H_4O_4$ (formula weight = 204.22) if the reaction is

$$NaOH(aq) + KHC_8H_4O_4 \rightarrow Na\ KC_8H_4O_4(aq) + H_2O(l)$$

    a. 1.82 ml
    b. 4.55 ml
! c. 45.5 ml
    d. 75.9 ml
    e. 550 ml

90. How many mL of 6.00 molar HCl(aq) solution are required to completely consume a 27.5 g sample of zinc metal (atomic weight = 65.39) if the reaction is

$$Zn(s) + HCl(aq) \rightarrow ZnCl_2(aq) + H_2(g)$$

    a. 126 ml
! b. 140 ml
    c. 280 ml
    d. 1.26×10^3 ml
    e. 2.52×10^3 ml

91. A 50.0 mL sample of 0.200 molar $AgNO_3(aq)$ was allowed to react with an excess of NaCl(aq). The AgCl precipitate which resulted from the reaction as shown below was carefully dried and weighed. How many grams of precipitate should be obtained?

$$AgNO_3(aq) + NaCl(aq) \rightarrow AgCl(s) + NaNO_3(aq)$$

    a. 1.08 g
! b. 1.43 g
    c. 1.70 g
    d. 3.13 g
    e. 62.6 g

92. A 50.0 mL sample of a 0.200 molar aqueous solution of Na_3PO_4 was added to 50.0 mL of a 0.100 molar aqueous solution of $BaCl_2$. The mixture was stirred and the precipitate was collected, dried carefully, and weighed. How many grams of precipitate should be obtained? The reaction is shown below

$$Na_3PO_4(aq) + BaCl_2(aq) \rightarrow Ba_3(PO_4)_2(s) + NaCl(aq)$$

! a. 1.00 g
    b. 1.50 g
    c. 3.01 g
    d. 4.01 g
    e. 9.03 g

93. A 100.0 mL sample of a 0.200 molar aqueous solution of K_2CrO_4 was added to 100.0 mL of a 0.100 molar aqueous solution of $BaCl_2$. The mixture was stirred and the precipitate was collected, dried carefully, and weighed. How many grams of precipitate should be obtained? The reaction is shown below

$$K_2CrO_4(aq) + BaCl_2(aq) \rightarrow BaCrO_4(s) + KCl(aq)$$

    a. 2.05 g
! b. 2.53 g
    c. 5.07 g
    d. 6.16 g
    e. 7.60 g

Fill in the Blanks

94. A sample of naturally occurring carbon contains 0.800 moles of C atoms. How many atoms are there in the sample? _____ (! 4.82×10^{23} atoms)

95. The mass, in grams, of 3.00 moles of phosphorus (P_4), is _____ grams. (! 372)

96. A sample of Na_2SO_4 weighing 7.10 grams contains _____ moles. (! 0.0500)

97. One formula unit of $(NH_4)_2ClO_4$ contains _____ nitrogen atoms. (! 15)

98. The number of moles of iron atoms which are combined with 7.28 moles of oxygen atoms in a sample of the compound, Fe_3O_4, is _____ (! 5.46)

99. A sample of ozone, O_3, contains 3.011×10^{12} atoms (10^{12} represents a trillion). This also represents _____ moles of ozone. (! 1.667×10^{-12})

100. The percent, by weight, of sulfur in $(NH_4)_2SO_4$ is _____ (! 24.267 %)

101. An aqueous solution of 0.2200 molar ammonium nortonate (M = 159.83 g mol^{-1}) contains 26.37 grams of solute. What is the volume of the solution, in ml? _____ (! 750.0 ml)

102. How many grams of iron are there in a sample of Fe_3O_4 which weighs 8.338 grams? _____ (! 6.033 g)

103. Students in a laboratory class were provided with 6.00 molar hydrochloric acid solution from the stockroom. The instructions in the experiment for that day called for 250 mL of 2.00 molar hydrochloric acid per student. How many liters of the 6.00 molar solution should be used to prepare enough hydrochloric acid solution for a lab class with 12 students if the students work individually and the one student assigned the task of preparing the batch is told to make 25.0% more than they actually need. _____ (! 1.25 liters)

104. A 250.0 mL sample of a solution containing potassium dichromate as the only solute was evaporated to dryness, then the residue was carefully dried in the oven at the recommended temperature. The oven-dried residue weighed 16.58 grams. What was the molarity of the potassium dichromate solution? _____ (! 0.2254 molar)

True and False

105. A mole of oxygen, O_2, and a mole of phosphorus, P_4, do not contain the same number of molecules. (! F)

106. The molecular formula for a substance can never contain fewer atoms than the empirical formula for the same substance. (! T)

107. A mole of naturally occurring neon weighs more than a mole of naturally occurring oxygen. ____ (! F)

108. NaCl, a compound which can be prepared from a highly toxic gaseous element and a highly poisonous metal, is a very toxic substance. (! F)

109. A 0.540 molar aqueous solution of sodium tetrafluoroborate (M = 109.79 g mol^{-1}) contains 14.82 grams of solute in 250 mL of solution. (! T)

110. A mole of nitrogen gas, N_2, and a mole of carbon dioxide gas, CO_2, contain the same number of molecules. (! T)

Critical Thinking

111. In a quantitative analysis study, 4.624 grams of a compound containing carbon, hydrogen, and oxygen only yielded 7.210 g of CO_2 and 2.656 g of H_2O in a combustion analysis apparatus. Determine the empirical formula of the compound.

      a. $C_9H_{16}O_8$
! b. $C_{10}H_{18}O_9$
      c. $C_{11}H_{20}O_{10}$
      d. $C_{12}H_{22}O_{11}$
      e. $C_{13}H_{24}O_{12}$

112. The reactant and product in a chemical reaction are shown below,
$$P_4O_{10} + Ca(OH)_2 \rightarrow Ca_3(PO_4)_2 + H_2O$$
If you start with 2.40 moles of P_4O_{10} and 3.30 moles of $Ca(OH)_2$ and only the excess remains,

! a. 1.10 moles of $Ca_3(PO_4)_2$ are produced
    b. 0.90 moles of $Ca(OH)_2$ are left over
    c. 2.40 moles of $Ca_3(PO_4)_2$ are produced
    d. 1.65 moles of $Ca_3(PO_4)_2$ are produced
    e. 0.60 moles of P_4O_{10} are consumed

113. A 5.000 g sample of a mixture which contains $MgCO_3$ *and* sand (SiO_2) was strongly heated for 2.30 hours until no further reaction occurred. It was then cooled and the residue, which contained MgO and unchanged sand, was weighed. The reaction is: $MgCO_3 \rightarrow MgO + CO_2(g)$. The residue remaining (minus the CO_2 which was completely driven off) weighed 3.397 grams. Calculate the percent, by weight, of $MgCO_3$ in the original sample.

    a. 22.59 %
    b. 50.00 %
  ! c. 61.42 %
    d. 90.40 %
    e. 95.01 %

114. A mixture, weighing 6.000 grams, contains Na_3PO_4 (41.50%) and $BaCl_2$ (58.50 % of the mixture, by weight). When dissolved in water, a precipitate forms via the double displacement reaction:
$$BaCl_2(aq) + Na_3PO_4(aq) \rightarrow NaCl(aq) + Ba_3(PO_4)_2(s)$$
If the reaction is quantitative, the yield of the solid barium phosphate should be

  ! a. 3.382 grams
    b. 3.357 grams
    c. 4.571 grams
    d. 3.510 grams
    e. 1.983 grams

115. A mixture containing silver nitrate ($AgNO_3$) and potassium nitrate (KNO_3), weighing 5.000 grams, was treated with an **excess** of potassium chloride. A **quantitative** reaction, the reaction of silver nitrate with potassium chloride occurred, and 1.582 grams of a white precipitate, silver chloride, was obtained. Determine the percent, by weight, of silver nitrate in the original mixture.

    a. 32.55 %
  ! b. 37.50 %
    c. 42.50 %
    d. 62.50 %
    e. 62.74 %

116. Lead sulfide, in ores, can be assayed by the reaction:
$2\, PbS(s) + 6\, HNO_3(aq) + K_2Cr_2O_7(aq) \rightarrow$
$$2\, PbCrO_4(s) + 2\, S(s) + 4\, NO_2(g) + 2\, KNO_3(aq) + 3\, H_2O$$
A 6.053 g sample of ore, treated with excess nitric acid and potassium dichromate yielded 6.094 g of $PbCrO_4(s)$. Calculate the percent, by weight, of lead sulfide in the ore.

    a. 68.22%
  ! b. 74.53%
    c. 77.22%
    d. 79.16%
    e. 83.11%

117. A student is working on a research project. The instructions in the book on how to prepare $Ni(NH_3)_6Cl_2$ say that the percent yield in this preparation is 75.5 %. If the limiting reagent is $NiCl_2·6H_2O$, and the student needs 50.0 grams of the $Ni(NH_3)_6Cl_2$ for the next step, how many grams of the $NiCl_2·6H_2O$ should the student start with to prepare the desired quantity of the $Ni(NH_3)_6Cl_2$? _____ (! 67.9 grams)

118. A laboratory manual gave precise instructions for carrying out the reaction described in the chemical equation, $C_2H_6O + O_2 \rightarrow C_2H_4O_2 + H_2O$. It stated that if you bubble oxygen gas through a solution containing the reactant for 24 hours under a well defined set of conditions, then the yield of $C_2H_4O_2$ would be 7.50% of the theoretical amount. If you desire to produce 700 grams of the $C_2H_4O_2$ in a single batch, how many kg of C_2H_6O should you begin with? _____ (! 7.16 kg)

119. Calcium nortonate, $CaNtO_4$, is 54.698% nortonium, by weight. Calculate the percent, by weight, of sodium in sodium nortonate. _____ (! 19.513%)

120. A high school friend who is working part time as a technician in a chemical manufacturing plant needs help with this problem. He has some 6.00 molar aqueous sulfuric acid and some 0.500 molar aqueous sulfuric acid. The water supply has been shut off, and he wants to make up 2.000 liters of 1.20 molar aqueous sulfuric acid from just the two reagents above. How many mL of each should he take to make up the 2.000 liters? _____ (! 255 mL of 6.00 molar and 1745 mL of 0.500 molar)

121. An sample being given as a laboratory unknown is a mixture of calcium carbonate and magnesium carbonate. Both substances decompose to form the respective binary oxide and carbon dioxide when heated at a high temperature for a prolonged period. An unknown sample weighing 5.424 grams was decomposed by heating for several hours at 950 °C. The oxide residue which remained weighed 2.791 grams. From this laboratory data calculate the percent, by weight, of calcium carbonate in the unknown. _____ (! 44.42 %)

122. The mineral dolomite has the formula, $CaCO_3·MgCO_3$. When dolomite is heated for an extended period of time at elevated temperatures it decomposes to give carbon dioxide and a mixture of calcium oxide and magnesium oxide. If a 5.424 g sample of this mineral substance is heated for several hours at 950 °C, how many grams should the mixed oxide residue remaining weigh? _____ (! 2.835 g)

Chemicals in Our World 2: Silicon—An Element for the Twenty-first Century

123. Which one of the following applications is *not* one for which silicon has a present of projected future application?

      a. transistors
      b. computer chips
      c. micro-electromechanical systems (MEMS)
      d. biochips
  ! e. magnetic resonance imaging (MRI)

124. Which one of the following is not a property of silicon which makes it useful for industrial purposes?

      a. stability to heat
      b. natural abundance in readily available minerals
      c. chemical stability
      d. ease of fabrication by machining
 !   e. high electrical conductivity

123. Silicon can be found in a nearly pure state (96 % pure or better) in nature. (! F)

124. The mineral substance from which most of the silicon used in industry is obtained is

      a. silicon carbide
      b. calcium silicate
      c. iron(II) silicate
 !   d. sand
      e. aluminum silicate

Chapter 4 Reactions between Ions in Aqueous Solution

Multiple Choice

1. Which one of the following is a nonelectrolyte?

     a. aqueous barium nitrate solution
     b. aqueous calcium chloride solution
     c. aqueous lithium phosphate solution
   ! d. aqueous methyl alcohol solution
     e. aqueous potassium sulfate solution

2. Which one of the following is an electrolyte?

     a. aqueous maple syrup solution
   ! b. aqueous calcium chloride solution
     c. aqueous sucrose solution
     d. aqueous acetone solution
     e. aqueous ethyl alcohol solution

3. Which one of the following is an electrolyte?

     a. aqueous glucose solution
     b. aqueous acetone solution
     c. aqueous ethylene glycol solution
     d. aqueous methyl alcohol solution
   ! e. aqueous potassium sulfate solution

4. Which one of the following is a nonelectrolyte?

     a. aqueous ammonium chloride solution
   ! b. aqueous ethylene glycol solution
     c. aqueous nickel sulfate solution
     d. aqueous sodium perchlorate solution
     e. aqueous zinc nitrate solution

5. Given the following set of solutions
     A: aqueous sodium perchlorate   B: aqueous methyl alcohol
     C: aqueous glucose   D: aqueous calcium chloride
     E: aqueous nickel sulfate
    Which of these solutions are electrolyte solutions?

     a. A and E, only
     b. C, D and E, only
     c. A and D, only
   ! d. A, D and E, only
     e. B, D and E, only

6. Given the following set of solutions
    A: aqueous acetone B: aqueous silver nitrate
    C: aqueous ethylene glycol D: aqueous calcium chloride
    E: aqueous ammonium bromide
    Which of these solutions are electrolyte solutions?

        a. A and E, only
        b. C, D and E, only
        c. A and D, only
        d. A, D and E, only
    !   e. B, D and E, only

7. Which one of the following compounds produces 4 ions per formula unit by dissociation when dissolved in water?

        a. $(NH_4)_2SO_4$
        b. Hg_2Cl_2
        c. $Ca(NO_3)_2$
    !   d. Li_3PO_4
        e. $(NH_4)_4Fe(CN)_6$

8. Which one of the following compounds produces 4 ions per formula unit by dissociation when dissolved in water?

        a. $K_2C_2O_4$
    !   b. $Al(NO_3)_3$
        c. $Hg_2(NO_3)_2$
        d. $NaBrO_3$
        e. $Na_2S_2O_3$

9. Which one of the following compounds produces 3 ions per formula unit by dissociation when dissolved in water?

        a. sodium nitrate
        b. nickel sulfate
    !   c. calcium perchlorate
        d. aluminum sulfate
        e. ammonium bromate

10. Which one of the following compounds produces 3 ions per formula unit by dissociation when dissolved in water?

        a. Hg_2SO_4
        b. $NaClO_2$
        c. $LiClO_4$
        d. $KClO$
    !   e. $(NH_4)_2SO_4$

11. How many ions are produced in solution by dissociation of 1 formula unit of $NiCl_2 \cdot 6H_2O$?

      a. 2
! b. 3
      c. 4
      d. 6
      e. 9

12. How many ions are produced in solution by dissociation of 1 formula unit of $Co(NO_3)_2 \cdot 6H_2O$?

      a. 2
! b. 3
      c. 4
      d. 6
      e. 9

13. In the reaction, $K_2SO_4(aq) + Ba(NO_3)_2(aq) \rightarrow BaSO_4(s) + 2\ KNO_3(aq)$, which ions are the spectator ions?

      a. Ba^{2+} and SO_4^{2-}
      b. Ba^{2+} and K^+
      c. Ba^{2+} and NO_3^-
      d. K^+ and SO_4^{2-}
! e. K^+ and NO_3^-

14. In the reaction, $KHS(aq) + HCl(aq) \rightarrow KCl(aq) + H_2S(g)$, which ions are the spectator ions?

! a. K^+ and Cl^-
      b. K^+ and H^+
      c. H^+ and HS^-
      d. K^+ and HS^-
      e. HS^- and Cl^-

15. The equation for the reaction,
$$Pb(NO_3)_2(aq) + NaCl(aq) \rightarrow PbCl_2(s) + NaNO_3(aq)$$
can be written as a net ionic equation. In this net ionic equation, the spectator ions are

      a. Na^+ and Pb^{2+}
      b. Na^+ and Cl^-
      c. Pb^{2+} and Cl^-
      d. Pb^{2+} and NO_3^-
! e. Na^+ and NO_3^-

16. The equation for the reaction,

$$BaCl_2(aq) + K_2CrO_4(aq) \rightarrow BaCrO_4(s) + KCl(aq)$$

can be written as a net ionic equation. In this net ionic equation, the spectator ions are

    a. Ba^{2+} and K^+
    b. K^+ and CrO_4^{2-}
! c. K^+ and Cl^-
    d. B^{2+} and CrO_4^{2-}
    e. Cl^- and CrO_4^{2-}

17. The equation for the reaction,

$$AgNO_3(aq) + K_2CrO_4(aq) \rightarrow Ag_2CrO_4(s) + KNO_3(aq)$$

can be written as a net ionic equation. In this net ionic equation, the spectator ions are

    a. Ag^+ and K^+
    b. Ag^+ and CrO_4^{2-}
    c. K^+ and CrO_4^{2-}
! d. K^+ and NO_3^-
    e. CrO_4^{2-} and NO_3^-

18. Which set of compounds below is a set in which all members are considered soluble in water?

    a. $BaCO_3$, $NaBrO_3$, $Ca(OH)_2$, and $PbCl_2$
! b. $NaCl$, $BaCl_2$, NH_4NO_3, and $LiClO_4$
    c. $NiCO_3$, $PbSO_4$, $AgCl$, and $Mg(OH)_2$
    d. $NaCl$, $AgBr$, Na_2CO_3, and $Hg_2(NO_3)_2$
    e. $PbCl_2$, $Pb(NO_3)_2$, $AgClO_4$, and $HgCl_2$

19. Which set of compounds below is a set in which all members are considered insoluble in water?

    a. $BaCO_3$, $NaBrO_3$, $Ca(OH)_2$, and $PbCl_2$
    b. $NaCl$, $BaCl_2$, NH_4NO_3, and $LiClO_4$
    c. $NaCl$, $AgBr$, Na_2CO_3, and $Hg_2(NO_3)_2$
! d. $NiCO_3$, $PbSO_4$, $AgCl$, and $Mg(OH)_2$
    e. $PbCl_2$, $Pb(NO_3)_2$, $AgClO_4$, and $HgCl_2$

20. Which set of compounds below is a set in which all members are considered insoluble in water?

    a. $BaSO_4$, $BaCl_2$, $BaCO_3$, and $Ba(OH)_2$
    b. $CrSO_4$, $CrCl_2$, $Cr(ClO_4)_2$, and Cr
    c. Na_2SO_4, $NaCl$, Na_2CO_3, and $NaOH$
    d. $NiSO_4$, $NiCl_2$, $Ni(C_2H_3O_2)_2$, and $NiCO_3$
! e. $PbSO_4$, $PbCl_2$, $PbCO_3$, and $Pb(OH)_2$

21. According to the Arrhenius theory of Acids and Bases, acids are substances which

    a. exhibit a sour taste
    b. react with all metals to release hydrogen gas
    c. react with all metals to release carbon dioxide gas
 ! d. release hydrogen ions when dissolved in water to form a solution
    e. turn litmus paper from blue to red

22. Which one of the equations below represents what occurs when $HC_2H_3O_2$ is dissolved in some water?

    a. $HC_2H_3O_2 + H_2O \rightarrow H_3O^+(aq) + C_2H_3O_2^-(aq)$
 ! b. $HC_2H_3O_2 + H_2O \rightleftharpoons H_3O^+(aq) + C_2H_3O_2^-(aq)$
    c. $HC_2H_3O_2 + H_2O \rightleftharpoons C_2H_3O_2^+(aq) + OH^-(aq)$
    d. $HC_2H_3O_2 + H_2O \rightleftharpoons H_3O^-(aq) + C_2H_3O_2^+(aq)$
    e. $HC_2H_3O_2 + H_2O \rightleftharpoons 2H^+(aq) + OH^-(aq) + C_2H_3O_2^-(aq)$

23. Which one of the following listed species is a molecular base?

    a. $NaOH(s)$
 ! b. $NH_3(g)$
    c. $C_2H_5OH(l)$
    d. $Li_2O(s)$
    e. $NH_4^+(aq)$

24. Which one of the following is the acid anhydride for the acid, $HCl(aq)$?

    a. ClO
    b. ClO_2
    c. Cl_2O_7
 ! d. $HCl(aq)$ does not have an anhydride
    e. H_2O

25. Which one of the following is the acid anhydride for the acid, $HClO_4$?

    a. ClO
    b. ClO_2
    c. ClO_3
    d. ClO_4
 ! e. Cl_2O_7

26. Which one of the following is a basic anhydride?

    a. $SO_2(g)$
    b. $CO_2(g)$
    c. $O_2(g)$
    ! d. $BaO(s)$
    e. $N_2O_5(s)$

27. The chemical species present in all solutions which are moderately to strongly acidic, which is responsible for the acidic property is

    a. $H_2O(aq)$
    b. $OH^-(aq)$
    c. $H_2O^+(aq)$
    d. $H_3O^+(l)$
    ! e. $H_3O^+(aq)$

28. The anhydride of orthophosphoric acid, H_3PO_4, is

    a. PO_2
    b. PO_3
    c. P_2O_3
    ! d. P_4O_{10}
    e. P_2O

29. Which one of the following substances will *ionize* when dissolved in water to form an aqueous solution?

    a. $NaClO_4(s)$
    ! b. $HNO_3(l)$
    c. $C_6H_{12}O_6(s)$
    d. $(NH_4)_2SO_4(s)$
    e. $Ba(OH)_2(s)$

30. Which statement below is correctly worded and states a fact?

    a. Ionic acids are strong electrolytes and ionize completely when dissolved in water.
    b. Ionic bases are weak electrolytes and ionize completely when dissolved in water.
    c. Ionic bases are strong electrolytes and ionize completely when dissolved in water.
    ! d. Ionic salts are strong electrolytes and dissociate completely when dissolved in water.
    e. Ionic salts are weak electrolytes and ionize partially when dissolved in water.

31. Which statement below is correctly worded and states a fact?

    a. All acids are strong electrolytes and dissociate completely when dissolved in water.
    ! b. Some acids are strong electrolytes and ionize completely when dissolved in water.
    c. Some acids are strong electrolytes and dissociate completely when dissolved in water.
    d. Some acids are weak electrolytes and ionize completely when dissolved in water.
    e. Some acids are weak electrolytes and dissociate partially when dissolved in water.

32. Which one of the following species is a weak electrolyte?

    a. $HClO_4(aq)$
    b. $HCl(aq)$
    c. $NaOH(aq)$
    ! d. $NH_3(aq)$
    e. $LiOH(aq)$

33. Which one of the following acids is NOT a known strong acid?

    a. $HBr(aq)$
    b. $HCl(aq)$
    c. $HClO_3(aq)$
    ! d. $HF(aq)$
    e. $HI(aq)$

34. Which one of the following bases is NOT a known strong base?

    a. $Ca(OH)_2(aq)$
    b. $Ba(OH)_2(aq)$
    c. $KOH(aq)$
    d. $NaOH(aq)$
    ! e. $NH_3(aq)$

35. Which one of the following acids is NOT a known strong acid?

    a. $HBr(aq)$
    ! b. $HC_2H_3O_2(aq)$
    c. $HClO_3(aq)$
    d. $HClO_4(aq)$
    e. $HNO_3(aq)$

36. Which one of the following acids is a known strong acid?

    a. $HBrO(aq)$
    b. $HClO_2(aq)$
    c. $HF(aq)$
    ! d. $HI(aq)$
    e. $H_3PO_3(aq)$

37. Which set below represents a group containing *only* weak electrolytes?

       a. $HNO_3(aq)$, $H_2SO_4(aq)$, $HCN(aq)$
       b. $KOH(aq)$, $H_3PO_4(aq)$, $NaClO_4(aq)$
!   c. $NH_3(aq)$, $HC_2H_3O_2(aq)$, $HCN(aq)$
       d. $NH_4Cl(aq)$, $HClO_2(aq)$, $HCN(aq)$
       e. $NaOH(aq)$, $H_2SO_4(aq)$, $HC_2H_3O_2(aq)$

38. An acid-base neutralization is the reaction of

       a. $H_2(g)$ with $O_2(g)$ to form $H_2O(l)$
       b. $H_2(aq)$ with $OH^-(aq)$ to form $H_2O(l)$
       c. $H^+(aq)$ with $O_2(g)$ to form $H_2O(l)$
!   d. $H^+(aq)$ with $OH^-(aq)$ to form $H_2O(l)$
       e. $Na^+(aq)$ with $OH^-(aq)$ to form $NaOH(aq)$

39. Which one of the following listed solutions is the least acidic (contains the lowest concentration of hydronium ions due to small degree of ionization)?

       a. 1.0 molar $HCl(aq)$
       b. 1.0 molar $H_2SO_4(aq)$
       c. 1.0 molar $HClO_4(aq)$
       d. 1.0 molar $HNO_3(aq)$
!   e. 1.0 molar $HCHO_2(aq)$

40. Which set below represents a group containing only weak acids?

!   a. $HC_2H_3O_2(aq)$, $HCN(aq)$, $HNO_2(aq)$
       b. $HC_2H_3O_2(aq)$, $HCN(aq)$, $HNO_3(aq)$
       c. $HC_2H_3O_2(aq)$, $HCl(aq)$, $HNO_2(aq)$
       d. $HClO(aq)$, $HCN(aq)$, $HBrO_3(aq)$
       e. $HNO_2(aq)$, $HC_2H_3O_2(aq)$, $HI(aq)$

41. A dynamic equilibrium is soon reached when acetic acid is dissolved in water. Which of the species shown below is present in largest amount in the solution?

       a. $C_2H_3O_2^-$
       b. H^+
!   c. $HC_2H_3O_2$
       d. H_3O^+
       e. OH^-

42. CH_3NH_2 is the formula for a molecular base. When this base is dissolved in water a small fraction of it ionizes. The formula for one of the products of this ionization is

      a. NH_2^+
      b. CH_3NH^-
      c. $CH_3NH_2^+$
  ! d. $CH_3NH_3^+$
      e. NH_3^+

43. Boiler scale can be formed from ground water due to

  ! a. transformation of HCO_3^- ions to CO_3^{2-} ions which then form precipitates with the "hardness ions", Ca^{2+}, Mg^{2+}, Fe^{2+}, and/or Fe^{3+}
      b. transformation of HSO_3^- ions to SO_3^{2-} ions which then form precipitates with the "hardness ions", Ca^{2+}, Mg^{2+}, Fe^{2+}, and/or Fe^{3+}
      c. transformation of HSO_4^- ions to SO_4^{2-} ions which then form precipitates with the "hardness ions", Ca^{2+}, Mg^{2+}, Fe^{2+}, and/or Fe^{3+}
      d. transformation of $H_2PO_4^-$ ions to PO_4^{3-} ions which then form precipitates with the "hardness ions", Ca^{2+}, Mg^{2+}, Fe^{2+}, and/or Fe^{3+}
      e. reaction of the CO_3^{2-} ions present in all ground water with the "hardness ions", Ca^{2+}, Mg^{2+}, Fe^{2+}, and/or Fe^{3+}

44. The "hardness ions", Ca^{2+}, Mg^{2+}, Fe^{2+}, and/or Fe^{3+}, which are present in all ground water, can be removed by pretreating the water before use with

      a. $CaCl_2$
      b. KNO_3
  ! c. $Na_2CO_3 \cdot 10H_2O$
      d. $PbSO_4$
      e. 0.0100 M HCl(*aq*)

45. Which one of the following is *not* an example of an acid salt?

      a. aluminum bicarbonate
      b. barium dihydrogen phosphate
      c. nickel(II) bichromate
  ! d. potassium monohydrogen chloride
      e. sodium monohydrogen sulfate

46. Which one of the following is *not* an example of an acid salt?

      a. ammonium dihydrogen arsenate
      b. barium bicarbonate
      c. chromium(III) monohydrogen sulfate
  ! d. cobalt(II) monohydrogen acetate
      e. nickel(II) bichromate

47. Which statement below is *not* correct?

 ! a. Acid salts can be formed by partial neutralization of a monoprotic acid by a monoprotic base.
   b. Acid salts can be formed by partial neutralization of a diprotic acid by a monoprotic base.
   c. Acid salts can be formed by partial neutralization of a diprotic acid by a diprotic base.
   d. Acid salts can be formed by partial neutralization of a triprotic acid by a diprotic base.
   e. Acid salts can be formed by partial neutralization of a polyprotic acid by a monoprotic base.

48. The reaction, $BaCl_2(aq) + H_2SO_4(aq) \rightarrow BaSO_4(s) + 2\,HCl(aq)$ is an example of

   a. An ionic redox reaction
   b. An ionic neutralization reaction
   c. A molecular neutralization reaction
 ! d. A molecular precipitation reaction
   e. A molecular redox reaction

49. Complete neutralization of orthophosphoric acid with barium hydroxide yields $Ba_3(PO_4)_2$ as one of the products when it is separated and dried. This indicates the orthophosphoric acid is a

   a. monoprotic acid
   b. diprotic acid
 ! c. triprotic acid
   d. tetraprotic acid
   e. hexaprotic acid

50. One of the phosphoric acids, when fully neutralized by treatment with barium hydroxide yields, as one of its products, a substance with the formula, $Ba_2P_2O_7$. The parent acid for the anion in this compound is a

   a. monoprotic acid
   b. diprotic acid
   c. triprotic acid
 ! d. tetraprotic acid
   e. hexaprotic acid

51. Which one of the reactions below will yield $NiCr_2O_7$ as one of its products?

 ! a. nickel(II) hydroxide and dichromic acid
   b. nickelic acid and chromium(II) hydroxide
   c. nickel(II) hydroxide and chromic acid
   d. nickel(II) hydroxide and chromate acid
   e. nickel(II) hydroxide and bichromic acid

52. $ZnCO_3(s)$ is insoluble in water, but dissolves in excess 6.0 molar $HCl(aq)$. Which set below best fits as a description of what takes place?

    a. $ZnCO_3(s) \rightarrow Zn^{2+}(aq) + CO_3^{2-}(aq)$
    b. $ZnCO_3(s) + H_2O(l) \rightarrow ZnO(aq) + H_2CO_3(aq)$
! c. $ZnCO_3(s) + 2 H^+(aq) \rightarrow Zn^{2+}(aq) + H_2O(l) + CO_2(g)$
    d. $ZnCO_3(s) + 2 H_2O(l) \rightarrow Zn(OH)_2(aq) + H_2CO_3(aq)$
    e. $ZnCO_3(s) + 2 H_2O(l) \rightarrow Zn(OH)_2(aq) + H_2O(l) + CO_2(g)$

53. Which one of the following choices represents the net reaction which actually takes place in solution when $HClO_4(aq)$ is added to $NH_3(aq)$?

    a. $HClO_4(aq) + NH_3(aq) \rightarrow NH_4ClO_4(aq)$
    b. $H^+(aq) + OH^-(aq) \rightarrow H_2O(l)$
    c. $HClO_4(aq) + OH^-(aq) \rightarrow ClO_4^-(aq) + H_2O(l)$
! d. $H^+(aq) + NH_3(aq) \rightarrow NH_4^+(aq)$
    e. $HClO_4(aq) + NH_4OH(aq) \rightarrow H_2O(l) + NH_4ClO_4(aq)$

54. Which one of the following choices represents the net reaction which actually takes place in solution when $HC_2H_3O_2(aq)$ is added to $Ba(OH)_2(aq)$?

    a. $HC_2H_3O_2(aq) + Ba(OH)_2(aq) \rightarrow Ba(C_2H_3O_2)_2(aq) + H_2O(l)$
    b. $H^+(aq) + OH^-(aq) \rightarrow H_2O(l)$
! c. $HC_2H_3O_2(aq) + OH^-(aq) \rightarrow C_2H_3O_2^-(aq) + H_2O(l)$
    d. $H^+(aq) + Ba(OH)_2(aq) \rightarrow Ba^{2+}(aq) + H_2O(l)$
    e. $HC_2H_3O_2(aq) + Ba^{2+}(aq) \rightarrow Ba(C_2H_3O_2)_2(aq) + H^+(aq)$

55. Which one of the following choices represents the net reaction which actually takes place in solution when $HC_2H_3O_2(aq)$ is added to $NH_3(aq)$?

! a. $HC_2H_3O_2(aq) + NH_3(aq) \rightarrow NH_4^+(aq) + C_2H_3O_2^-aq)$
    b. $H^+(aq) + OH^-(aq) \rightarrow H_2O(l)$
    c. $HC_2H_3O_2(aq) + OH^-(aq) \rightarrow C_2H_3O_2^-(aq) + H_2O(l)$
    d. $H^+(aq) + NH_4OH(aq) \rightarrow NH_4^+(aq) + H_2O(l)$
    e. $HC_2H_3O_2(aq) + NH_4OH(aq) \rightarrow H_2O(l) + NH_4ClO_4(aq)$

56. Which one of the following choices represents the net reaction which actually takes place in solution when $HClO_3(aq)$ is added to $KOH(aq)$?

    a. $HClO_3(aq) + KOH(aq) \rightarrow KClO_3(aq) + H_2O(l)$
! b. $H^+(aq) + OH^-(aq) \rightarrow H_2O(l)$
    c. $HClO_3(aq) + OH^-(aq) \rightarrow ClO_3^-(aq) + H_2O(l)$
    d. $H^+(aq) + KOH(aq) \rightarrow K^+(aq) + H_2O(l)$
    e. $HClO_3(aq) + K^+(aq) \rightarrow KClO_3(aq) + H^+(aq)$

57. Which one of the following choices represents the net reaction which actually takes place in solution when $HNO_3(aq)$ is added to $Mg(OH)_2(s)$?

    a. $HNO_3(aq) + Mg(OH)_2(s) \rightarrow Mg(NO_3)_2(aq) + H_2O(l)$
    b. $H^+(aq) + OH^-(aq) \rightarrow H_2O(l)$
    c. $HNO_3(aq) + OH^-(s) \rightarrow NO_3^-(aq) + H_2O(l)$
! d. $H^+(aq) + Mg(OH)_2(s) \rightarrow Mg^{2+}(aq) + H_2O(l)$
    e. $HNO_3(aq) + Mg^{2+}(aq) \rightarrow Mg(NO_3)_2(aq) + H^+(aq)$

58. Which one of the following choices represents the net reaction which actually takes place in solution when $HNO_3(aq)$ is added to $Fe_2O_3(s)$?

    a. $HNO_3(aq) + Fe_2O_3(s) \rightarrow Fe(NO_3)_3(aq) + H_2O(l)$
    b. $H^+(aq) + OH^-(aq) \rightarrow H_2O(l)$
    c. $HNO_3(aq) + OH^-(s) \rightarrow NO_3^-(aq) + H_2O(l)$
! d. $H^+(aq) + Fe_2O_3(s) \rightarrow Fe^{3+}(aq) + H_2O(l)$
    e. $HNO_3(aq) + Fe^{3+}(aq) \rightarrow Fe(NO_3)_3(aq) + H^+(aq)$

59. Which one of the following choices represents the net reaction which actually takes place in solution when $HCl(aq)$ is added to $CaCO_3(s)$?

    a. $HCl(aq) + CaCO_3(s) \rightarrow CaCl_2(aq) + CO_2(g) + H_2O(l)$
! b. $H^+(aq) + CaCO_3(s) \rightarrow Ca^{2+}(aq) + CO_2(g) + H_2O(l)$
    c. $HCl(aq) + CO_3^{2-}(aq) \rightarrow Cl^-(aq) + H_2O(l) + CO_2(g)$
    d. $Cl^-(aq) + CaCO_3(s) \rightarrow CaCl_2(aq) + CO_3^{2-}(aq)$
    e. $HCl(aq) + CaCO_3(s) \rightarrow Ca^{2+}(aq) + Cl_2(g) + CO_2(g) + H_2O(l)$

60. Which one of the following choices represents the net reaction which actually takes place in solution when $Ba(OH)_2(aq)$ is added to $NH_4Cl(aq)$?

! a. $NH_4^+(aq) + OH^-(aq) \rightarrow NH_3(aq) + H_2O(l)$
    b. $NH_4^+(aq) + Ba(OH)_2(aq) \rightarrow Ba^{2+}(aq) + NH_3(aq) + H_2O(l)$
    c. $NH_4Cl(aq) + OH^-(aq) \rightarrow NH_3(aq) + H_2O(l) + Cl^-(aq)$
    d. $H^+(aq) + Cl^-(aq) \rightarrow HCl(aq)$
    e. $Ba(OH)_2(aq) + NH_4Cl(aq) \rightarrow BaCl_2(aq) + NH_4OH(aq)$

61. Which of the following properties is NOT a characteristic of solutions of strong acids

! a. react with metals to yield CO_2 gas
    b. exhibit a sour taste
    c. turn litmus from blue to red
    d. neutralize bases
    e. react with carbonate salts to yield CO_2 gas

62. Which reaction below can be used to produce carbon dioxide gas?

        a. react aqueous ammonia with aqueous sodium carbonate
        b. react aqueous barium hydroxide solution with solid calcium carbonate
        c. react aqueous barium hydroxide solution with aqueous carbonic acid (H_2CO_3)
 !   d. react aqueous sulfuric acid and solid calcium carbonate
        e. react sodium metal with aqueous carbonic acid (H_2CO_3)

63. Which reaction below can be used to produce sulfur dioxide gas?

        a. react aqueous barium hydroxide solution with aqueous sodium sulfite solution
        b. react aqueous nitric acid solution with aqueous sodium sulfate solution
        c. react aqueous nitric acid solution with concentrated sodium sulfide solution
 !   d. react aqueous sulfuric acid solution with solid sodium sulfite
        e. react solid barium sulfate with aqueous nitric acid solution

64. Lactic acid, ($HC_3H_5O_3$), is a monoprotic acid that forms when milk becomes sour. In one laboratory exercise for students taking a food chemistry course, a 40.00 mL sample of an aqueous lactic acid solution required 26.50 mL of 0.140 molar NaOH(aq) to neutralize it during the course of a titration. From this data, what is the molar concentration of lactic acid in the solution?

 !   a. 0.0928 molar
        b. 0.148 molar
        c. 0.211 molar
        d. 0.757 molar
        e. 0.928 molar

65. Vinegar contains acetic acid ($HC_2H_3O_2$), which is responsible for its acidity. In one analysis of a commercial (off the shelf) vinegar brand, a 15.00 mL sample was titrated with 0.450 molar NaOH(aq). It required 30.5 mL of this sodium hydroxide titrant to neutralize the acid in the vinegar sample. What is the molar concentration of acetic acid in the vinegar?

        a. 0.102 molar
        b. 0.221 molar
        c. 0.305 molar
        d. 0.458 molar
 !   e. 0.915 molar

66. Ascorbic acid (Vitamin C, $H_2C_6H_6O_6$), is a diprotic acid. In a laboratory exercise, a vitamin C tablet was analyzed by titration using 0.125 molar NaOH(aq). On the average, it required 29.5 mL of the base to neutralize the acid in the one tablet. How many mg of Vitamin C are there in one tablet?

        a. 100 mg
        b. 162 mg
        c. 273 mg
 !   d. 325 mg
        e. 649 mg

67. An aqueous solution contains three solutes. One liter contains: 0.200 moles of calcium chloride, 0.150 moles of magnesium chloride, and 0.750 moles of sodium chloride. How many grams of Cl are there per liter of this solution?

     a. 39.0 g
!   b. 51.4 g
     c. 78.0 g
     d. 80.3 g
     e. 103 g

68. A 3.50 g sample of solid $Mg(OH)_2$ was treated with 50.0 mL of 0.500 molar $H_2SO_4(aq)$. After the reaction was over, some of the $Mg(OH)_2$ remained undissolved. Calculate how many g of solid $Mg(OH)_2$ would have remained undissolved.

     a. 1.00 g
     b. 1.46 g
     c. 1.75 g
!   d. 2.04 g
     e. 3.47 g

69. A 36.0 mL sample of aqueous sulfuric acid was titrated with 0.250 molar NaOH(aq) until the chemical indicator signaled that the solution was exactly neutralized. The mixture was then carefully evaporated to dryness, then the residue was dried in a drying oven. The residue was then weighed and a value of 861 mg was obtained for its mass. Calculate a value for the molarity of the sulfuric acid solution from this data.

     a. 0.0842 molar
!   b. 0.168 molar
     c. 0.244 molar
     d. 0.337 molar
     e. 0.597 molar

70. A 36.0 mL sample of aqueous sulfuric acid was titrated with 0.250 molar KOH(aq) until the chemical indicator signaled that the solution was exactly neutralized. The mixture was then carefully evaporated to dryness, then the residue was dried in a drying oven. The residue was then weighed and a value of 861 mg was obtained for its mass. Calculate a value for the quantity of the potassium hydroxide solution that was used in the titration from this data.

     a. 12.7 ml
     b. 19.8 ml
     c. 25.4 ml
!   d. 39.5 ml
     e. 79.1 ml

71. An ore containing lead carbonate, $PbCO_3$, was analyzed. All the lead in a 1.836 gram sample was converted to $PbSO_4(s)$ using a standard procedure involving treatment with $HNO_3(aq)$ followed by treatment with Na_2SO_4 solution. The lead sulfate which was recovered weighed 333 mg. What is the percent, by weight, of lead in the ore?

    a. 1.99 %
  ! b. 12.4 %
    c. 16.0 %
    d. 18.1 %
    e. 20.6 %

72. A solid laboratory unknown contains two substances, lead carbonate and potassium carbonate. A 5.000 g sample of this unknown was treated with aqueous nitric acid to dissolve it, then, after further treatment to adjust the acidity, it was treated with an excess of potassium chromate solution. The precipitate which formed, when dried carefully and weighed, has a mass of 2.697 grams. Calculate the percent, by weight, of lead carbonate in this laboratory unknown.

  ! a. 44.60 %
    b. 50.00 %
    c. 65.91 %
    d. 72.93 %
    e. 77.38 %

73. A solid laboratory unknown contains two substances, lead carbonate and barium carbonate. A 5.000 g sample of this unknown was treated with aqueous nitric acid to dissolve it, then, after further treatment to adjust the acidity, it was treated with an excess of potassium chromate solution. The precipitate which formed, when dried carefully and weighed, has a mass of 6.276 grams. Calculate the percent, by weight, of lead carbonate in this laboratory unknown.

    a. 34.60 %
  ! b. 38.42 %
    c. 45.91 %
    d. 52.93 %
    e. 67.38 %

74. Morenosite is a hydrate of nickel sulfate with the formula, $NiSO_4 \cdot XH_2O$. A student was assigned to determine the value of X in the formula. This student took a 5.095 g sample of the hydrate, dissolved it in water and treated it with an excess of barium chloride solution. After carefully collecting the precipitate and drying it in an oven, He obtained a mass of 4.234 g for the precipitate. From this data, determine the value of X in the formula

    a. 4
    b. 5
    c. 6
  ! d. 7
    e. 8

75. $NaHCO_3$ can be used to neutralize excess acid in situations such as, for instance, acid spills in the laboratory. The reaction is: $H^+ + HCO_3^- \rightarrow H_2O + CO_2(g)$. How many grams of $NaHCO_3$ would be required to neutralize the acid in 75.5 mL of 1.00 molar nitric acid?

     a. 0.899 grams
     b. 1.11 grams
!   c. 6.34 grams
     d. 7.55 grams
     e. 75.5 grams

76. In a commercial laboratory, the acid in sulfuric acid waste can be readily neutralized using finely ground limestone chips. The reaction is:
$$H_2SO_4(aq) + CaCO_3(s) \rightarrow H_2O + CO_2(g) + CaSO_4(s)$$
The nice thing about the process--the sludge contains both the reaction product and the excess limestone, and all the acid is "killed". A large bath holds 10,000 liters of solution, which is enough to fill 50 of the 200 liter drums. The acid content of the "spent" bath was determined to be 1.50 molar in H_2SO_4. How many metric tons (1 metric ton = 1000 kg) of $CaCO_3$ would be the minimum amount to neutralize the acid in this bath?

     a. 0.750 metric tons
     b. 1.02 metric tons
!   c. 1.50 metric tons
     d. 2.04 metric tons
     e. 3.54 metric tons

Fill in the Blanks

77. How many ions per formula unit are produced in solution by dissociation when $(NH_4)_3AsO_4$ dissolves in water? _____ (! 4)

78. How many ions per formula unit are produced in solution by dissociation when Hg_2SO_4 dissolves in water? _____ (! 2)

79. All acids share the common property of reacting with water to produce _____ (! hydronium ions)

80. Ionization differs from dissociation in that there are no _____ existing prior to the ionization step. (! ions)

81. Write the equation for the ionization reaction of perchloric acid with water. _____
(! $HClO_4(l) + H_2O(l) \rightarrow H_3O^+(aq) + ClO_4^-(aq)$)

82. Write the net ionic equation for the reaction which occurs when $HClO_4(aq)$ reacts with $Ba(OH)_2(aq)$: _____ (! $H^+(aq) + OH^-(aq) \rightarrow H_2O(l)$)

83. A sample from each of the following solutions,

         0.10 M $Ba(NO_3)_2(aq)$ 0.10 M $Ca(NO_3)_2(aq)$

         0.10 M $AgNO_3(aq)$ 0.10 M $Pb(NO_3)_2(aq)$

         0.10 M $Zn(NO_3)_2(aq)$

was treated with some 0.10 M $H_2SO_4(aq)$. How many of the solutions will show a net reaction? _____ (! 3)

84. A sample from each of the following solutions,

         0.10 M $Na_2SO_3(aq)$ 0.10 M $NH_4NO_3(aq)$

         0.10 M $K_2S(aq)$ 0.10 M $Li_3PO_4(aq)$

         0.10 M $Ni(ClO_4)_2(aq)$

was treated with some 1.00 M $H_2SO_4(aq)$. How many solutions will show a reaction? _____ (! 2)

85. A sample from each of the following solutions,

         1.00 M $H_2SO_4(aq)$ 1.00 M $Ni(NO_3)_2(aq)$

         1.00 M $BaCl_2(aq)$ 1.00 M $AgNO_3(aq)$

         1.0 M $K_2SO_4(aq)$

was treated with some 0.500 M $Na_2CO_3(aq)$. How many solutions will show a reaction? ___ (! 4)

86. In the course of a titration of barium ion in a sample by sulfate ion in a titrant solution, 83.5 mL of 0.200 molar $Na_2SO_4(aq)$ was required to precipitate all the barium ion. How many grams will the dried precipitate weigh? _____ (! 3.90 grams)

87. A 250.0 mL sample of a solution containing potassium dichromate was evaporated to dryness. The residue was then carefully dried in the oven at the recommended temperature. The residue weighed 16.58 grams. What is the molarity of this potassium dichromate solution? _____ (! 0.2254 molar)

88. A student in laboratory was provided with some 6.00 molar hydrochloric acid solution. The instructions call for 250 mL of 2.00 molar hydrochloric acid solution. How many mL of the 6.00 molar solution should be used to prepare 500 mL of the 2.00 molar solution, so the student will have some in case of bad luck? _____ (! 167 ml)

True and False

89. When solid calcium nitrate dissolves in water, the process can be represented by the equation,

     $Ca(NO_3)_2(s) \rightarrow Ca^{2+}(l) + 2\ NO_3^-(l)$ (! F)

90. When solid nickel sulfate dissolves in water, the process can be represented by the equation,

     $NiSO_4(s) \rightarrow Ni^{2+}(aq) + S^{2-}(aq) + 2\ O_2(g)$ (! F)

91. The symbol, $H^+(aq)$, is often used as a substitute for $H_2(aq)$. (! F)

92. When a solution of sodium carbonate is mixed with a solution of nitric acid, a precipitate will form. (! F)

93. When a solution of nitric acid is mixed with a solution of sodium sulfate, a gas is formed and escapes from the mixture. (! F)

94. Nitric acid will dissolve a solid sample of calcium carbonate and no solid residue will remain. (! T)

95. All sulfates are insoluble except those of Group IA, Group IIA, and Al^{3+}. (! F)

96. Mixing an aqueous ammonium chloride solution with an aqueous barium nitrate solution will cause formation of a precipitate. (! F)

97. Addition of some aqueous sodium sulfate to a solution containing three solutes, silver nitrate, ammonium nitrate, and barium nitrate, will cause formation of a precipitate. (! T)

98. An aqueous solution contains one solute which is either sodium carbonate, sodium sulfate, or potassium nitrate. Addition of some barium chloride to a sample of the solution did not cause any visible chemical change. A student stated that is possible to tell exactly which solute is present from this preliminary test. Is this true or false? (! T)

Critical Thinking

99. A finely powdered well mixed sample is a mixture containing NaCl and KCl. A 4.624 gram sample of the mixture was dissolved in 80.00 mL of water and treated with 0.264 molar $AgNO_3(aq)$. It required 277.0 mL of the $AgNO_3(aq)$ solution to combine with all of the chloride ion present. The percent, by weight, of NaCl in the mixture is therefore _____ % (! 64.9 or 65.0)

100. A 50.0 mL sample of an aqueous solution of sodium chromate was treated with an excess amount of lead chloride solution. The precipitate, which was obtained in quantitative yield (theoretical yield) was carefully dried and weighed. A mass of 4.04 grams was obtained. What is the molarity of the sodium chromate solution? _____ (! 0.250 molar)

101. Hydrochloric acid solution can be neutralized by using lime (CaO). The reaction is:
$HCl(aq) + CaO(s) \rightarrow CaCl_2(aq) + H_2O(l)$. How many kg of CaO (formula mass = 56.077) are required for neutralization of 35.50 gallons of 2.40M $HCl(aq)$? _____ (! 9.04 kg)

102. Vinegar contains acetic acid ($HC_2H_3O_2$), which is responsible for its acidity. In one analysis of a commercial (off the shelf) vinegar brand, a 15.00 mL sample was titrated with 0.450 molar $NaOH((aq)$. It required 30.5 mL of this sodium hydroxide titrant to neutralize the acid in the vinegar sample. If 1.000 liters of this vinegar weighs 1.004 kg, what is the percent, by weight, of acetic acid in this vinegar brand? _____ (! 5.47 %)

103. A student in laboratory was performing a titration to find out the exact molarity of her unknown $KOH(aq)$ solution. She weighed out 2.465 g of $KHC_8H_4O_4$, dissolved it in 100 mL of water and titrated it with the base. The equation for the reaction is:
$$OH^-(aq) + HC_8H_4O_4^-(aq) \rightarrow H_2O + C_8H_4O_4^{2-}(aq)$$
The indicator showed that 42.5 mL of the base were required to neutralize the $KHC_8H_4O_4$ sample. What is the molarity of the potassium hydroxide solution? _____ (! 0.284 molar)

104. A student is analyzing a laboratory unknown sample which contains calcium sulfate and calcium carbonate. In this procedure a 5.000 gram sample of the unknown was treated with 30.0 mL of 1.00 molar HCl(aq), an amount which was in excess. The reaction is:

$$CaCO_3(s) + 2H^+(aq) \rightarrow H_2O(l) + Ca^{2+}(aq) + CO_2(g)$$

The excess acid required was titrated with 0.155 molar NaOH(aq). 25.55 mL were required to neutralize it. What is the percent, by weight, of $CaCO_3$ in the sample? _____ (! 26.1 %)

105. A solid diprotic acid which we will call H_2A has a molar mass whose determination is the subject of today's question. Following the procedure, a student weighed out 0.647 grams of the H_2A sample, dissolved it in 50.0 mL of water and titrated it with 0.235 molar sodium hydroxide solution. It required 37.45 mL of the base to exactly neutralize the H_2A sample. Based on this data, what is the molar mass of H_2A to three significant digits? _____ (! 147 g)

106. A student performing his work study assignment in the chemistry laboratory stockroom made up the following mixture: 16.336 g of magnesium chloride, 4.662 g of sodium chloride, and 5.442 grams of potassium chloride dissolved together in enough water to make 500 mL of solution. Using a pipet, he gave each student in the lab 50.0 mL of this mixture. They were to treat it with silver nitrate solution, collect the precipitate and dry it according to instructions, weigh it, report its mass, and also the mass of chloride ion in their sample. What value should each student report for these two items? _____ , _____ (! 7.11 g, 1.76 g)

107. A dry lab exercise was worded as follows: Three solutions, labeled A, B, and C each contain one solute. One is barium chloride, one is sodium sulfate, and one is potassium nitrate. Devise a scheme, in which you mix a few drops of one with a few drops of another and tell what results you observe, and which solution is which. _____

_____

(! The one which does not give a precipitate with either of the other two is KNO_3. That's all you can say!)

Chapter 5 Oxidation-Reduction Reactions

Multiple Choice

1. What is the oxidation number of each sulfur atom in the $S_2O_8^{2-}$ ion?

    a. -2
    b. +1
    c. +3
    d. +5
    ! e. +7

2. What is the oxidation number of the chlorine atom in the $HClO_4$ molecule?

    a. -1
    b. +3
    c. +5
    ! d. +7
    e. +9

3. What is the oxidation number of each oxygen atom in the compound, BaO_2?

    ! a. -1
    b. -2
    c. +1
    d. +2
    e. +3

4. What is the oxidation number of the sodium atom in the compound, NaO_2?

    a. -1
    b. -1
    ! c. +1
    d. +2
    e. +4

5. What is the oxidation number of each boron atom in the compound, $Na_2B_4O_7$?

    a. -3
    b. +1
    c. +5
    ! d. +3
    e. +6

82

6. What is the oxidation number of each cobalt atom in the compound, $Co_2(SO_4)_3$?

    ! a. +3
    b. +6
    c. +9
    d. +15
    e. +30

7. What is the oxidation number of each carbon atom in the compound, $K_2C_2O_4$?

    a. 0
    b. -4
    ! c. +3
    d. +4
    e. +6

8. What is the oxidation number of each sulfur atom in the compound, $Rb_2S_2O_4$?

    a. -2
    b. +1
    ! c. +3
    d. +5
    e. +6

9. What is the oxidation number of the vanadium atom in the compound, $(NH_4)_3VO_4$?

    a. +2
    b. +3
    ! c. +5
    d. +6
    e. +7

10. What is the oxidation number of each nitrogen atom in $(NH_4)_2SO_4$?

    ! a. -3
    b. -2
    c. +1
    d. +2
    e. +3

11. What is the oxidation number of the arsenic atom in the AsO_4^{3-} ion?

    a. +1
    b. +3
    c. +4
    ! d. +5
    e. +6

12. Which one of the following processes represents an oxidation?

     a. $Ba^{2+}(aq) + CrO_4^{2-}(aq) \rightarrow BaCrO_4(s)$
     b. $2\,H^+(aq) + CO_3^{2-}(aq) \rightarrow H_2O(l) + CO_2(g)$
     c. $Fe^{3+}(aq) \rightarrow Fe^{2+}(aq)$
! d. $MnO_2(s) \rightarrow MnO_4^-(aq)$
     e. $2\,CrO_4^{2-}(aq) + 2\,H^+(aq) \rightarrow Cr_2O_7^{2-}(aq) + H_2O(l)$

13. Which one of the following processes represents a reduction?

     a. $Ba^{2+}(aq) + CrO_4^{2-}(aq) \rightarrow BaCrO_4(s)$
     b. $2\,H^+(aq) + CO_3^{2-}(aq) \rightarrow H_2O(l) + CO_2(g)$
! c. $CrO_4^{2-}(aq) \rightarrow Cr^{3+}(aq)$
     d. $MnO_2(s) \rightarrow MnO_4^-(aq)$
     e. $2\,CrO_4^{2-}(aq) + 2\,H^+(aq) \rightarrow Cr_2O_7^{2-}(aq) + H_2O(l)$

14. Which one of the following processes represents an oxidation?

     a. $Ca^{2+}(aq) + CO_3^{2-}(aq) \rightarrow CaCO_3(s)$
     b. $2\,H^+(aq) + SO_3^{2-}(aq) \rightarrow H_2O(l) + SO_2(g)$
     c. $VO_4^{3-}(aq) \rightarrow VO^{2+}(aq)$
! d. $CrO_2^-(aq) \rightarrow CrO_4^{2-}(aq)$
     e. $2\,S_2O_7^{2-}(aq) + H_2O(l) \rightarrow 2\,SO_4^{2-}(aq) + 2\,H^+(aq)$

15. Which one of the following processes represents a reduction?

     a. $Ca^{2+}(aq) + CO_3^{2-}(aq) \rightarrow CaCO_3(s)$
     b. $2\,H^+(aq) + SO_3^{2-}(aq) \rightarrow H_2O(l) + SO_2(g)$
! c. $VO_4^{3-}(aq) \rightarrow VO^{2+}(aq)$
     d. $CrO_2^-(aq) \rightarrow CrO_4^{2-}(aq)$
     e. $2\,S_2O_7^{2-}(aq) + H_2O(l) \rightarrow 2\,SO_4^{2-}(aq) + 2\,H^+(aq)$

16. The sulfite ion was involved in a chemical reaction in which it underwent oxidation. Which one of the products listed below is a possible oxidation product of the sulfite ion?

     a. $S_2O_3^{2-}(aq)$
     b. $SO_2(g)$
     c. $S^{2-}(aq)$
     d. $S(s)$
! e. $SO_4^{2-}(aq)$

17. The nitrogen molecule was involved in a chemical reaction in which it underwent reduction. Which one of the products listed below is a possible reduction product of the nitrogen molecule?

! a. N_2H_4 (aq)
   b. $NO(g)$
   c. $NO_2^-(aq)$
   d. $NO_2(g)$
   e. $NO_3^-(aq)$

18. The $ClO_2(g)$ molecule was involved in a chemical reaction in which it underwent oxidation. Which one of the products listed below is a possible oxidation product of the ClO_2 molecule?

   a. $ClO^-(aq)$
   b. $Cl^-(aq)$
   c. $ClO_2^-(aq)$
   d. $Cl_2(g)$
! e. $ClO_3^-(aq)$

19. The $NO(g)$ molecule was involved in a chemical reaction. Though the formula of the product was not given, it was stated that the NO molecule underwent oxidation in the process. Which one of the products listed below is a possible oxidation product of the NO molecule?

   a. N_2H_4 (aq)
   b. $NH_3(aq)$
   c. $N_2(g)$
! d. $NO_2^-(aq)$
   e. $NH_2OH(aq)$

20. Balance the half reaction, $NO_3^-(aq) \rightarrow NH_4^+(aq)$, taking place in acidic media. Which answer below describes how many electrons are needed to balance the half reaction?

   a. 2 electrons, left side
   b. 3 electrons, right side
   c. 4 electrons, left side
! d. 8 electrons, left side
   e. 8 electrons, right side

21. Balance the half reaction, $H_2S(aq) \rightarrow S(s)$, taking place in acidic media. Which answer below describes how many electrons are needed to balance the half reaction?

   a. 2 electrons, left side
! b. 2 electrons, right side
   c. 4 electrons, left side
   d. 4 electrons, right side
   e. 8 electrons, right side

22. Balance the half reaction, $Cl_2O_7(g) \rightarrow HClO(aq)$, taking place in acidic media. Which answer below describes how many electrons are needed to balance the half reaction?

    a. 2 electrons, left side
    b. 3 electrons, right side
!   c. 12 electrons, left side
    d. 6 electrons, right side
    e. 8 electrons, left side

23. Balance the half reaction, $C_5O_5^{2-}(g) \rightarrow CO_3^{2-}(aq)$, taking place in basic media. Which answer below describes how many hydroxide ions are needed to balance the half reaction?

    a. 8 ions, left side
    b. 12 ions, right side
    c. 12 ions, left side
!   d. 20 ions, left side
    e. 20 ions, right side

24. Balance the half reaction, $C_5O_5^{2-}(g) \rightarrow CO_3^{2-}(aq)$, taking place in basic media. Which answer below describes how many electrons are needed to balance the half reaction?

    a. 4 electrons, left side
    b. 8 electrons, right side
    c. 8 electrons, left side
    d. 12 electrons, left side
!   e. 12 electrons, right side

25. Balance the half reaction, $C_2H_6O(aq) \rightarrow HC_2H_3O_2(aq)$, taking place in acidic media. How many electrons are needed to balance the charge?

    a. 2
    b. 3
!   c. 4
    d. 6
    e. 8

26. Balance the half reaction, $C_8H_{10}(l) \rightarrow C_8H_4O_4^{2-}(aq)$, taking place in basic media. Which answer below describes how many electrons are needed to balance the half reaction?

    a. 4 electrons, left side
    b. 8 electrons, right side
    c. 8 electrons, left side
    d. 12 electrons, left side
!   e. 12 electrons, right side

27. When you balance the redox equation below,
$$C_4H_{10}(g) + Cr_2O_7^{2-}(aq) + H^+(aq) \rightarrow H_6C_4O_4(aq) + Cr^{3+}(aq) + H_2O(l)$$
the reducing agent is

   ! a. $C_4H_{10}(g)$
      b. $Cr_2O_7^{2-}(aq)$
      c. $H^+(aq)$
      d. $H_6C_4O_4(aq)$
      e. $Cr^{3+}(aq)$

28. When you balance the redox equation,
$$C_4H_{10}(l) + Cr_2O_7^{2-}(aq) + H^+(aq) \rightarrow H_6C_4O_4(s) + Cr^{3+}(aq) + H_2O(l)$$
the oxidizing agent is

      a. $C_4H_{10}(l)$
   ! b. $Cr_2O_7^{2-}(aq)$
      c. $H^+(aq)$
      d. $H_6C_4O_4(s)$
      e. $Cr^{3+}(aq)$

29. When you balance the redox equation below,
$$VO_4^{3-}(aq) + SO_2(g) + 2 H^+(aq) \rightarrow VO^{2+}(aq) + SO_4^{2-}(aq) + H_2O(l)$$
the reducing agent is

      a. $VO_4^{3-}(aq)$
      b. $VO^{2+}(aq)$
      c. $H^+(aq)$
   ! d. $SO_2(g)$
      e. $SO_4^{2-}(aq)$

30. When you balance the redox equation,
$$VO_4^{3-}(aq) + SO_2(g) + 2 H^+(aq) \rightarrow VO^{2+}(aq) + SO_4^{2-}(aq) + H_2O(l)$$
the oxidizing agent is

   ! a. $VO_4^{3-}(aq)$
      b. $VO^{2+}(aq)$
      c. $H^+(aq)$
      d. $SO_2(g)$
      e. $SO_4^{2-}(aq)$

31. In the reaction, $C_4H_{10}(l) + Cr_2O_7^{2-}(aq) + H^+(aq) \rightarrow H_6C_4O_4(s) + Cr^{3+}(aq) + H_2O(l)$
the change in the oxidation number of the chromium atom is

      a. -6
   ! b. -3
      c. +3
      d. +5
      e. +8

32. Complete the balancing of the following half reaction, taking place in basic media,
$$Br^-(aq) \rightarrow BrO_3^-(aq)$$
Which answer below describes how many electrons are needed to balance the half reaction?

      a. 2 electrons, left side
      b. 2 electrons, right side
      c. 4 electrons, right side
 ! d. 6 electrons, right side
      e. 6 electrons, left side

33. Complete the balancing of the following half reaction, taking place in basic media,
$$Br^-(aq) \rightarrow BrO_3^-(aq)$$
Which answer below describes how many hydroxide ions are needed to balance the half reaction?

      a. 2, on the left side
      b. 4, on the left side
      c. 4, on the right side
 ! d. 6, on the left side
      e. 6, on the right side

34. Complete the balancing of the following half reaction, taking place in basic media,
$$Cr(OH)_4^-(aq) \rightarrow CrO_4^{2-}(aq)$$
Which answer below describes how many electrons are needed to balance the half reaction?

      a. 1 electron, on the left side
      b. 2 electrons, on the right side
 ! c. 3 electrons, on the right side
      d. 3 electrons, on the left side
      e. 4 electrons, on the right side

35. Complete the balancing of the following half reaction, taking place in basic media,
$$Cr(OH)_4^-(aq) \rightarrow CrO_4^{2-}(aq)$$
Which answer below describes how many hydroxide ions are needed to balance the half reaction?

      a. 1, on the left side
      b. 3, on the right side
      c. 3, on the left side
 ! d. 4, on the left side
      e. 4, on the right side

36. In the reaction, $CrO_4^{2-}(aq) + H_2O(l) \rightarrow CrO_2^-(aq) + OH^-(aq)$, the change in the oxidation number of the chromium atom is

      a. -6
 ! b. -3
      c. +3
      d. +5
      e. +8

37. Complete the balancing of the following half reaction, taking place in basic media,
$$NtO_4^{2-}(aq) \rightarrow Nt(OH)_2(s)$$
Which answer below describes how many electrons are needed to balance the half reaction?

      a. 2 electrons, on the left side
      b. 3 electrons, on the right side
!   c. 4 electrons, on the left side
      d. 4 electrons, on the right side
      e. 6 electrons, on the right side

38. Complete the balancing of the following half reaction, taking place in basic media,
$$NtO_4^{2-}(aq) \rightarrow Nt(OH)_2(s)$$
Which answer below describes how many water molecules are needed to balance the half reaction?

      a. 2, on the left side
!   b. 4, on the left side
      c. 4, on the right side
      d. 6, on the left side
      e. 6, on the right side

39. When the balancing of the equation for the reaction,
$$C_8H_{10}(l) + NtO_4^{2-}(aq) + H^+(aq) \rightarrow C_8H_4O_4^{2-}(aq) + Nt^{2+}(aq) + H_2O(l)$$
taking place in acidic media is completed, what is the sum of ALL the coefficients in the equation?

      a. 12
      b. 20
      c. 24
!   d. 26
      e. 32

40. When the balancing of the equation for the reaction,
$$Fe^{2+}(aq) + Cr_2O_7^{2-}(aq) + H^+(aq) \rightarrow Cr^{3+}(aq) + Fe^{3+}(aq) + H_2O(l)$$
taking place in acidic media is properly completed, what is the sum of ALL the coefficients in the equation?

      a. 6
      b. 22
      c. 30
      d. 32
!   e. 36

41. When the balancing of the equation for the reaction,

$$MnO_4^-(aq) + H_2C_2O_4(aq) + H^+(aq) \rightarrow Mn^{2+}(aq) + CO_2(g) + H_2O(l)$$

taking place in acidic media is properly completed, what is the sum of ALL the coefficients in the equation?

     a. 29
     b. 30
     c. 31
     d. 32
! e. 33

42. When the balancing of the equation for the reaction,

$$HSO_3^-(aq) + MnO_4^-(aq) \rightarrow MnO_2(s) + HSO_4^-(aq)$$

taking place in slightly acidic media is properly completed, what is the sum of ALL the coefficients in the equation?

     a. 7
     b. 9
! c. 13
     d. 15
     e. 19

43. When the balancing of the equation for the reaction,

$$Bi_2O_3(s) + OCl^-(aq) \rightarrow Cl^-(aq) + BiO_3^-(aq)$$

taking place in basic solution media is properly completed, what is the sum of ALL the coefficients in the equation?

     a. 6
     b. 8
     c. 9
! d. 10
     e. 14

44. When the balancing of the equation for the reaction,

$$CrO_4^{2-}(aq) + Br^-(aq) \rightarrow CrO_2^-(aq) + BrO_3^-(aq)$$

taking place in basic solution media is properly completed, what is the sum of ALL the coefficients in the equation?

     a. 6
     b. 8
! c. 9
     d. 10
     e. 14

45. In a chemical reaction, zinc metal reacts with perchloric acid solution to produce zinc perchlorate (in solution) and hydrogen gas, which escapes. The species being oxidized in this reaction is

      a. $HClO_4(aq)$
      b. $H_2(g)$
      c. $Zn^{2+}(aq)$
  ! d. $Zn(s)$
      e. $Zn(ClO_4)_2(aq)$

46. In a chemical reaction, zinc metal reacts with nitric acid solution to produce zinc nitrate (in solution), ammonium nitrate (in solution), and water. The species being oxidized in this reaction is

      a. $HNO_3(aq)$
      b. $NH_4^+(aq)$
      c. $Zn^{2+}(aq)$
  ! d. $Zn(s)$
      e. $Zn(NO_3)_2(aq)$

47. In a chemical reaction, magnesium metal reacts with aqueous sulfuric acid solution to produce magnesium sulfate (in solution) and hydrogen gas. In the course of the reaction, which element undergoes an increase in oxidation number?

      a. hydrogen, only
  ! b. magnesium, only
      c. oxygen, only
      d. sulfur, only
      e. magnesium and hydrogen

48. In a series of chemical test reactions the following observations were made when some metallic element samples were treated with 3.00 molar hydrochloric acid solution. Zn: metal dissolves, hydrogen gas is emitted. Cu: no reaction. Ag: no reaction. Mg: metal dissolves, hydrogen gas is emitted. Mn: metal dissolves, hydrogen gas is emitted. Which statement below is true?

      a. Mg, Mn, Zn are more reactive than Ag, Cu; but less reactive than H_2.
      b. Mg, Mn, Zn are less reactive than Ag, Cu; but more reactive than H_2.
  ! c. Mg, Mn, Zn are more reactive than Ag, Cu; and more reactive than H_2.
      d. Mg, Mn, Zn are less reactive than Ag, Cu; and less reactive than H_2.
      e. These observations are insufficient to form any judgment about relative reactivity
         of any of the elements listed above.

49. In which situation described below can the product of the chemical reaction be predicted with a high degree of confidence?

  ! a. an active metal reacting with a non-oxidizing monoprotic acid
      b. an active metal reacting with an oxidizing monoprotic acid
      c. an active metal reacting with a non-oxidizing diprotic acid
      d. an active metal reacting with an oxidizing diprotic acid
      e. an active metal reacting with a non-oxidizing triprotic acid

50. Three metallic elements, copper, gold and zinc, can be distinguished from one another on the basis of how they react with two strong acids, $HNO_3(aq)$ and $HCl(aq)$ Which set below, using the abbreviations R (for reaction occurs) and NR (for no reaction) correctly describes what occurs?

    a. Au: HCl(R), HNO_3(NR)   Cu: HCl(R), HNO_3(NR)   Zn: HCl(R), HNO_3(NR)

    b. Au: HCl(NR), HNO_3(NR) Cu: HCl(R), HNO_3(R)   Zn: HCl(R), HNO_3(NR)

! c. Au: HCl(NR), HNO_3(NR) Cu: HCl(NR), HNO_3(R) Zn: HCl(R), HNO_3(R)

    d. Au: HCl(NR), HNO_3(NR) Cu: HCl(R), HNO_3(R)   Zn: HCl(NR), HNO_3(R)

    e. Au: HCl(NR), HNO_3(NR) Cu: HCl(R), HNO_3(NR) Zn: HCl(R), HNO_3(R)

51. Three metallic elements, copper, magnesium and gold, can be distinguished from one another on the basis of how they react with two strong acids, $HNO_3(aq)$ and $HCl(aq)$ Which set below, using the abbreviations R (for reaction occurs) and NR (no reaction) correctly describes what occurs?

    a. Au: HCl(R), HNO_3(NR)   Cu: HCl(R), HNO_3(NR)   Mg: HCl(R), HNO_3(NR)

    b. Au: HCl(NR), HNO_3(NR) Cu: HCl(R), HNO_3(R)   Mg: HCl(R), HNO_3(NR)

    c. Au: HCl(NR), HNO_3(NR) Cu: HCl(R), HNO_3(R)   Mg: HCl(NR), HNO_3(R)

    d. Au: HCl(NR), HNO_3(NR) Cu: HCl(R), HNO_3(NR) Mg: HCl(R), HNO_3(R)

! e. Au: HCl(NR), HNO_3(NR) Cu: HCl(NR), HNO_3(R) Mg: HCl(R), HNO_3(R)

52. In terms of activity, the series in increasing order for metals is found to be,
$$Au < Ag < Cu < Sn < Cd < Zn < Al < Mg < Na < Cs$$
Which reaction below *does not occur spontaneously* upon mixing the reagents shown?

! a. $Cd(s) + Al^{3+}(aq) \rightarrow Cd^{2+}(aq) + Al(s)$

    b. $Cd(s) + Cu^{2+}(aq) \rightarrow Cd^{2+}(aq) + Cu(s)$

    c. $Zn(s) + Cu^{2+}(aq) \rightarrow Zn^{2+}(aq) + Cu(s)$

    d. $Al(s) + Ag^{+}(aq) \rightarrow Al^{3+}(aq) + Ag(s)$

    e. $Cu(s) + Au^{3+}(aq) \rightarrow Cu^{2+}(aq) + Au(s)$

53. In terms of activity, the series in increasing order for metals is found to be,
$$Au < Ag < Cu < Sn < Cd < Zn < Al < Mg < Na < Cs$$
Which reaction below *occurs spontaneously* upon mixing the reagents shown?

    a. $Sn(s) + Zn^{2+}(aq) \rightarrow Sn^{2+}(aq) + Zn(s)$

    b. $Ag(s) + Mg^{2+}(aq) \rightarrow Ag^{+}(aq) + Mg(s)$

! c. $Zn(s) + Au^{3+}(aq) \rightarrow Zn^{2+}(aq) + Au(s)$

    d. $Ag(s) + Mn^{2+}(aq) \rightarrow Ag^{+}(aq) + Mn(s)$

    e. $Sn(s) + Al^{3+}(aq) \rightarrow Sn^{2+}(aq) + Al(s)$

54. The most reactive metallic elements of the groups listed below are the metals of

! a. Group 1A

    b. Group 2A

    c. Group 3A

    d. Group 1B

    e. Group 2B

55. The least reactive metallic elements of the groups listed below are the metals of

    a. Group 1A
    b. Group 2A
    c. Group 3A
    d. Group 1B
!   e. Group 2B

56. In terms of activity, the series in increasing order for metals is found to be,
    $$Au < Ag < Cu < Sn < Cd < Zn < Al < Mg < Na < Cs$$
    Based on this list, which one of the elements presented below would undergo oxidation most readily?

    a. Ag
!   b. Al
    c. Cu
    d. Cd
    e. Zn

57. In terms of activity, the series in increasing order for metals is found to be,
    $$Au < Ag < Cu < Sn < Cd < Zn < Al < Mg < Na < Cs$$
    Based on this list, which one of the elements presented below would undergo oxidation most readily?

!   a. Mg
    b. Al
    c. Cu
    d. Cd
    e. Zn

58. In terms of activity, the series in increasing order for metals is found to be,
    $$Au < Ag < Cu < Sn < Cd < Zn < Al < Mg < Na < Cs$$
    Based on this list, which one of the elements presented below would undergo oxidation least readily?

    a. Mg
    b. Al
!   c. Cu
    d. Cd
    e. Zn

59. In terms of activity, the series in increasing order for metals is found to be,
    $$Au < Ag < Cu < Sn < Cd < Zn < Al < Mg < Na < Cs$$
    Based on this list, which one of the elements presented below would undergo oxidation least readily?

!   a. Ag
    b. Al
    c. Cu
    d. Cd
    e. Zn

60. In terms of activity, the series in increasing order for metals is found to be,
$$Au < Ag < Cu < Sn < Cd < Zn < Al < Mg < Na < Cs$$
Based on this list, which one of the elements presented below would react most readily with a 0.10 molar aqueous solution of hydrofluoric acid?

      a. Ag
      b. Sn
      c. Cu
      d. Cd
!   e. Zn

61. Which one of the following elements would you expect to react most rapidly, if at all, with water?

      a. Ag
      b. Al
      c. Cu
!   d. Na
      e. Zn

62. Which one of the following elements would you expect to react most rapidly, if at all, with water?

      a. Al
      b. Cd
!   c. Cs
      d. Mg
      e. Zn

63. When the hydrocarbon, C_8H_{16}, undergoes complete combustion, a specific set of products are formed. If you write the equation for the reaction and balance it, the sum of the coefficients for the reagents in the balanced equation will be

      a. 17
      b. 19
      c. 21
      d. 26
!   e. 29

64. When the carbohydrate, $C_{12}H_{22}O_{11}$, undergoes complete combustion, a specific set of products are formed. If you write the equation for the reaction and balance it, the sum of the coefficients for the reagents in the balanced equation will be

      a. 24
      b. 35
!   c. 36
      d. 47
      e. 83

65. When the carbohydrate, $C_{12}H_{22}O_{11}$, undergoes complete combustion, the reducing agent in the reaction is

        a. oxygen
!   b. the carbohydrate
        c. hydrogen
        d. carbon
        e. carbon dioxide

66. Iron in a sample with non-interfering substances can be determined by a titration using dichromate ion in acidic solution. The iron is converted to $Fe^{2+}(aq)$ ions which are then titrated by the dichromate ion. The reaction is:

$$6\ Fe^{2+}(aq)\ +\ 1\ Cr_2O_7{}^{2-}(aq)\ +\ \underline{\quad}\ \rightarrow\ 6\ Fe^{3+}(aq)\ +\ \underline{\quad}\ Cr^{3+}(aq)\ +\ \underline{\quad}$$

How many grams of iron are there present in a sample if it required 42.7 mL of 0.0180 molar $Na_2Cr_2O_7(aq)$ solution for the titration described by the incomplete equation above?

        a. 0.043 g
!   b. 0.258 g
        c. 3.61 g
        d. 7.07 g
        e. 7.15 g

67. In general chemistry laboratory, the reaction

$$1\ Cu(s)\ +\ 4\ HNO_3(aq)\ \rightarrow\ Cu(NO_3)_2(aq)\ +\ \underline{\quad}\ NO_2(g)\ +\ \underline{\quad}\ H_2O(l)$$

is used to dissolve the copper metal. If a 1.000 g sample of copper is used, and instructions say to use **four** times as much acid as the calculated amount, how many mL (to the nearest ml) of 15.0 M nitric acid would be used in the procedure for this sample?

        a. 4 ml
        b. 5 ml
        c. 10 ml
!   d. 17 ml
        e. 25 ml

68. $Fe^{2+}(aq)$ reacts with $MnO_4{}^-(aq)$ ion in acidic solution to yield $Fe^{3+}(aq)$ ions and $Mn^{2+}(aq)$ ions.

$$5\ Fe^{2+}(aq)\ +\ 1\ MnO_4{}^-(aq)\ +\ \underline{\quad}\ \rightarrow\ 5\ Fe^{3+}(aq)\ +\ \underline{\quad}\ Mn^{2+}(aq)\ +\ \underline{\quad}$$

A sample of melanterite, $FeSO_4 \cdot 7H_2O$, was analyzed for purity using this reaction by titration of an aqueous solution of the sample. One such sample required 47.35 mL of 0.0175350 molar permanganate solution to completely titrate all the iron in the sample by the reaction shown above. How much did the sample weigh, if it was in fact pure melanterite?

        a. 0.596 g
        b. 0.184 g
        c. 0.461 g
!   d. 1.15 g
        e. 4.87 g

69. Hydrogen peroxide, H_2O_2, can be determined by titration with permanganate solution by titration. The reaction is:

$$2\ MnO_4^-(aq) + 5\ H_2O_2(aq) + \underline{\quad} \rightarrow 5O_2(g) + \underline{\quad} Mn^{2+}(aq) + \underline{\quad\quad}$$

If it required 80.0 mL of 0.0220 molar $MnO_4^-(aq)$ solution to titrate 5.0 mL of a $H_2O_2(aq)$ solution, what is the molarity of the $H_2O_2(aq)$ solution?

    a. 0.14 molar
    b. 0.18 molar
    c. 0.35 molar
    d. 0.62 molar
  ! e. 0.88 molar

70. Zinc reacts with permanganate ion to form $Zn^{2+}(aq)$ ions and $Mn^{2+}(aq)$ ions . The reaction is:

$$\underline{\quad} Zn(s) + 2\ MnO_4^-(aq) + \underline{\quad\quad} \rightarrow \underline{\quad} Zn^{2+}(aq) + \underline{\quad} Mn^{2+}(aq) + \underline{\quad\quad}$$

How many grams of zinc are required to completely react with 100.0 mL of a 0.0150 molar solution of $KMnO_4(aq)$?

    a. 0.0392 g
    b. 0.0981 g
  ! c. 0.245 g
    d. 10.2 g
    e. 43.9 g

71. SO_2 in air can be determined by the reaction,

$$\underline{\quad\quad} MnO_4^-(aq) + \underline{\quad} SO_2(g) + \underline{\quad} \rightarrow \underline{\quad} SO_4^{2-}(aq) + \underline{\quad} Mn^{2+}(aq) + \underline{\quad\quad}$$

It required 185 mL of 0.0200 molar $MnO_4^-(aq)$ solution to completely react with all the SO_2 in a sample of air. How many grams of SO_2 were there in the sample?

    a. 3.70 g
    b. 9.25 g
    c. 0.237 g
    d. 0.0948 g
  ! e. 0.593 g

Fill in the Blanks

72. Is the process, $Cr_2O_7^{2-}(aq) \rightarrow Cr^{3+}(aq)$ an oxidation or a reduction? _____ (! reduction)

73. Is the process, $NO_3^-(aq) \rightarrow NO(g)$ an oxidation or a reduction? _____ (! reduction)

74. Is the process, $S_2O_3^{2-}(aq) \rightarrow S_4O_6^{2-}(aq)$ an oxidation or a reduction? _____ (! oxidation)

75. Is the process, $C_2O_4^{2-}(aq) \rightarrow CO_3^{2-}(aq)$ an oxidation or a reduction? _____ (! oxidation)

76. When a metal displaces hydrogen from a non-oxidizing acid, which substance is the oxidizing agent? _____ (! the H^+ ion)

77. When a metal displaces hydrogen from a non-oxidizing acid, which substance is the reducing agent? _____ (! the metal itself)

78. When the equation, $Al(s) + NO_3^-(aq) \rightarrow NO(g) + Al^{3+}(aq)$ is balanced, the Al/NO_3^- ratio is _____ (! 1:1)

79. When the equation, $Zn(s) + NO_3^-(aq) \rightarrow NH_4^+(aq) + Zn^{2+}(aq)$ is balanced, the Zn/NO_3^- ratio is _____ (! 4:1)

80. Which one of the six substances involved in the reaction described in the balanced equation,
$$BrO_3^-(aq) + 3\,Zn(s) + 6\,H^+(aq) \rightarrow Br^-(aq) + 3\,Zn(s) + 3\,H_2O(l)$$
is the oxidizing agent? _____ (! $BrO_3^-(aq)$)

81. Which one of the six substances involved in the reaction described in the balanced equation,
$$5\,H_2O(l) + 4\,Cl_2(g) + S_2O_3^{2-}(aq) \rightarrow 2\,SO_4^{2-}(aq) + 8\,Cl^-(aq) + 10\,H^+(aq)$$
is the reducing agent? _____ (! $S_2O_3^{2-}(aq)$)

82. Which one of the six substances involved in the reaction described just below is the reducing agent?
$$C_6H_{12}O_6(aq) + NO_3^-(aq) + H^+(aq) \rightarrow C_6H_{12}O_6(aq) + NO_2(g) + H_2O(l)$$
_____ (! $C_6H_{12}O_6(aq)$)

83. A solution was made by taking 2.500g of $KMnO_4$ and dissolving it in enough water to make 1.000 liter of solution. This solution was used to titrate $H_2C_2O_4 \cdot 2H_2O$, which can be readily obtained in high purity. In acidic media, the reaction is:
____ $MnO_4^-(aq) +$ ____ $H_2C_2O_4(aq) +$ ____ $\rightarrow$ ____ $CO_2(g) +$ ____ $Mn^{2+}(aq) +$ ____
How many mL of this solution are required to titrate a 0.480 g sample of $H_2C_2O_4 \cdot 2H_2O$? _____
(! 96.3 ml)

True and False

84. The reaction, $HCl(aq) + Na_2CO_3(aq) \rightarrow NaCl(aq) + H_2O(l) + CO_2(g)$ involves changes in oxidation number and is therefore classified as a redox reaction. (! F)

85. The reaction, $Al(s) + HClO_4(aq) \rightarrow Al(ClO_4)_3(aq) + H_2(g)$ involves changes in oxidation number and is therefore classified as a redox reaction. (! T)

86. The reaction, $Cl_2(g) + NaBr(aq) \rightarrow NaCl(aq) + Br_2(l)$, involves changes in oxidation number and is therefore classified as a redox reaction. (! T)

87. The reaction, $NiS(s) + O_2(g) \rightarrow NiO(s) + SO_2(g)$, involves changes in oxidation number and is therefore classified as a redox reaction. (! T)

88. The reaction, $AgNO_3(aq) + NH_4Br(aq) \rightarrow AgCl(s) + NH_4NO_3(aq)$, involves changes in oxidation number and is therefore classified as a redox reaction. (! F)

89. Magnesium metal will displace hydrogen from non-oxidizing acids (! T)

90. In terms of activity, the series, in decreasing order for metals is found to be,

$$Au < Ag < Cu < Sn < Cd < Zn < Al < Mg < Na < Cs$$

This means that cadmium will displace aluminum from aqueous solutions of aluminum sulfate (! F)

91. The metals of Group 1A undergo reduction more readily than those in any other group in the periodic table. (! F)

92. When organic compounds which contain sulfur under complete combustion with oxygen, one of the products is hydrogen sulfide. (! F)

93. When hydrocarbon compounds undergo combustion, the carbon is always converted into carbon dioxide. (! F)

94. Even though this does not happen at ordinary temperature and pressures, nitrogen can undergo combination with oxygen to form nitrogen oxides. (! T)

Critical Thinking

95. Which reaction below ***does not occur spontaneously*** upon mixing the reagents shown?

  ! a. $Cd(s) + Al^{3+}(aq) \rightarrow Cd^{2+}(aq) + Al(s)$
   b. $Cd(s) + Cu^{2+}(aq) \rightarrow Cd^{2+}(aq) + Cu(s)$
   c. $Zn(s) + Cu^{2+}(aq) \rightarrow Zn^{2+}(aq) + Cu(s)$
   d. $Al(s) + Ag^{+}(aq) \rightarrow Al^{3+}(aq) + Ag(s)$
   e. $Cu(s) + Au^{3+}(aq) \rightarrow Cu^{2+}(aq) + Au(s)$

96. When the balancing of the half reaction, $C_{10}H_8(s) \rightarrow C_8H_6O_4(s) + CO_2(g)$, taking place in acidic media is completed, the number of electrons showing in the half reaction is _____ (! 18)

97. What is the oxidation number of the sulfur in the compound, FeS_2? In order to think about this problem, consider the existence of H_2O_2, BaO_2, NaO_2, KO_2, among others, and the periodic relationships between these and the species under consideration. What is your best reasoned response? _____ (! -1)

98. A solution was made by taking 2.500g of $KMnO_4$ and dissolving it in enough water to make 1.000 liter of solution. This solution was used to titrate $H_2C_2O_4 \cdot 2H_2O$, a very pure substance. In acidic media, the reaction is

$$MnO_4^-(aq) + H_2C_2O_4(aq) + \_\_\_ \rightarrow CO_2(g) + Mn^{2+}(aq) + \_\_\_$$

How many mL of this solution are required to titrate a 0.480 g sample of $H_2C_2O_4 \cdot 2H_2O$? _____ (! 96.3 ml)

99. It is proposed to analyze for CO gas present in air samples by passing the gas through a solution of potassium permanganate. The reaction that occurs is,

$$\underline{\quad} MnO_4^-(aq) + \underline{\quad} CO(g) + \underline{\quad\quad} \rightarrow \underline{\quad} CO_2(g) + \underline{\quad} Mn^{2+}(aq) + \underline{\quad\quad}$$

In a trial run, it required 102 liters of air containing CO (no other substances that would react with permanganate were present) to completely decolorize 250 mL of 0.0150 molar $MnO_4^-(aq)$ solution in a scrubber. If air weighs 1.29 g/liter, what is the percent by weight of CO in the air?_____
(! 0.200 %)

100. A student in the honors program working on her research project is going to do a synthesis which involves bubbling chlorine gas through the aqueous reaction mixture in a closed system. The outlet from the system goes through a scrubber which contains some sodium thiosulfate solution. The sodium thiosulfate will react with the chlorine passing through the scrubber to produce harmless chloride ion and sulfate ion. This prevents the chlorine from going up the exhaust system and polluting the atmosphere on campus grounds. The reaction is,

$$Cl_2(g) + S_2O_3^{2-}(aq) \rightarrow SO_4^{2-}(aq) + Cl^-(aq)$$

The reaction calls for 15.5 grams of chlorine gas. The student wants enough thiosulfate in the scrubber to be able to handle *twice* this amount to be on the safe side. How many grams of crystal sodium thiosulfate (which is actually sodium thiosulfate pentahydrate) should the student weigh out for use in the scrubber? _____ (! 27.1 g)

Critical Thinking Level III

101. A student in the honors program is going to prepare a significant quantity of a gold compound which will be used in her research project as well as other projects in their research group. The first step calls for the reaction of the gold metal with aqua regia (a 3:1 v/v mix of commercial concentrated hydrochloric acid and commercial concentrated nitric acid). In her procedure, she is to use 6 times as much aqua regia as the stoichiometric quantity required. A graduate student performed the calculation and indicated that aqua regia mixed according to directions has a nitrate concentration of 3.08 molar and a chloride concentration of 6.96 molar, while the hydrogen ion concentration is 10.04 molar. The reaction is,

$$Au(s) + NO_3^-(aq) + Cl^-(aq) + H^+(aq) \rightarrow NO_2(g) + AuCl_4^-(aq) + H_2O(l)$$

The piece of gold wire that is the starting material weighs 9.562 grams. Calculate the volume, in ml, of aqua regia which is required, based on the consideration stated above. *hint*: Which component of the mix will be the limiting reagent, the HNO_3, the HCl, or the H^+ ions? _____ (! 284 ml)

Chemicals in Our World 3: Xenon--Star Wars Propulsion "Fuel" Today

102. What type of engine uses the element xenon in its propulsion system?

     ! a. ion propulsion engine
       b. magnetic induction engine
       c. electric field engine
       d. magnetic resonance engine (MRE)
       e. nuclear reaction engine

103. The energy source in the engine used in deep space research vehicles which employs xenon as one of its components is

       a. nuclear disintegration of radium
       b. nuclear fission using uranium
       c. nuclear fission using plutonium
       d. nuclear fusion of xenon nuclei
!   e. solar energy

104. The energy source in the engine used in deep space research vehicles which employs xenon as one of its components is

       a. nuclear fusion of hydrogen nuclei
!   b. solar energy
       c. nuclear fission using plutonium
       d. electrons from a radium source
       e. oxidation reduction reaction involving xenon ions

105. Characteristics of xenon which make it desirable and convenient for use in deep space vehicles which employ xenon as one of the components are

       a. availability as a byproduct from natural gas wells and ease with which it undergoes nuclear fusion reactions
       b. availability as a byproduct from natural gas wells and ease with which it undergoes nuclear fission reactions
       c. high ionization energy and availability as a byproduct of nuclear reactions of the nuclear engine fuel
!   d. high atomic mass and low ionization energy
       e. ease of storage as the xenon-containing compound $XePtF_6$, a gas with high molar mass and high potential energy

Chapter 6 Energy and Thermochemistry

Multiple Choice

1. Which one of the following is a unit of energy, but not an SI unit of energy?

    a. joule
    b. newton
    c. pascal
    d. watt
    ! e. calorie

2. Which one of the following is a unit of energy?

    a. pascal
    b. newton
    ! c. joule
    d. watt
    e. ampere

3. Chemical energy is

    a. the kinetic energy resulting from violent decomposition of energetic chemicals
    b. the heat energy associated with combustion reactions
    c. the electrical energy produced by fuel cells
    ! d. the potential energy which resides in chemical bonds
    e. the energy living plants receive from solar radiation

4. Which one of the following statements is true?

    a. Molecules in gases possess kinetic energy since they are in constant motion, while molecules in liquids and solids are not in constant motion and hence possess no kinetic energy.
    b. Molecules in gases and liquids possess kinetic energy since they are in constant motion, while molecules in solids are not in constant motion and hence possess no kinetic energy.
    ! c. Molecules in gases, liquids and solids possess kinetic energy since they are in constant motion.
    d. Polyatomic molecules possess kinetic energy in the liquid and gaseous states since the atoms can move about in the molecule even if the molecule cannot move.
    e. Since solids are rigid, their molecules do not possess kinetic energy unless the solid is melted.

5. A chemical reaction has just occurred in an insulated isolated system which caused an overall increase in the potential energy of the system. Which statement below is true?

      a. Heat was taken in from the surroundings by the system.
      b. Heat was given off to the surroundings by the system.
      c. The temperature of the system increased.
 ! d. The temperature of the system decreased.
      e. The total energy of the system increased.

6. A chemical reaction has just occurred in an insulated isolated system which caused an overall decrease in the potential energy of the system. Which statement below is true?

      a. Heat was taken in from the surroundings by the system.
      b. Heat was given off to the surroundings by the system.
 ! c. The temperature of the system increased.
      d. The temperature of the system decreased.
      e. The total energy of the system decreased.

7. An exothermic chemical reaction has just occurred in an insulated isolated system. Which statement below is true?

      a. Heat was taken in from the surroundings by the system.
      b. Heat was given off to the surroundings by the system.
      c. The potential energy of the system increased.
 ! d. The potential energy of the system decreased.
      e. The total energy of the system increased.

8. During an exothermic chemical reaction,

      a. a system becomes warmer, and the chemical substances undergo an increase in potential energy
 ! b. a system becomes warmer, and the chemical substances undergo a decrease in potential energy
      c. a system becomes cooler, and the chemical substances undergo an increase in potential energy
      d. a system becomes cooler, and the chemical substances undergo a decrease in potential energy
      e. a system becomes warmer, and additional heat is gained from the surroundings

9. The internal energy of a chemical system is described by one of the equations below. Which one?

 ! a. $E_{system} = (Kinetic\ Energy)_{system} + (Potential\ Energy)_{system}$
      b. $E_{system} = (Kinetic\ Energy)_{system} - (Potential\ Energy)_{system}$
      c. $E_{system} = (Potential\ Energy)_{system} - (Kinetic\ Energy)_{system}$
      d. $E_{system} = (Kinetic\ Energy)_{system}$
      e. $E_{system} = (Potential\ Energy)_{system}$

10. During an endothermic chemical reaction,

    a. a system becomes warmer, and the chemical substances undergo an increase in potential energy
    b. a system becomes warmer, and the chemical substances undergo a decrease in potential energy
    ! c. a system becomes cooler, and the chemical substances undergo an increase in potential energy
    d. a system becomes cooler, and the chemical substances undergo a decrease in potential energy
    e. a system becomes warmer, and additional heat is gained from the surroundings

11. For a chemical reaction taking place at constant pressure, which one of the following is *not* true?

    a. $\Delta E = E_{final} - E_{initial}$
    b. $\Delta E = E_{products} - E_{reactants}$
    c. $\Delta E = q + w$
    ! d. $\Delta E = $ Kinetic Energy - Potential Energy
    e. $\Delta E = \Delta H - P\Delta V$

12. For a chemical reaction taking place at constant pressure, which one of the following is true?

    a. $\Delta H_{system} = $ (Kinetic Energy)$_{system}$ + (Potential Energy)$_{system}$
    b. $\Delta H_{system} = $ (Kinetic Energy)$_{system}$ - (Potential Energy)$_{system}$
    c. $\Delta H_{system} = \Delta E_{system} - q_p$
    ! d. $\Delta H_{system} = \Delta E_{system} + P\Delta V_{system}$
    e. $\Delta H_{system} = \Delta E_{system} + q_p$

13. Which statement below is true?

    a. A state function is one whose value in a system depends on the method of preparation of the reactants and products.
    b. Hess' law states that the enthalpy of the products is always greater than the enthalpy of the reactants.
    c. The molar heat capacity of a substance is the number of joules in one mole of the substance
    d. A state function is one whose value in a system is determined by the temperature of the system, and not on the composition of the system.
    ! e. A state function is one whose value in a system is determined by the composition of the system, the volume, the temperature, and the pressure.

14. In the course of measuring fuel content values, a reaction for the conversion of HC's (crude oil fuel) into water and carbon dioxide is carried out in two steps

$$\text{HC's} + \text{oxygen} \rightarrow CO(g) + H_2O$$
$$CO(g) + \text{oxygen} \rightarrow CO_2(g)$$

The net reaction taking place is simply, HC's + oxygen $\rightarrow CO_2(g) + H_2O$. Actually, a large fraction of the raw material in converted in one step, and the second step is just to catch the fraction that was just partially burned the first time. Anyway, for the overall or net process, which statement below is definitely always true?

    a. ΔH is independent of the time interval between the two steps, but dependent on the fraction which had to be converted in two steps.

    b. ΔH is dependent on the time interval between the two steps, but dependent on the fraction which had to be converted in two steps.

!   c. ΔH is independent of the time interval between the two steps, and also independent of the fraction which had to be converted in two steps.

    d. ΔH is dependent on the time interval between the two steps, but independent of the fraction which had to be converted in two steps.

15. An endothermic reaction is one in which th ere is

    a. a positive value for the work (w > 0 joules)
    b. a negative value for the work (w < 0 joules)
    c. a negative value for ΔH (ΔH < 0 joules)
!   d. a positive value for ΔH (ΔH > 0 joules)

16. For the reaction, $A_2(g) + 2\,BX(g) \rightarrow B_2(s) + 2\,AX(g)$ taking place in an insulated system, the enthalpy of the products is lower than that of the reactants. Which one of the following statements is true for the system?

    a. The kinetic energy of the system decreases as the reactants are converted to products.
!   b. The potential energy of the system decreases as the reactants are converted to products.
    c. The total energy of the system decreases as the reactants are converted to products.
    d. The total mass of the system decreases as the reactants are converted to products.

17. A chemical reaction took place in a 6 liter cylindrical enclosure fitted with a piston (like the cylinder in an internal combustion engine of the piston driven type). Over the time required for the reaction to be complete, the system underwent a volume change from 0.400 liters to 3.20 liter. Which statement below is true beyond doubt or qualification?

    a. Work was performed on the system.
!   b. Work was performed by the system.
    c. The internal energy of the system increased.
    d. The internal energy of the system decreased.
    e. The internal energy of the system remained unchanged.

18. A chemical reaction took place in a 5 liter cylindrical enclosure fitted with a piston (like the cylinder in an internal combustion engine of the piston driven type). Over the time required for the reaction to be complete, the system underwent a volume change from 1.40 liters to 3.70 liters. Which statement below is true beyond doubt or qualification?

     a. The enthalpy of the system remained unchanged.
     b. The enthalpy of the system decreased.
     c. The enthalpy of the system increased.
!   d. Work was performed by the system.
     e. Work was performed on the system.

19. For a change in a system taking place at constant pressure, which statement below is true?

     a. $\Delta H = \Delta E$
     b. $\Delta H = q_p - P \Delta V$
     c. $\Delta H = \Delta E - q_p$
!   d. $\Delta H = q_p$
     e. $\Delta E = q_p$

20. A closed, uninsulated system fitted with a movable piston so no matter is exchanged with the surroundings was assembled. Introduction of 430 J of heat caused the system to expand, doing 238 J of work in the process against a constant pressure of 101 kPa (kilopascals). What is the value of ΔE for this process?

     a. (430 + 238) joules
!   b. (430 - 238) joules
     c. (238 - 430) joules
     d. 430 joules
     e. (-238 - 430) joules

21. A closed, uninsulated system fitted with a movable piston so no matter is exchanged with the surroundings was assembled. Introduction of 430 J of heat caused the system to expand, doing 238 J of work in the process against a constant pressure of 101 kPa (kilopascals). What is the value of ΔH for this process?

     a. (430 + 238) joules
     b. (430 - 238) joules
     c. (238 - 430) joules
!   d. 430 joules
     e. (-238 - 430) joules

22. A closed, uninsulated system fitted with a movable piston so no matter is exchanged with the surroundings was assembled. Introduction of 238 J of heat caused the system to expand, doing 430 J of work in the process against a constant pressure of 101 kPa (kilopascals). What is the value of ΔE for this process?

      a. (430 + 238) joules
      b. (430 - 238) joules
!   c. (238 - 430) joules
      d. 430 joules
      e. (-238 - 430) joules

23. A 500.0 gram sample of aluminum is initially at 25.0 °C. It absorbs 32.60 kJ of heat from its surroundings. What is its final temperature, in °C? (specific heat = 0.9930 J g^{-1} °C^{-1} for aluminum)

      a. 40.4 °C
      b. 64.7 °C
      c. 65.7 °C
      d. 89.7 °C
!   e. 90.7 °C

24. A 350.0 gram sample of copper is initially at 25.0 °C. It absorbs 12.50 kJ of heat from its surroundings. What is its final temperature, to the nearest tenth of a degree? (specific heat = 0.3874 J g^{-1} °C^{-1} for copper)

      a. 38.8 °C
      b. 67.2 °C
      c. 92.2 °C
!   d. 117.2 °C
      e. 156.7 °C

25. A calorimeter consists of metal parts with a heat capacity of 850.0 J °C^{-1} and 1100 grams of oil with a specific heat of 2.184 J g^{-1} °C^{-1}. What is the heat capacity, in joules per degree, of the *entire* assembly?

      a. 1354 J °C^{-1}
      b. 1952 J °C^{-1}
      c. 2956 J °C^{-1}
!   d. 3252 J °C^{-1}
      e. 4259 J °C^{-1}

26. A calorimeter consists of metal parts with a heat capacity of 925.0 J °C^{-1} and 1100 grams of oil with a specific heat of 2.814 J g^{-1} °C^{-1}. What is the heat capacity, in joules per degree, of the *entire* assembly?

        a. 1321 J °C^{-1}
        b. 2028 J °C^{-1}
        c. 3703 J °C^{-1}
  ! d. 4020 J °C^{-1}
        e. 5698 J °C^{-1}

27. A certain oil used in industrial transformers has a density of 1.086 g ml^{-1} and a specific heat of 1.826 J g^{-1} °C^{-1}. Calculate the heat capacity of one gallon of this oil. (1 gallon = 3.785 liters)

        a. 0.4442 kJ °C^{-1}
        b. 0.5239 kJ °C^{-1}
        c. 2.251 kJ °C^{-1}
        d. 6.364 kJ °C^{-1}
  ! e. 7.506 kJ °C^{-1}

28. A certain oil used in industrial transformers has a density of 1.068 g ml^{-1} and a specific heat of 1.628 J g^{-1} °C^{-1}. Calculate the heat capacity of one gallon of this oil. (1 gallon = 3.785 liters)

        a. 0.3747 kJ °C^{-1}
        b. 0.4027 kJ °C^{-1}
        c. 2.483 kJ °C^{-1}
        d. 5.770 kJ °C^{-1}
  ! e. 6.581 kJ °C^{-1}

29. A calorimeter consists of metal parts with a heat capacity of 950.0 J °C^{-1} and 850 grams of oil with a specific heat of 2.418 J g^{-1} °C^{-1}. Calculate the amount of heat energy required, in kJ, to raise its temperature from 25.00 °C to 31.60 °C.

        a. 4.91 kJ
        b. 11.9 kJ
  ! c. 19.8 kJ
        d. 20.8 kJ
        e. 28.7 kJ

30. A calorimeter consists of metal parts with a heat capacity of 925.0 J °C^{-1} and 1100 grams of oil with a specific heat of 2.184 J g^{-1} °C^{-1}. Calculate the heat required, in kJ, to raise its temperature from 24.40 °C to 29.75 °C.

        a. 0.827 kJ
        b. 7.64 kJ
  ! c. 17.8 kJ
        d. 23.7 kJ
        e. 99.0 kJ

31. A coffee cup calorimeter contains 480.0 grams of water at 25.00 °C. To it are added:

    380.0 grams of water at 53.5 °C
    525.0 grams of water at 65.5 °C

Assuming the heat absorbed by the styrofoam is negligible, calculate the expected final temperature. The specific heat of water is 4.184 J g^{-1} °C^{-1}.

    a. 38.2 °C
 ! b. 48.2 °C
    c. 67.6 °C
    d. 88.7 °C
    e. 94.4 °C

32. A coffee cup calorimeter contains 525.0 grams of water at 25.0 °C. To it are added:

    350.0 grams of water at 48.3 °C
    480.0 grams of water at 63.8 °C

Neglect the heat absorbed by the styrofoam, and calculate the final temperature. The specific heat of water is 4.184 J g^{-1} °C^{-1}.

    a. 39.6 °C
    b. 45.7 °C
 ! c. 44.8 °C
    d. 66.7 °C
    e. 92.4 °C

33. A calorimeter consists of metal parts with a heat capacity of 850.0 J °C^{-1} and 1050 grams of oil with a specific heat of 2.148 J g^{-1} °C^{-1}. Both are at 24.50 °C. A 500 g copper slug, at 220.0 °C is added. What is the final temp? Specific heat of copper = 0.3874 J g^{-1} °C^{-1}.

    a. 33.4 °C
 ! b. 36.0 °C
    c. 36.8 °C
    d. 89.7 °C
    e. 120.5 °C

34. A calorimeter has metal parts (heat capacity of 850.0 J °C^{-1}) and 1100 grams of oil (specific heat = 2.184 J g^{-1} °C^{-1}), both at 24.50 °C. Adding a 460 g slug, at 240.0 °C, caused the temperature to rise to 32.5 °C. Find the specific heat of the metal!

    a. 0.236 J g^{-1} °C^{-1}
 ! b. 0.273 J g^{-1} °C^{-1}
    c. 0.309 J g^{-1} °C^{-1}
    d. 0.357 J g^{-1} °C^{-1}
    e. 2.28 J g^{-1} °C^{-1}

35. A calorimeter has metal parts (heat capacity of 925.0 J °C^{-1}) and 1100 grams of oil (specific heat = 2.824 J g^{-1} °C^{-1}), both at 25.40 °C. Adding a 550 g slug, at 220.0 °C caused the temperature to rise to 35.2 °C. Find the specific heat of the metal!

     a. 0.365 J g^{-1} °C^{-1}
!   b. 0.389 J g^{-1} °C^{-1}
     c. 0.395 J g^{-1} °C^{-1}
     d. 0.551 J g^{-1} °C^{-1}
     e. 1.20 J g^{-1} °C^{-1}

36. When pure sodium hydroxide is dissolved in water, heat is evolved. In a laboratory experiment to measure the molar heat of solution of sodium hydroxide, the following procedure was followed. To a calorimeter containing 300 g of water at 20.00 °C, 10.65 g of NaOH, also at 20.00 °C was added. The temperature change, which was monitored by a digital probe with negligible heat capacity, stopped when it reached a temperature of 28.50 °C. If the specific heat of the mixture is 4.184 J g^{-1} °C^{-1}, and the small heat capacity of the calorimeter is ignored, what is the heat evolved, per mole of sodium hydroxide?

     a. -37.4 kJ
!   b. -41.5 kJ
     c. -45.5 kJ
     d. -90.5 kJ
     e. -153 kJ

37. When pure sulfuric acid is dissolved in water, heat is evolved. In a laboratory experiment to measure the molar heat of solution of sulfuric acid, the following procedure was followed. To a calorimeter containing 300 g of water at 20.00 °C, 10.65 g of H$_2$SO$_4$, also at 20.00 °C was added. The temperature change, which was monitored by a digital probe with negligible heat capacity, ceased when it reached a temperature of 26.55 °C. If the specific heat of the mixture is 4.184 J g^{-1} °C^{-1}, and the small heat capacity of the calorimeter is ignored, what is the heat evolved, per mole of sulfuric acid?

     a. -27.4 kJ
     b. -72.8 kJ
!   c. -78.4 kJ
     d. -84.6 kJ
     e. -292 kJ

38. The values associated with the term, "standard reference conditions" in a thermochemical situation are

     a. temperature: 0.00 K; pressure: 1.000 standard atmosphere
     b. temperature: 0.00 °C; pressure: 1.000 standard atmosphere
     c. temperature: 273.15 K; pressure: 1.000 Pascal
!   d. temperature: 298.15 K; pressure: 1.000 standard atmosphere
     e. temperature: 298.15 K; pressure: 1.000 Pascal

39. The thermochemical equation which is associated with ΔH_f^o, the standard enthalpy of formation, for HCl(g), is

        a. $H(g) + Cl(g) \rightarrow HCl(g)$
        b. $H_2(g) + Cl_2(g) \rightarrow 2\,HCl(g)$
 ! c. $\frac{1}{2}\,H_2(g) + \frac{1}{2}\,Cl_2(g) \rightarrow HCl(g)$
        d. $H_2(g) + Cl_2(l) \rightarrow 2\,HCl(g)$
        e. $\frac{1}{2}\,H_2(g) + \frac{1}{2}\,Cl_2(l) \rightarrow HCl(g)$

40. The thermochemical equation which is associated with ΔH_f^o, the standard enthalpy of formation, for urea, $CO(NH_2)_2(s)$, is

        a. $CO(g) + 2\,NH_3(g) \rightarrow CO(NH_2)_2(s) + H_2(g)$
        b. $CO(g) + 2\,H_2(g) + N_2(g) \rightarrow CO(NH_2)_2(s)$
        c. $C(s) + O(g) + N_2(g) + 2\,H_2(g) \rightarrow CO(NH_2)_2(s)$
 ! d. $C(s) + \frac{1}{2}\,O_2(g) + N_2(g) + 2\,H_2(g) \rightarrow CO(NH_2)_2(s)$
        e. $C(s) + \frac{1}{2}\,O_2(g) + 2\,NH_2(g) \rightarrow CO(NH_2)_2(s)$

41. Given the reaction, $4B + 3A \rightarrow 4C + 7D$, and some standard enthalpies of formation, ΔH_f^o:
       A: +15.7 kJ mol^{-1} B: -86.4 kJ mol^{-1} C: -52.7 kJ mol^{-1} D: -71.6 kJ mol^{-1}
What is the standard enthalpy of reaction, in kJ for the reaction shown?

        a. -53.6 kJ
 ! b. -413.5 kJ
        c. -515.6 kJ
        d. -853.6 kJ
        e. -908.4 kJ

42. Given the reaction, $3B + 5A \rightarrow 7C + 3D$, and some standard enthalpies of formation, ΔH_f^o:
       A: -15.7 kJ mol^{-1} B: -86.4 kJ mol^{-1} C: -52.7 kJ mol^{-1} D: -71.6 kJ mol^{-1}
What is the standard enthalpy of reaction, in kJ for the reaction shown?

        a. +26.6 kJ
        b. -53.6 kJ
        c. -198.8 kJ
 ! d. -403.0 kJ
        e. -413.5 kJ

43. The standard enthalpy of combustion for xylene, $C_8H_{10}(l)$, is -3908 kJ mol^{-1}. Using this data and the standard enthalpies of formation, ΔH_f^o: $H_2O(l)$ = -285.9 kJ mol^{-1}; $CO_2(g)$ = -393.5 kJ mol^{-1}, calculate the standard enthalpy of formation of $C_8H_{10}(l)$, in kJ mol^{-1}.

   ! a. -669.5 kJ
     b. +3228.6 kJ
     c. -3228.6 kJ
     d. +4587.4 kJ
     e. +8485.5 kJ

44. A chemical compound has a molecular weight of 89.05 g/mole. 1.400 grams of this compound underwent complete combustion under constant pressure conditions in a calorimeter with a heat capacity of 2980 J °C^{-1} (metal shell, water substitute--a special oil, thermocouple, *etc*). The temperature went up by 11.95 degrees. Calculate the molar heat of combustion of the compound.

     a. 35.6 kJ mol^{-1}
     b. 686.2 kJ mol^{-1}
     c. 1681 kJ mol^{-1}
     d. 1886 kJ mol^{-1}
   ! e. 2265 kJ mol^{-1}

45. The standard enthalpy of combustion for naphthalene, $C_{10}H_8(s)$, is -5156.8 kJ mol^{-1}. Using this data and the standard enthalpies of formation, ΔH_f^o: $H_2O(l)$ = -285.9 kJ mol^{-1}; $CO_2(g)$ = -393.5 kJ mol^{-1}, calculate the standard enthalpy of formation of $C_{10}H_8(s)$, in kJ mol^{-1}.

   ! a. +78.2 kJ
     b. +935.9 kJ
     c. -1065.4 kJ
     d. +3619.7 kJ
     e. -10235.4 kJ

46. When aluminum metal reacts with iron(III) oxide to form aluminum oxide and iron metal, 429.6 kJ of heat are given off for each mole of aluminum metal consumed, under constant pressure and standard conditions. What is the correct value for the standard enthalpy of reaction in the thermochemical equation below?

$$2\ Al(s)\ +\ Fe_2O_3(s)\ \rightarrow\ 2\ Fe(s)\ +\ Al_2O_3(s)$$

     a. +429.6 kJ
     b. -429.6 kJ
     c. +859.2 kJ
   ! d. -859.2 kJ
     e. -1289 kJ

47. Complete combustion of hydrocarbons, or compounds with C,H, and O as the only elements, gives CO_2 and H_2O as the only products. If carried out under standard conditions, the CO_2 is a gas while the H_2O is a liquid. Given these standard enthalpies of **combustion**:

$C_2H_4(g)$ = -1411.08 kJ mol^{-1} $C_2H_2(g)$ = -1299.65 kJ mol^{-1}

$H_2(g)$ = -285.90 kJ mol^{-1} $C(s)$ = -393.50 kJ mol^{-1}

Calculate the standard enthalpy of reaction for the process, $C_2H_2(g) + H_2(g) \rightarrow C_2H_4(g)$

! a. -174.47 kJ
   b. +397.33 kJ
   c. -961.47 kJ
   d. -2424.83 kJ
   e. -2996.63 kJ

48. Complete combustion of hydrocarbons, or compounds with C,H, and O as the only elements, gives CO_2 and H_2O as the only products. If carried out under standard conditions, the CO_2 is a gas while the H_2O is a liquid. Given these standard enthalpies of **combustion**: $C_6H_{12}(l)$ = -3919.86 kJ mol^{-1}, $C_6H_6(l)$ = -3267.80 kJ mol^{-1}, $H_2(g)$ = -285.90 kJ mol^{-1}, $C(s)$ = -393.50 kJ mol^{-1}. Calculate the standard enthalpy of reaction for the process, $C_6H_6(l) + 3 H_2(g) \rightarrow C_6H_{12}(l)$

! a. -205.64 kJ
   b. +366.16 kJ
   c. +759.66 kJ
   d. +2155.36 kJ
   e. +5684.36 kJ

49. A check of the formulas of methane, water, and methanol suggests that the reaction,

$$CH_4(g) + H_2O(g) \rightarrow CH_3OH(l) + H_2(g)$$

could be made to occur under the correct conditions. This is a wild idea, but Mike G. says it's just a matter of the right catalyst combination, reactor temperature, and pressure. Using the values in the table below, what is the calculated value of $\Delta H°$ for Mike G.'s proposed reaction?

$C(s) + 2 H_2(g) \rightarrow CH_4(g)$ $\Delta H°$ = -74.848 kJ

$H_2(g) + \frac{1}{2} O_2(g) \rightarrow H_2O(g)$ $\Delta H°$ = -241.8 kJ

$H_2(g) + \frac{1}{2} O_2(g) \rightarrow H_2O(l)$ $\Delta H°$ = -285.9 kJ

$C(s) + 2 H_2(g) + \frac{1}{2} O_2(g) \rightarrow CH_3OH(l)$ $\Delta H°$ = -238.6 kJ

$2 C(s) + 3 H_2(g) + \frac{1}{2} O_2(g) \rightarrow C_2H_5OH(l)$ $\Delta H°$ = -277.63 kJ

$2 C(s) + 2 H_2(g) \rightarrow C_2H_4(g)$ $\Delta H°$ = +52.284 kJ

   a. -78.0 kJ
! b. +78.0 kJ
   c. -122.1 kJ
   d. +122.1 kJ
   e. +368.9 kJ

50. A check of the formulas of ethylene, water, and ethanol suggests that the reaction,
$$C_2H_4(g) + H_2O(g) \rightarrow C_2H_5OH(l)$$
could be made to occur under the correct conditions. This is a wild idea, but Mike G. says it's just a matter of the right catalyst combination, reactor temperature, and pressure. Using the values in the table below, what is the calculated value of $\Delta H°$ for Mike G.'s proposed reaction?

$$C(s) + 2 H_2(g) \rightarrow CH_4(g) \qquad\qquad \Delta H° = -74.848 \text{ kJ}$$
$$H_2(g) + ½ O_2(g) \rightarrow H_2O(g) \qquad\qquad \Delta H° = -241.8 \text{ kJ}$$
$$H_2(g) + ½ O_2(g) \rightarrow H_2O(l) \qquad\qquad \Delta H° = -285.9 \text{ kJ}$$
$$C(s) + 2 H_2(g) + ½ O_2(g) \rightarrow CH_3OH(l) \quad \Delta H° = -238.6 \text{ kJ}$$
$$2 C(s) + 3 H_2(g) + ½ O_2(g) \rightarrow C_2H_5OH(l) \; \Delta H° = -277.63 \text{ kJ}$$
$$2 C(s) + 2 H_2(g) \rightarrow C_2H_4(g) \qquad\qquad \Delta H° = +52.284 \text{ kJ}$$

  a. -39.0 kJ
  b. -44.0 kJ
  c. +44.0 kJ
! d. -88.1 kJ
  e. +88.1 kJ

51. For the reaction, $D_2(s) + 2 AX(g) \rightarrow A_2(g) + 2 DX(g)$ taking place in an insulated system, the enthalpy of the reactants is lower than that of the products. Which one of the following is true for the system?

  ! a. the kinetic energy of the system decreases as the reactants are converted to products
    b. the potential energy of the system decreases as the reactants are converted to products
    c. the total energy of the system decreases as the reactants are converted to products
    d. the total mass of the system decreases as the reactants are converted to products

Fill in the Blanks

52. A 500.0 gram sample of water is initially at 25.0 °C. It absorbs 50.0 kJ of heat from its surroundings. What is its final temperature, in °C? Specific heat of water = 4.184 J g^{-1} °C^{-1}.
_____ (! 48.9)

53. A calorimeter consists of metal parts with a heat capacity of 925.0 J °C^{-1} and 975 grams of oil with a specific heat of 2.214 J g^{-1} °C^{-1}. Both are at 25.40 °C. A 550 g iron slug, at 240.0 °C is added. What is the final temperature? Specific heat of iron = 0.4998 J g^{-1} °C^{-1}. _____ (! 43.0 °C)

54. A sample of zinc weighing 425 grams was initially at a temperature of 25.40 °C. It required 1360 joules of heat energy to increase the temperature to 33.70 °C. What is the molar heat capacity of the zinc? _____ (! 25.2 J mol^{-1} °C^{-1})

55. A sample of nickel weighing 425 grams was initially at a temperature of 26.20 °C. It required 975 joules of heat energy to increase the temperature to 31.55 °C. What is the specific heat of the nickel? _____ (! 0.429 J g^{-1} °C^{-1})

56. Complete combustion of hydrocarbons, or compounds with C,H, and O as the only elements give CO_2 and H_2O as the only products. If carried out under standard conditions, the CO_2 is a gas while the H_2O is a liquid. Given these standard enthalpies of *combustion*: $C_2H_4(g)$ = -1411.08 kJ mol^{-1}, $C_6H_{12}(l)$ = -3919.86 kJ mol^{-1}, $H_2(g)$ = -285.90 kJ mol^{-1}, $C(s)$ = -393.50 kJ mol^{-1}. Calculate the standard enthalpy of reaction for the process, $3 C_2H_4(g) \rightarrow C_6H_{12}(l)$. _____ (! -313.38 kJ)

57. A sample of chromium weighing 254 g was initially at a temperature of 25.88 °C. It required 843 joules of heat energy to increase the temperature to 32.75 °C. What is the molar heat capacity of the chromium? _____ (! 25.1 J mol^{-1} °C^{-1})

58. Complete combustion of hydrocarbons, or compounds with C,H, and O as the only elements give CO_2 and H_2O as the only products. If carried out under standard conditions, the CO_2 is a gas while the H_2O is a liquid. Given these standard enthalpies of *combustion*: $CH_3CHO(l)$ = -1166.37 kJ mol^{-1}, $C_6H_{12}O_3(l)$ = -3340.34 kJ mol^{-1}, $H_2(g)$ = -285.90 kJ mol^{-1}, $C(s)$ = -393.50 kJ mol^{-1}. Calculate the standard enthalpy of reaction for the process, $3 CH_3CHO(l) \rightarrow C_6H_{12}O_3(l)$. _____ (! -158.77 kJ)

59. Complete combustion of hydrocarbons, or compounds with C,H, and O as the only elements give CO_2 and H_2O as the only products. If carried out under standard conditions, the CO_2 is a gas while the H_2O is a liquid. Given these standard enthalpies of *combustion*: $C_2H_2(g)$ = -1299.65 kJ mol^{-1}, $C_6H_6(l)$ = -3267.80 kJ mol^{-1}, $H_2(g)$ = -285.90 kJ mol^{-1}, $C(s)$ = -393.50 kJ mol^{-1}. Calculate the standard enthalpy of reaction for the process, $3 C_2H_2(g) \rightarrow C_6H_6(l)$. _____ (! -631.15 kJ)

60. For the reaction, $N_2(g) + 3 H_2(g) \rightarrow 2 NH_3(g)$, $\Delta H°$ = -46.11 kJ per mole of nitrogen
What is the value of $\Delta H°$ for the reaction, $NH_3(g) \rightarrow \frac{1}{2} N_2(g) + ?? H_2(g)$? _____ (! +23.1 kJ)

61. For the reaction, $3 N_2(g) + H_2(g) \rightarrow 2 HN_3(g)$, $\Delta H°$ = +264 per mole of hydrogen
What is the value of $\Delta H°$ for the reaction, $HN_3(g) \rightarrow \frac{1}{2} H_2(g) + ?? N_2(g)$? _____ (! -132 kJ)

62. Use these reactions and standard enthalpies, $\Delta H°$

$$2 ZbO(s) + \frac{1}{2} O_2(g) \rightarrow Zb_2O_3(s) \qquad -128.0 \text{ kJ}$$
$$ZbO(s) + \frac{1}{2} O_2(g) \rightarrow ZbO_2(s) \qquad -380.0 \text{ kJ}$$
$$2 ZbO(s) + 3/2 O_2(g) \rightarrow Zb_2O_5(s) \qquad -344.5 \text{ kJ}$$

find the value for
$$Zb_2O_3(s) + O_2(g) \rightarrow Zb_2O_5(s) \qquad _____ (! -216.5 \text{ kJ})$$

63. Use these reactions and standard enthalpies, $\Delta H°$

$$2 ZbO(s) + \frac{1}{2} O_2(g) \rightarrow Zb_2O_3(s) \qquad -128.0 \text{ kJ}$$
$$ZbO(s) + \frac{1}{2} O_2(g) \rightarrow ZbO_2(s) \qquad -380.0 \text{ kJ}$$
$$2 ZbO(s) + 3/2 O_2(g) \rightarrow Zb_2O_5(s) \qquad -344.5 \text{ kJ}$$

find the value for
$$Zb_2O_3(s) + Zb_2O_5(s) \rightarrow 4 ZbO(s) + 2 O_2(g) \qquad _____ (! +472.5 \text{ kJ})$$

64. Given the thermochemical equation, $2 M_2O_5(s) \rightarrow 4 MO_2(s) + O_2(g)$ with a standard enthalpy of reaction = +74.2 kJ, calculate a value for the standard enthalpy of reaction in the thermochemical reaction, $2 MO_2(s) + \frac{1}{2} O_2(g) \rightarrow M_2O_5(s)$ _____ (! -37.1 kJ)

65. Given the reaction, $7A + 5B \rightarrow 3C + 4D$, and some standard enthalpies of formation, ΔH_f^o :

   A: 15.7 kJ mol^{-1} B: -86.4 kJ mol^{-1} C: -52.7 kJ mol^{-1} D: -71.6 kJ mol^{-1}

   What is the standard enthalpy of reaction, in kJ for the reaction shown? _____ (! -122.4 kJ)

66. Using the standard enthalpies of formation, ΔH_f^o :

   $H_2O(l)$ = -285.9 kJ mol^{-1}; $C_2H_4(g)$ = 52.284 kJ mol^{-1}; $C_2H_5OH(l)$ = -277.63 kJ mol^{-1}

   calculate the standard enthalpy of reaction for

   $C_2H_4(g) + H_2O(l) \rightarrow C_2H_5OH(l)$ _____ (! -44.0 kJ)

67. Using the standard enthalpies of formation, ΔH_f^o :

   $NO(g)$ = 90.37 kJ mol^{-1} $NO_2(g)$ = 33.8 kJ mol^{-1}
   $SO_2(g)$ = -296.9 kJ mol^{-1} $SO_3(g)$ = -395.2 kJ mol^{-1}

   calculate the standard enthalpy of reaction for

   $SO_2(g) + NO_2(g) \rightarrow SO_3(g) + NO(g)$ _____ (! -41.7 kJ)

68. Using the standard enthalpies of formation, ΔH_f^o :

   $CO(g)$ = -110.5 kJ mol^{-1} $CO_2(g)$ = -393.5 kJ mol^{-1}
   $SO_2(g)$ = -296.9 kJ mol^{-1} $SO_3(g)$ = -395.2 kJ mol^{-1}

   calculate the standard enthalpy of reaction for

   $CO_2(g) + SO_2(g) \rightarrow SO_3(g) + CO(g)$ _____ (! 184.7 kJ)

69. Using the standard enthalpies of formation, ΔH_f^o :

   $CO(g)$ = -110.5 kJ mol^{-1} $CO(NH_2)_2(s)$ = -333.19 kJ mol^{-1} $NH_3(g)$ = -46.19 kJ mol^{-1}

   calculate the standard enthalpy of reaction for

   $CO(NH_2)_2(s) + H_2(g) \rightarrow 2NH_3(g) + CO(g)$ _____ (! 130.3 kJ)

70. Given the thermochemical equation, $3\ M(s) + 3\ O_2(g) \rightarrow 3\ MO_2(s)$ with a standard enthalpy of reaction = -1443 kJ, calculate a value for the standard enthalpy of reaction in the thermochemical reaction, $MO_2(s) \rightarrow$ __ $M(s) +$ __ $O_2(g)$. _____ (! +481 kJ)

True and False

71. An exothermic chemical reaction in an open system is a type of adiabatic change. (! F)

72. The statement, "the total energy of the universe (system + surroundings) is constant", is a logical extension of the law of conservation of energy. (! T)

73. Heat energy can always be quantitatively converted into various other forms of energy. (! F)

74. The first law of thermodynamics is expressed in the equation, $\Delta H = q + w$. (! F)

75. The first law of thermodynamics is expressed in the equation, ΔE = Kinetic Energy - Potential Energy. (! F)

76. Based on the terms and symbols used in the discussions on thermochemistry, is the expression, $\Delta E = \Delta H - P\Delta V$ correct? (! T)

77. For a chemical reaction taking place at constant pressure in which all reactants and products are solids or liquids, $\Delta E \approx q_p$. (! T)

Critical Thinking

78. A calorimeter has metal parts (heat capacity of 850.0 J °C^{-1}) and 1020 grams of oil (specific heat = 2.248 J g^{-1} °C^{-1}), both at 24.50 °C. Two metal slugs, one a 460.0 g piece of cobalt and the other a 360.0 g piece of cadmium were removed from an oven which was maintained at 240.0 °C and added to the calorimeter. If no heat was lost to the surroundings, what would be the final temperature in the calorimeter? (cadmium, *molar* heat capacity = 25.34 J mol^{-1} °C^{-1}; cobalt, *molar* heat capacity = 25.12 J mol^{-1} °C^{-1}) _____ (! 42.0 °C)

79. Use these reactions, and the standard enthalpies as shown $\Delta H°$

$M(s) + CO_2(g) \rightarrow CO(g) + MO(s)$ -140.0 kJ

$3\,MO(s) + CO_2(g) \rightarrow CO(g) + M_3O_4(s)$ + 1.20 kJ

$2\,M_3O_4(s) + CO_2(g) \rightarrow CO(g) + 3\,M_2O_3(s)$ -380.0 kJ

$M_2O_3(s) + CO_2(g) \rightarrow CO(g) + 2\,MO_2(s)$ -121.8 kJ

$2\,MO_2(s) + CO_2(g) \rightarrow CO(g) + M_2O_5(s)$ +344.5 kJ

to find the value for

$3\,M_2O_5(s) + 7\,CO(g) \rightarrow 7\,CO_2(g) + 2\,M_3O_4(s)$ _____ (! -288.1 kJ)

80. Use these reactions, and the standard enthalpies as shown $\Delta H°$

$M(s) + CO_2(g) \rightarrow CO(g) + MO(s)$ -140.0 kJ

$3\,MO(s) + CO_2(g) \rightarrow CO(g) + M_3O_4(s)$ + 1.20 kJ

$2\,M_3O_4(s) + CO_2(g) \rightarrow CO(g) + 3\,M_2O_3(s)$ -380.0 kJ

$M_2O_3(s) + CO_2(g) \rightarrow CO(g) + 2\,MO_2(s)$ -121.8 kJ

$2\,MO_2(s) + CO_2(g) \rightarrow CO(g) + M_2O_5(s)$ +344.5 kJ

to find the value for

$M_2O_3(s) + 3\,CO(g) \rightarrow 3\,CO_2(g) + 2\,M(s)$ _____ (! +405.9 kJ)

81. Use these reactions, and the standard enthalpies as shown $\Delta H°$

$M(s) + CO_2(g) \rightarrow CO(g) + MO(s)$ -140.0 kJ

$3\,MO(s) + CO_2(g) \rightarrow CO(g) + M_3O_4(s)$ + 1.20 kJ

$2\,M_3O_4(s) + CO_2(g) \rightarrow CO(g) + 3\,M_2O_3(s)$ -380.0 kJ

$M_2O_3(s) + CO_2(g) \rightarrow CO(g) + 2\,MO_2(s)$ -121.8 kJ

$2\,MO_2(s) + CO_2(g) \rightarrow CO(g) + M_2O_5(s)$ +344.5 kJ

to find the value for

$MO_2(s) + CO(g) \rightarrow CO_2(g) + MO(s)$ _____ (! 123.8 kJ)

82. The standard enthalpy of combustion for oxalic acid, $H_2C_2O_4(s)$, is -251.9 kJ mol^{-1}. Using this data and the standard enthalpies of formation, ΔH_f^o:

$$H_2O(l) = -285.9 \text{ kJ mol}^{-1} \qquad CO_2(g) = -393.5 \text{ kJ mol}^{-1}$$

calculate the standard enthalpy of formation of $H_2C_2O_4(s)$, in kJ mol^{-1}. _____ (! -821.0 kJ)

83. The standard enthalpy of combustion for ethylene glycol, $C_2H_6O_2(l)$, is -1179.5 kJ mol^{-1}. Using this data and the standard enthalpies of formation, ΔH_f^o:

$$H_2O(l) = -285.9 \text{ kJ mol}^{-1}; \ CO_2(g) = -393.5 \text{ kJ mol}^{-1}$$

calculate the standard enthalpy of formation of $C_2H_6O_2(l)$, in kJ mol^{-1}. _____ (! -465.2 kJ)

84. 500.0 ml of 0.220 molar HCl(aq) was added to a high quality insulated calorimeter containing 500.0 ml of 0.200 molar NaOH(aq). Both solutions have a density of 1.000 g ml^{-1} and a specific heat of 4.184 J g^{-1} °C^{-1}. The calorimeter had a heat capacity of 850.0 J °C^{-1}. The temperature of the *entire* system rose from 25.60 °C to 26.70 °C. Calculate the heat of reaction, in kJ, per mole of NaOH(aq). _____ (! 55.4 kJ)

85. 600.0 ml of 0.240 molar perchloric acid, HClO$_4$(aq) was added to a high quality insulated calorimeter containing 400.0 ml of 0.300 molar KOH(aq). Both solutions have a density of 1.000 g ml^{-1} and a specific heat of 4.184 J g^{-1} °C^{-1}. The calorimeter had a heat capacity of 950.0 J °C^{-1}. The temperature of the *entire* system rose from 25.30 °C to 26.59 °C. Calculate the heat of reaction, in kJ, per mole of NaOH(aq). _____ (! 55.2 kJ)

86. Some workers in central research were talking around the lunch table. They claim to have an idea for a process which might possibly convert $C_2H_4(g)$ to $C_2H_5OH(l)$, an alternative fuel. It would work in two steps:

$$NaOH(s) + C_2H_4(g) \xrightarrow{catalyst, heat, pressure} NaC_2H_5O(s)$$
$$NaC_2H_5O(s) + H_2O(g) \rightarrow C_2H_5OH(l) + NaOH(aq)$$

It is known that for the reaction, NaOH(s) $\rightarrow$ NaOH(aq), ΔH^o = -44.505 kJ. Using the values in the table below, what is the calculated value of ΔH^o for the proposed reaction? _____ (! -132.6 kJ)

$$
\begin{array}{ll}
C(s) + 2\,H_2(g) \rightarrow CH_4(g) & \Delta H^o = -74.848 \text{ kJ} \\
H_2(g) + \tfrac{1}{2}\,O_2(g) \rightarrow H_2O(g) & \Delta H^o = -241.8 \text{ kJ} \\
H_2(g) + \tfrac{1}{2}\,O_2(g) \rightarrow H_2O(l) & \Delta H^o = -285.9 \text{ kJ} \\
C(s) + 2\,H_2(g) + \tfrac{1}{2}\,O_2(g) \rightarrow CH_3OH(l) & \Delta H^o = -238.6 \text{ kJ} \\
2\,C(s) + 3\,H_2(g) + \tfrac{1}{2}\,O_2(g) \rightarrow C_2H_5OH(l) & \Delta H^o = -277.63 \text{ kJ} \\
2\,C(s) + 2\,H_2(g) \rightarrow C_2H_4(g) & \Delta H^o = +52.284 \text{ kJ}
\end{array}
$$

Chapter 7 Atomic and Electronic Structure

Multiple Choice

1. The frequency of an electromagnetic wave is

    a. the number of complete oscillations or cycles over a distance of one meter
    ! b. the number of complete oscillations or cycles in a one second time interval
    c. the distance between successive maxima in the wave in one complete cycle
    d. the number of complete oscillations or cycles over a distance of one centimeter
    e. the distance between successive nodes in the wave

2. The wavelength of an electromagnetic wave is

    a. the number of complete oscillations or cycles over a distance of one meter
    b. the number of complete oscillations or cycles in a one second time interval
    ! c. the distance between successive maxima in the wave
    d. the number of complete oscillations or cycles over a distance of one centimeter
    e. the distance between a minimum and the nearest maximum in the oscillation

3. What is the wavelength of electromagnetic radiation which has a frequency of 4.464×10^{14} s^{-1}?

    a. 1.338×10^{23} m
    b. 1.489×10^{-6} m
    c. 6.716×10^{-7} nm
    ! d. 671.6 nm
    e. 7.472×10^{-15} nm

4. What is the wavelength of electromagnetic radiation which has a frequency of 3.818×10^{14} s^{-1}?

    a. 1145 nm
    b. 1.274×10^{-1} nm
    c. 1.274×10^{-7} m
    d. 7.852×10^{-7} nm
    ! e. 7.852×10^{-7} m

5. Calculate the frequency of visible light having a wavelength of 464.1 nm

    a. 139.1 s^{-1}
    b. 1.548×10^{-6} s^{-1}
    c. 1.548×10^{-15} s^{-1}
    ! d. 6.460×10^{14} s^{-1}
    e. 6.460×10^{5} s^{-1}

6. A police radar unit is operating on a frequency of 9.527 Gigahertz. What is the wavelength of the radiation being employed?

    a. 314.7 nm
    b. 314.7 m
!   c. 3.147 cm
    d. 314.7 cm
    e. 31.78 m

7. Calculate the frequency of visible light having a wavelength of 568.8 nm

    a. 170.5 s^{-1}
    b. $1.897 \times 10^{6} \text{ s}^{-1}$
    c. $1.897 \times 10^{15} \text{ s}^{-1}$
    d. $5.271 \times 10^{-9} \text{ s}^{-1}$
!   e. $5.271 \times 10^{14} \text{ s}^{-1}$

8. Which one of the following types of radiation has the lowest frequency?

!   a. FM radio waves
    b. infrared waves
    c. microwaves
    d. x-rays
    e. ultraviolet rays

9. Which one of the following types of radiation has the highest frequency?

!   a. blue visible light
    b. FM radio
    c. infrared waves
    d. microwave radiation
    e. short wave radio waves

10. Which one of the following types of radiation has the shortest wavelength?

    a. FM radio waves
    b. infrared waves
    c. microwaves
    d. ultraviolet rays
!   e. x-rays

11. Which one of the following types of radiation has the longest wavelength?

    a. gamma rays
    b. green visible light
!   c. red visible light
    d. ultraviolet rays
    e. x-rays

12. What is the energy, in joules, of one photon of microwave radiation with a wavelength of 0.158 m?

!   a. 1.26×10^{-24} J
    b. 3.14×10^{-26} J
    c. 3.19×10^{25} J
    d. 3.49×10^{-43} J
    e. 7.15×10^{40} J

13. What is the energy, in joules, of one photon of visible radiation with a wavelength of 464.1 nm?

    a. 1.026×10^{-48} J
    b. 2.100×10^{35} J
    c. 2.341×10^{11} J
!   d. 4.280×10^{-19} J
    e. 4.280×10^{-12} J

14. What is the energy, in joules, of one mole of photons associated with visible light having a wavelength of 486.1 nm?

    a. 12.41 kJ
    b. 2.461×10^{-4} J
!   c. 2.461×10^{5} J
    d. 6.167×10^{14} J
    e. $8.776.15 \times 10^{25}$ J

15. What is the energy, in joules, of one mole of photons associated with visible light having a wavelength of 4.89×10^2 nm?

    a. 1.48×10^{42} J
    b. 1.95×10^{-16} J
!   c. 2.45×10^{5} J
    d. 3.24×10^{-40} J
    e. 4.06×10^{-19} J

16. What is the energy, in joules, of one mole of photons associated with radiation which has a frequency of 6.336×10^{15} Hz?

!   a. 2.528×10^{6} J
    b. 3.882×10^{14} J
    c. 3.955×10^{-7} J
    d. 4.198×10^{-18} J
    e. 6.298×10^{-26} J

120

17. What is the energy, in joules, of one mole of photons associated with radiation which has a frequency of 3.818×10^{15} Hz?

    a. 1.045×10^{-25} J
    ! b. 1.524×10^{6} J
    c. 2.530×10^{-18} J
    d. 6.564×10^{-7} J
    e. 9.568×10^{24} J

18. What is the wavelength, in nm, of radiation which has an energy of 3.371×10^{-19} joules per photon?

    a. 655.9 nm
    b. 152.5 nm
    c. 170.0 nm
    ! d. 589.3 nm
    e. 745.1 nm

19. What is the wavelength, in nm, of radiation which has an energy of 216.1 kJ mole^{-1} (of these photons)?

    a. 655.9 nm
    ! b. 546.1 nm
    c. 108.8 nm
    d. 589.3 nm
    e. 977.7 nm

20. What is the frequency, in sec^{-1}, of radiation which has an energy of 3.371×10^{-19} joules per photon?

    a. 1.697×10^{15} sec^{-1}
    b. 5.893×10^{-7} sec^{-1}
    ! c. 5.087×10^{14} sec^{-1}
    d. 1.966×10^{-15} sec^{-1}
    e. 6.626×10^{-34} sec^{-1}

21. What is the frequency, in sec^{-1}, of radiation which has an energy of 216.1 kJ per mole (of these photons)?

    a. 615.9×10^{14} sec^{-1}
    b. 1.624×10^{14} sec^{-1}
    c. 1.058×10^{-10} sec^{-1}
    ! d. 5.491×10^{14} sec^{-1}
    e. 3.588×10^{-19} sec^{-1}

22. Which statement among the ones presented below is true?

    a. The line spectra of elements are the same provided they belong to the same family.
    b. The line spectra of elements are the same provided they belong to the same family **and** are combined with oxygen.
    c. The line spectra of elements are the same provided they belong to the same family **and** are in the same physical state.
    d. The line spectra of elements can be used for separation of elements from mixtures.
!   e. The line·spectra of elements can be used for identification purposes.

23. Which statement among the ones presented below is true?

    a. The line spectra of atoms consists of a series of white lines superimposed on a colored background.
    b. The line spectra of atoms consists of a series of white lines superimposed on a dark background.
!   c. The line spectra of atoms consists of a series of colored lines superimposed on a dark background.
    d. The line spectra of atoms consists of a series of dark lines superimposed on a white background.
    e. The line spectra of atoms consists of a series of dark lines superimposed on a colored background.

24. Which statement among the ones presented below is true?

    a. The spectrum of sunlight consists of a series of white lines superimposed on a colored background.
    b. The spectrum of sunlight consists of a series of white lines superimposed on a dark background.
    c. The spectrum of sunlight consists of a series of colored lines superimposed on a dark background.
!   d. The spectrum of sunlight consists of a series of dark lines superimposed on a colored background.
    e. The spectrum of sunlight consists of a series of dark lines superimposed on a white background.

25. Which statement below is true with regard to Bohr's model of the atom?

    a. The model accounted for the absorption spectra of atoms but not for the emission spectra.
!   b. The model could account for the emission spectrum of hydrogen and for the Rydberg equation.
    c. The model was based on the wave properties of the electron.
    d. The model accounted for the emission spectra of atoms, but not for the absorption spectra.
    e. The model was generally successful for all atoms to which it was applied.

26. What is the energy, in joules, of one mole of photons whose wavelength is 5.461×10^2 nm?

      a. 2.191×10^{-4} J
      b. 2.437×10^{-12} J
!   c. 2.191×10^5 J
      d. 1.376×10^6 J
      e. 4.06×10^{-19} J

27. Which statement below is true about the spectrum of hydrogen obtained in gas discharge tubes experiments?

      a. A photon is absorbed as the electron goes from a state with a *higher* energy to one with a *lower* energy.
      b. A photon is absorbed as the electron goes from a state with a *lower* energy to one with a *higher* energy.
!   c. A photon is emitted as the electron goes from a state with a *higher* energy to one with a *lower* energy.
      d. A photon is emitted as the electron goes from a state with a *lower* energy to one with a *higher* energy.
      e. An electron is emitted as the photon goes from a state with a *higher* energy to one with a *lower* energy.

28. The definite energies associated with specific wavelengths in the emission spectrum of atomic hydrogen suggest that

      a. electrons have a smaller rest mass than photons
      b. photons have a smaller rest mass than electrons
!   c. energy states in the hydrogen atom are quantized
      d. atomic hydrogen is more stable and has a lower potential energy than molecular hydrogen
      e. the potential energy of electrons in the atom can have any arbitrary value over a period of time, but the kinetic energy may only have certain specific values

29. Calculate the energy required to excite a hydrogen atom by causing an electronic transition from the energy level with n = 1 to the level with n = 4. Recall that the quantized energies of the levels in the hydrogen atom are given by:

$$E_n = -\frac{21.79 x 10^{-19}}{n^2}\, joule$$

      a. 2.017×10^{-29} J
!   b. 2.043×10^{-18} J
      c. 2.192×10^5 J
      d. 2.254×10^{-18} J
      e. 3.275×10^{-17} J

30. Calculate the frequency of the light emitted by a hydrogen atom during a transition of its electron from the energy level with n = 4 to the level with n = 1. Recall that the quantized energies of the levels in the hydrogen atom are given by:

$$E_n = -\frac{21.79 \times 10^{-19}}{n^2}\ joule$$

    a. $1.028 \times 10^7\ s^{-1}$
    b. $1.215 \times 10^{-7}\ s^{-1}$
    c. $2.467 \times 10^{15}\ s^{-1}$
! d. $3.083 \times 10^{15}\ s^{-1}$
    e. $8.228 \times 10^6\ s^{-1}$

31. Calculate the wavelength of the light emitted by a hydrogen atom during a transition of its electron from the energy level with n = 4 to the level with n = 1. Recall that the quantized energies of the levels in the hydrogen atom are given by:

$$E_n = -\frac{21.79 \times 10^{-19}}{n^2}\ joule$$

    a. 0.6126 nm
    b. 6.856×10^{-18} nm
    c. 29.16 nm
! d. 97.24 nm
    e. 121.5 nm

32. Calculate the frequency of the light emitted by a hydrogen atom during a transition of its electron from the energy level with n = 6 to the level with n = 3. Recall that the quantized energies of the levels in the hydrogen atom are given by:

$$E_n = -\frac{21.79 \times 10^{-19}}{n^2}\ joule$$

    a. $1.665 \times 10^{-26}\ s^{-1}$
    b. $1.824 \times 10^{-15}\ s^{-1}$
! c. $2.740 \times 10^{14}\ s^{-1}$
    d. $3.649 \times 10^{-15}\ s^{-1}$
    e. $9.132 \times 10^{13}\ s^{-1}$

33. Calculate the energy required to excite a hydrogen atom by causing an electronic transition from the energy level with n = 3 to the level with n = 6. Recall that the quantized energies of the levels in the hydrogen atom are given by:

$$E_n = -\frac{21.79 \times 10^{-19}}{n^2}\ joule$$

    a. 1.211×10^{-19} J
! b. 1.816×10^{-19} J
    c. 2.421×10^{-19} J
    d. 3.632×10^{-19} J
    e. 6.658×10^{-19} J

34. Calculate the wavelength of the light emitted by a hydrogen atom during a transition of its electron from the energy level with n = 6 to the level with n = 3. Recall that the quantized energies of the levels in the hydrogen atom are given by:

$$E_n = -\frac{21.79 \times 10^{-19}}{n^2} \, joule$$

    a. 2.954×10^{-5} m
! b. 1094 nm
    c. 547 nm
    d. 821 nm
    e. 1640 nm

35. In an electron microscope, electrons are accelerated to high speeds. Using the de Broglie relation and ignoring relativistic effects, calculate the wavelength of an electron traveling with a speed of 6.550×10^4 meters per second. The electron has a mass of 5.485712×10^{-4} a.m.u.

! a. 1.111×10^{-8} m
    b. 1.111×10^{-11} m
    c. 1.844×10^{-35} m
    d. 2.426×10^{-12} m
    e. 5.528×10^{-27} m

36. Using the de Broglie relation and ignoring relativistic effects, calculate the wavelength of a $^{19}F^+$ ion which is moving with a speed of 4.255×10^5 m/s. The mass of ^{19}F is 18.9984 a.m.u.

    a. 4.936×10^{-17} m
! b. 4.936×10^{-14} m
    c. 1.484×10^{-29} m
    d. 1.484×10^{-26} m
    e. 4.936×10^{-20} m

37. Using the de Broglie relation, calculate the wavelength of a neutron which is moving with a speed of 4.505×10^4 m/s. The mass of the neutron is 1.008665 a.m.u.

    a. 1.458×10^{-38} m
    b. 2.632×10^{-3} m
    c. 4.372×10^{-30} m
    d. 8.781×10^{-15} m
! e. 8.781×10^{-12} m

38. The first full presentation describing the behavior of the electron in the hydrogen atom by application of the wave mechanics approach was presented by

    a. Louis de Broglie
    b. Werner von Heisenberg
    c. Wolfgang Pauli
    d. Ernest Rutherford
! e. Erwin Schrödinger

39. "No two electrons in the same atom can have all its quantum numbers the same." This statement is based on the work of

       a. Louis de Broglie
       b. Werner von Heisenberg
       c. Albert Einstein
 !   d. Wolfgang Pauli
       e. Erwin Schrödinger

40. Which statement below best summarizes the known facts about the quantum numbers which characterize the equations that describe the behavior of electrons in atoms?

       a. all of the quantum numbers are allowed to have values which are not integers
       b. only the principal quantum number is allowed to have values which are not integers
 !   c. only the spin quantum numbers are allowed to have values which are not integers
       d. only the secondary quantum number is allowed to have values which are not integers
       e. no quantum numbers are allowed to have values which are not integers

41. The wave functions which are solutions to the wave equation which describes the behavior of the electron in the hydrogen atom are described by how many quantum numbers?

       a. 1
       b. 2
 !   c. 3
       d. 4
       e. 5

42 . The letter designation for the subshell is based on

 !   a. the value of the secondary quantum number
       b. the value of the principal quantum number
       c. the value of the magnetic quantum number, m_l
       d. the value of the spin quantum number, m_s
       e. the transverse polarization of the optical emission from the H atom

43. The three quantum numbers which characterize the solutions to the wave equation describing the behavior of the electron in the H atom are usually designated as

       a. *1s 2s 2p*
       b. n l m_s
       c. m_l m_s m_p
 !   d. n l m_l
       e. l m_l m_s

44. All orbitals with the same value of the principal quantum number are said

   ! a. to belong to the same shell
   b. to belong to the same subshell
   c. to belong to the same group
   d. to belong to the same period
   e. to belong to the same class

45. The spectroscopic notation (number + letter designation) for the subshell with $n = 5$ and $l = 3$ is

   a. 5d subshell
   b. 5p subshell
   ! c. 5f subshell
   d. 5g subshell
   e. 5s subshell

46. The spectroscopic notation (number + letter designation) for the subshell with $n = 4$ and $l = 2$ is

   ! a. 4d subshell
   b. 4p subshell
   c. 4f subshell
   d. 4s subshell
   e. there is no subshell fitting this description

47. The maximum number of electrons that would be required to fill all the energy levels having a value of 4 for n, the principal quantum number, is

   a. n
   b. $n+1$
   c. $2n$
   d. n^2
   ! e. $2n^2$

48. The spectroscopic notation (number + letter designation) for the subshell with $n = 3$ and $l = 3$ is

   a. 3d subshell
   b. 3f subshell
   c. 3p subshell
   d. 3s subshell
   ! e. There is no subshell fitting this description

49. Given the following sets of quantum numbers for $n\ l\ m_l\ m_s$, which one of these sets is not a possible set for an electron in an atom?

	n	l	m_l	m_s
a.	3	2	2	-½
b.	3	1	-1	½
c.	4	3	2	½
d.	4	3	-2	-½
! e.	5	2	3	½

50. Given the following sets of quantum numbers for $n\ l\ m_l\ m_s$ which one of these sets is not a possible set for an electron in an atom?

	n	l	m_l	m_s
a.	4	2	2	-½
! b.	3	1	-1	-1
c.	4	3	2	½
d.	4	3	-2	-½
e.	5	2	2	½

51. Given the following sets of quantum numbers for $n\ l\ m_l\ m_s$ which one of these sets is not a possible set for an electron in an atom?

	n	l	m_l	m_s
a.	3	2	2	-½
b.	3	1	-1	½
c.	4	3	2	½
! d.	4	4	-3	-½
e.	5	2	-2	½

52. Given the following sets of quantum numbers for $n\ l\ m_l\ m_s$ which one of these sets is not a possible set for an electron in an atom?

	n	l	m_l	m_s
! a.	3	1	-1	0
b.	3	2	2	-½
c.	4	3	2	½
d.	4	3	-2	-½
e.	5	3	2	½

53. The statement that the ground state configuration of an atom is generated by filling in levels from the lowest (energy-wise) to the highest with electrons observing the maximum for each of these levels is

! a. the Aufbau principle
b. Bustamente's principle
c. Hund's Rule
d. Murphy's rule
e. the Pauli Principle

54. Given the following sets of quantum numbers for n l m_l m_s which one of these sets is not a possible set for an electron in an atom?

	n	l	m_l	m_s
a.	3	1	-1	½
! b.	3	3	2	-½
c.	4	3	2	½
d.	4	3	-2	-½
e.	5	3	2	½

55. There are several possible arrangements of electrons when you try to place 7 electrons in a 3d subshell. To determine the correct distribution for the ground state we are guided by

    a. the Aufbau principle
! b. Hund's Rule
    c. the Pauli Principle
    d. the wave particle duality principle
    e. the uncertainty principle

56. A correct description for the ground state configuration of the iron atom is

    a. [Ar] $3s^2 3d^6$, paramagnetic
    b. [Ar] $4s^2 3d^6$, diamagnetic
    c. [Ar] $4s^1 3d^7$, paramagnetic
    d. [Ar] $3d^8$, paramagnetic
! e. [Ar] $4s^2 3d^6$, paramagnetic

57. A correct description for the ground state configuration of the vanadium atom is

    a. [Ar] $4s^1 3d^4$, paramagnetic
! b. [Ar] $4s^2 3d^3$, paramagnetic
    c. [Ar] $4s^3 3d^2$, paramagnetic
    d. [Ar] $3d^5$, paramagnetic
    e. [Ar] $3s^2 3d^3$, paramagnetic

58. A correct description for the ground state configuration of the chromium atom is

! a. [Ar] $4s^1 3d^5$, paramagnetic
    b. [Ar] $4s^2 3d^4$, paramagnetic
    c. [Ar] $4s^3 3d^3$, paramagnetic
    d. [Ar] $3d^6$, paramagnetic
    e. [Ar] $3s^2 3d^4$, paramagnetic

59. A correct description for the ground state configuration of the selenium atom is

     a. [Ar] $4s^1 3d^{10} 4p^5$, paramagnetic
! b. [Ar] $4s^2 3d^{10} 4p^4$, paramagnetic
     c. [Ar] $4s^2 3d^8 4p^6$, paramagnetic
     d. [Ar] $3d^{10}, 4p^6$ diamagnetic
     e. [Ar] $4s^1 3d^9 4p^6$, paramagnetic

60. Which one of the following configurations represents an excited state configuration?

     a. [Ar] $4s^1 3d^5$
! b. [Ar] $4s^2 3d^4$
     c. [Xe] $5s^2 5p^1$
     d. [Xe] $6s^2 4f^7$
     e. [Rn] $7s^2$

61. Which one of the following configurations represent a situation that can not exist for ground state or for excited state?

     a. [Ar] $4s^2 3d^{10} 4p^5$
! b. [Xe] $5s^2 4d^{10} 5p^4$
     c. [Rn] $7s^2 4f^8$
     d. [Kr] $5s^1, 4d^6$
     e. [Ne] $6s^1$

62. An atom is described as having the ground state electronic configuration, [Ar] $4s^2 3d^5 4f^2$. Which element fits the description?

     a. one of the chalcogen family
     b. one of the halogen family
     c. one of the alkaline earth family
     d. one of the lanthanide elements
! e. there is no element which fits the description listed above

63. Using X to indicate a filled inner core and an arrow for a valence shell electron, indicate which of the following choices is the correct ground state electronic configuration for the sulfur atom.

     [Ne] <u>3s</u>   <u>   3p   </u>

     a. X ↑↓   ↑ ↑ ↑
! b. X ↑↓   ↑↓ ↑ ↑
     c. X ↑   ↑↓ ↑ ↑↓
     d. X ↑↓   ↑↓ ↑↓
     e. X ↑↓   ↑↓ ↑↓

64. Using X to indicate a filled inner core and an arrow for a valence shell electron, indicate which of the following choices is the correct ground state electronic configuration for the vanadium atom.

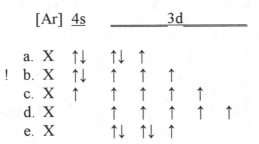

```
        [Ar] 4s _____  3d _____

      a.  X  ↑↓   ↑↓  ↑
   !  b.  X  ↑↓   ↑   ↑   ↑
      c.  X  ↑    ↑   ↑   ↑   ↑
      d.  X        ↑   ↑   ↑   ↑   ↑
      e.  X        ↑↓  ↑↓  ↑
```

65. Using X to indicate a filled inner core and an arrow for a valence shell electron, indicate which of the following choices is the correct ground state electronic configuration for the cobalt atom.

```
        [Ar] 4s _____  3d _____

      a.  X  ↑↓   ↑↓  ↑↓  ↑↓  ↑
      b.  X  ↑    ↑↓  ↑↓  ↑↓  ↑↓
      c.  X  ↑    ↑↓  ↑↓  ↑↓  ↑   ↑
      d.  X        ↑↓  ↑↓  ↑↓  ↑↓  ↑
   !  e.  X  ↑↓   ↑↓  ↑↓  ↑   ↑   ↑
```

66. Based on the Aufbau principle and other applicable guiding principles, what ground state electronic configuration would one reasonably expect to find for technetium (Z = 43)?

      a. $[Kr] 4s^2 3d^5$
      b. $[Kr] 4s^2 4d^5$
      c. $[Kr] 4d^7$
  ! d. $[Kr] 5s^2 4d^5$
      e. $[Kr] 5s^2 5d^5$

67. Which one of the following configurations represents a non-existent state?

      a. $[Ar] 4s^1 3d^5$
      b. $[Ar] 4s^2 3d^4$
  ! c. $[Xe] 5s^2 5p^1$
      d. $[Xe] 6s^2 4f^7$
      e. $[Rn] 7s^2$

68. Which one of the following configurations represents an alkaline earth element?

      a. $[Ar] 4s^1 3d^5$
      b. $[Ar] 4s^2 3d^4$
      c. $[Xe] 5s^2 5p^1$
      d. $[Xe] 6s^2 4f^7$
  ! e. $[Rn] 7s^2$

69. Which one of the following configurations represents a halogen element?

    a. [Ar] $4s^1 3d^5$
    b. [Ar] $4s^2 3d^4$
! c. [Kr] $5s^2 5p^5 4d^{10}$
    d. [Xe] $6s^2 4f^7$
    e. [Xe] $6s^2 4f^{14} 5d^{10} 6p^4$

70. An otherwise unidentified element is known to have an electronic configuration, $[X]ns^2$, in its ground state. This element must be in the same family as

    a. rubidium
! b. radium
    c. radon
    d. arsenic
    e. lead

71. A possible set of quantum numbers for an electron in the partially filled subshell in the gallium atom in its ground state configuration would be

	n	l	m_l	m_s
a.	3	1	0	-½
b.	3	1	1	½
c.	4	0	0	-½
! d.	4	1	0	½
e.	4	2	1	½

72. A possible set of quantum numbers for an electron in the partially filled subshell in the vanadium atom in its ground state configuration would be

	n	l	m_l	m_s
a.	3	1	0	-½
! b.	3	2	1	½
c.	4	0	0	-½
d.	4	1	0	½
e.	4	2	1	½

73. A possible set of quantum numbers for an electron in the partially filled subshell in the potassium atom in its ground state configuration would be

	n	l	m_l	m_s
a.	3	1	0	-½
b.	3	2	1	½
! c.	4	0	0	-½
d.	4	1	0	½
e.	4	2	1	½

74. A possible set of quantum numbers for an electron in the partially filled subshell in the germanium atom in its ground state configuration would be

	n	l	m_l	m_s
a.	3	1	1	½
b.	3	2	1	½
c.	4	0	0	-½
! d.	4	1	-1	½
e.	4	2	1	½

75. A possible set of quantum numbers for an electron in the partially filled subshell in the technetium atom in its ground state configuration would be

	n	l	m_l	m_s
a.	3	1	0	-½
b.	3	2	1	½
c.	4	0	0	-½
d.	4	1	0	½
! e.	4	2	1	½

76. Which one of the following situations is not ever encountered in the ground state configuration of an atom OR an ion?

    a. a . . . $3d^4$ with 4 unpaired electrons
! b. a . . . $3d^7$ with 7 unpaired electrons
    c. a . . . $3p^1$ with 1 unpaired electron
    d. a . . . $3d^9$ with 1 unpaired electron
    e. a . . . $4f^7$ with 7 unpaired electrons

77. Which one of the following situations is not ever encountered in the ground state configuration of an atom OR an ion?

    a. a . . . $3d^4$ with 4 unpaired electrons
    b. a . . . $3d^7$ with 3 unpaired electrons
    c. a . . . $3p^1$ with 1 unpaired electron
! d. a . . . $3d^9$ with 4 unpaired electron
    e. a . . . $4f^7$ with 7 unpaired electrons

78. Which one of the following statements is true?

    a. A 3f orbital is larger (extends farther) than a 3 p orbital in a particular atom.
    b. A 3p orbital has four lobes, one in each of the four quadrants.
    c. A $3f_{xyz}$ has eight lobes, one is each octant.
    d. All 3d orbitals have the same shape, just different orientations.
! e. The 7s orbital can be represented by a sphere.

79. Based on the expected ground state electronic configuration, element #120

        a. should be an inert gas element
        b. should have two unpaired electrons
        c. should be a chalcogen element
!   d. should be an alkaline earth element
        e. should have four unpaired electrons

80. Based on the order in which the subshells are filled in the ground state electronic configuration of atoms, element #111

!   a. should be a coinage metal
        b. should be an alkali metal
        c. should be a halogen element
        d. should be an actinide element
        e. should be an inert gas element

81. Which one of the species below should have the smallest radius?

        a. Ar
        b. Ca^{2+}
        c. K^+
!   d. Mg^{2+}
        e. Na^+

82. Which one of the species below should have the smallest radius?

        a. Cl^-
!   b. F^-
        c. O^{2-}
        d. S^{2-}
        e. Se^{2-}

83. Which one of the species below should have the largest radius?

!   a. Ar
        b. Ca^{2+}
        c. K^+
        d. Mg^{2+}
        e. Na^+

84. Which one of the atoms listed below has the largest value for its first ionization energy?

!   a. Al
        b. Sr
        c. Ga
        d. Cr
        e. Fr

85. Which one of the atoms listed below has the largest value for its electron affinity?

        a. O
        b. He
        c. Ga
        d. Cr
  ! e. F

86. Which one of the atoms represented by its symbol below has the largest value for its electron affinity?

        a. Al
        b. Sr
        c. Ga
  ! d. Cl
        e. Fl

87. The decrease in atomic radius as one progresses from element $Z = 11$ to $Z = 18$ in the periodic table can be related to

        a. the increase in the principal quantum number of the outermost occupied orbital in the atom
        b. the decrease in the principal quantum number of the outermost occupied orbital in the atom
  ! c. the increase in the effective nuclear charge being experienced by the electron(s) in the outermost occupied orbital in the atom
        d. the decrease in the effective nuclear charge being experienced by the electron(s) in the outermost occupied orbital in the atom
        e. the increase in the secondary quantum number of the outermost occupied orbital in the atom

88. The increase in atomic radius as one progresses *within the family* from element $Z = 3$ to $Z = 87$ in the periodic table can be related to

  ! a. the increase in the principal quantum number of the outermost occupied orbital in the atom
        b. the decrease in the principal quantum number of the outermost occupied orbital in the atom
        c. the increase in the effective nuclear charge being experienced by the electron(s) in the outermost occupied orbital in the atom
        d. the decrease in the effective nuclear charge being experienced by the electron(s) in the outermost occupied orbital in the atom
        e. the increase in the secondary quantum number of the outermost occupied orbital in the atom

Fill In The Blanks

89. The number of orbitals in a shell with $n = 3$ is _____ (! 9)

90. The number of orbitals in a subshell with $l = 3$ is _____ (! 7)

91. A particular energy level in a multielectron atom has a value of 3 for the secondary quantum number. What is the maximum number of electrons that can occupy this energy level? _____ (! 14)

92. The behavior of an electron in an atom can be described in terms of solutions to the wave equation. There are variable quantum numbers in these solutions (functions). How many variable quantum numbers are there for describing ONE electron in the atom? _____ (! 4)

93. Even though the _____ might suggest that the ground state configuration of the beryllium atom is $1s^4$, the _____ says otherwise. (! Aufbau method, Pauli principle)

94. How many completely filled subshells are there in the ground state configuration for a calcium atom? _____ (! 6)

95. How many unpaired electrons are there in the ground state electronic configuration for an iron atom? _____ (! 4)

96. Which one of the atoms in the set: Y, Cr, Mg, N, Ba, Se, Sn has the largest first ionization energy? _____ (! N)

97. Which one of the atoms in the set: Sr, Fr, Hg, Ga, Cr, Sn has the smallest first ionization energy? _____ (! Fr)

98. Which one of the atoms in the set: O, F, Ne, Ar, Cl, K, Ga has the greatest affinity for electrons? _____ (! F)

99. Which one of the atoms in the set: O, F, Ne, Ar, Cl, K, Ga has the largest first ionization energy? _____ (! Ne)

100. Which one of all the atoms has the smallest atomic radius? _____ (! He)

101. Which one of the atoms in the set: Ba, Cr, N, Sn, Mg, Sn, Se would you expect to have the largest atomic radius? _____ (! Ba)

102. Which one of the atoms in the set: Sr, Hf, Hg, Ga, Cr, Fr, Sn would you expect to have the largest atomic radius? _____ (! Fr)

103. Which one of the atoms in the set: Mg, Cr, N, Sn, Ba, Sn, Se would you expect to have the smallest first ionization energy? _____ (! Ba)

True and False

104. Even though the fluoride ion is larger than the fluorine atom, and the chloride ion is larger than the chlorine atom, the oxide ion is smaller than the oxygen atom. (! F)

105. The uncertainty principle was proposed to explain the fact that certain atoms, for instance silver, have different electronic configurations in their ground states than predicted by the Aufbau method. (! F)

106. In the tellurium atom, the valence shell electronic configuration is $ns^2 np^6$. (! F)

107. There are more unpaired electrons in the ground state electronic configuration for a chromium atom than there are for a manganese atom. (! T)

108. Generally speaking, anions and cations have larger radii than their parent atoms. (! F)

109. One of the ways in which very very small particles display wavelike behavior is in their ability to be diffracted when they are in particle beams. (! T)

110. The periodic structure of the periodic table can be correlated with periodic behavior of the electronic structural configuration of the elements. (! T)

Critical Thinking

111. A phototube in a photoelectric device has a photosensitive element. When this element is beamed with radiation having a wavelength of 374.2 nm, electrons are emitted. The maximum kinetic energy observed for these electrons is 1.488×10^{-19} J/electron. What is the wavelength of a laser which will turn the photocell on and cause electrons to be ejected which have absolutely no excess energy? _____ (! 520 nm)

112. A phototube in a photoelectric device has a photosensitive element. When this element is beamed with radiation having a wavelength of 354.2 nm, electrons are emitted. The maximum kinetic energy observed for these electrons is 1.988×10^{-19} J/electron. What is the wavelength of a laser which will turn the photocell on and cause electrons to be ejected which have absolutely no excess energy? _____ (! 549 nm)

113. When one thinks of an atom as being related to the region occupied by the electron cloud for the outermost electrons, a "radius" can be imagined. Typically, for an atom this "radius" would be about

      a. 2.00 picometers
      b. 20.0 picometers
  ! c. 200 picometers
      d. 2.00 nanometers
      e. 20.0 nanometers

114. Kevin Vitellan is working on a summer project in which he is using a tunable dye laser. At first, he was using radiation on a wavelength of 488.5 nm. After two weeks or so, his research advisor told him to increase the energy by another 55.0 kJ per mole and repeat the radiation effect tests. What wavelength should he now be using? _____ (! 398.9 nm)

115. Later in the summer, Kevin Vitellan is continuing work on a project in which he is using a tunable dye laser. Last week, the radiation he was using, 488.5 nm, was too energetic for the dyes in the matrix he was studying so his research advisor told him to decrease the laser energy by 55.0 kJ per mole and repeat the series of tests. What wavelength should he now be using? _____ (! 630.0 nm)

Chemicals in Our World 4: Greenhouse Gases and Global Warming

116. The insulating effect, the so called "greenhouse" effect is caused by

       a. atmospheric carbon dioxide, only
       b. most atmospheric gases, including oxygen, nitrogen, carbon dioxide
!   c. atmospheric methane, HC's, and carbon dioxide, among others
       d. the inert gases--helium, neon, argon, krypton, and xenon
       e. the atmospheric pollutants carbon monoxide, nitrogen oxides (NOx) and unburned HC's only

117. The buildup of carbon dioxide in the earth's atmosphere is controlled and prevented through

       a. natural photosynthesis only
!   b. natural photosynthesis and formation of carbonate deposits
       c. reactions with naturally occurring radon gas
       d. reaction with water vapor in the upper atmosphere to produce methane
       e. reaction with nitrogen oxides (NOx) formed through action of radiation on upper atmosphere gases

118. "Greenhouse" gases

       a. absorb incoming solar energy and radiate it downward through the potential gravity field
!   b. absorb outgoing energy and reradiate some of it back to the earth's surface
       c. absorb incoming solar energy and reradiate it back to the earth's surface during the night hours
       d. absorb heat generated by various earth sources and prevent any of it from escaping
       e. convert incoming radiant energy to heat energy and radiate it down to the earth's surface

119. Research studies employing the scientific method have led to establishment of a definite causal relation between the "greenhouse effect" and insect pest proliferation. (! F)

120. Research studies have established the link between the "greenhouse effect" and the continuing decrease in size of ice fields, the glaciers, and the polar ice caps. (! T)

121. A major cause of global warming comes from the heat released by the rapidly increasing numbers of forest fires on the various land masses of the planet. (! F)

122. Which one of the following "greenhouse" gases, found in the Earth's atmosphere, is not produced by chemical reactions which take place in nature?

      a. CO_2
      b. CH_4
      c. N_2O
  ! d. CCl_2F_2
      e. O_2

123. Gases which trap heat contribute to the greenhouse effect by

      a. preventing CO_2 from escaping into outer space from the earth's atmosphere
      b. preventing absorption of heat energy from the solar radiation
  ! c. preventing the radiation of heat from the earth's surface back into space
      d. facilitating the chemical reaction between CH_4 and O_2 in the upper atmosphere which produces extra heat
      e. preventing the reaction between N_2 and O_2 in the upper atmosphere to produce N_2O which consume energy and produce a cooling trend

124. Since the Earth's mean temperature is much lower than that of the sun, the amount of energy received at the Earth's surface from the solar source is significantly greater than the net amount of energy lost from the Earth's surface in turn. (! F)

Chapter 8 Chemical Bonding: General Concepts

Multiple Choice

1. Sodium tends to form ions which have the electronic configuration of a noble gas. What is the electronic configuration of the noble gas which the sodium ion mimics?

       a. $1s^2$
       b. $1s^2\,2p^6$
  ! c. $1s^2\,2s^2\,2p^6$
       d. $1s^2\,2s^2\,2p^6\,3s^2$
       e. $1s^2\,2s^2\,2p^6\,3s^2\,3p^6$

2. Bromine tends to form simple ions which have the electronic configuration of a noble gas. What is the electronic configuration of the noble gas which the bromide ion mimics?

       a. $1s^2\,2s^2\,2p^6\,3s^2\,3p^6\,3d^{10}\,4p^6$
       b. $1s^2\,2s^2\,2p^6\,3s^2\,3p^6\,4p^6\,4d^{10}$
       c. $1s^2\,2s^2\,2p^6\,3s^2\,3p^6\,4s^2\,4p^6$
  ! d. $1s^2\,2s^2\,2p^6\,3s^2\,3p^6\,3d^{10}\,4s^2\,4p^6$
       e. $1s^2\,2s^2\,2p^6\,3s^2\,3p^6\,3d^{10}\,4s^2\,4p^6\,4d^{10}$

3. Which one of the following reactions is exothermic to a substantial degree?

  ! a. $F(g) + e^- \rightarrow F^-(g)$
       b. $F^-(g) + e^- \rightarrow F^{2-}(g)$
       c. $F^{2-}(g) + e^- \rightarrow F^{3-}(g)$
       d. $F^{3-}(g) + e^- \rightarrow F^{4-}(g)$
       e. $F^{4-}(g) + e^- \rightarrow F^{5-}(g)$

4. Which one of the following reactions is exothermic to a substantial degree?

  ! a. $Cl(g) + e^- \rightarrow Cl^-(g)$
       b. $He(g) + e^- \rightarrow He^-(g)$
       c. $Ar(g) + e^- \rightarrow Ar^-(g)$
       d. $O^-(g) + e^- \rightarrow O^{2-}(g)$
       e. $N^{2-}(g) + e^- \rightarrow N^{3-}(g)$

5. If the octet rule were firmly obeyed by arsenic atoms, which one of the following ions of arsenic would be found in binary arsenic compounds?

       a. As^-
       b. As^{2-}
  ! c. As^{3-}
       d. As^{4-}
       e. As^{5-}

6. The octet rule appears to hold true for cations of which of the following sets?

     a. post transition metals and transition metals
! b. Group Ia and Group IIa metals
     c. Group IVa elements
     d. lanthanide elements
     e. actinide elements

7. Which of the following possible states of the element uranium is the one which obeys the octet rule?

     a. U^{2+}
     b. U^{3+}
     c. U^{4+}
! d. U^{6+}
     e. U^{2-}

8. The ions below do not follow the octet rule, with the exception of

     a. Fe^{3+}
     b. Sn^{2+}
     c. Ni^{2+}
! d. Ti^{4+}
     e. Cr^{3+}

9. The ions below do not follow the octet rule, with the exception of

     a. Fe^{3+}
     b. Ni^{2+}
! c. Sc^{3+}
     d. V^{3+}
     e. Cr^{3+}

10. The valence electrons in the potassium ions present in potassium nitrate are

     a. the 2p electrons only
     b. the 3s electrons only
     c. the 3s and 3p electrons only
     d. the 3p electrons only
! e. there are no valence electrons in the potassium ions in the compound above

11. The valence electrons in the chloride ions present in potassium chloride are

     a. the 2p electrons only
     b. the 3s electrons only
! c. the 3s and 3p electrons only
     d. the 3p electrons only
     e. there are no valence electrons in the chloride ions in the compound above

12. Which one of the elements below has 5 valence electrons in its Lewis symbol?

      a. actinium
      b. americium
      c. argon
!   d. arsenic
      e. astatine

13. Which one of the elements below has 3 valence electrons in its Lewis symbol?

!   a. gallium
      b. fluorine
      c. iron
      d. nickel
      e. sulfur

14. Which one of the species below has 8 valence electrons in its Lewis symbol?

      a. Ar^+
      b. F^+
      c. Mg^+
!   d. S^{2-}
      e. Si

15. Which one of the elements below has no valence electrons in its Lewis symbol?

      a. Ar^+
      b. Ga^+
!   c. Mg^{2+}
      d. S^{2-}
      e. F^-

16. Covalent bonds formed by the sharing of electrons are most likely to be formed between

      a. an atom with a high electron affinity and an atom with a low ionization energy
      b. an atom with a low electron affinity and an atom with a high ionization energy
!   c. two atoms with high electron affinities and high ionization energies
      d. two atoms with low electron affinities and low ionization energies
      e. an atom with a low electronegativity and an atom with a high ionization energy

17. The atoms in the nitrogen molecule, N_2, are held together by

      a. a single covalent bond
      b. a double covalent bond
!   c. a triple covalent bond
      d. an ionic bond
      e. a magnetic dipole bond

18. The atoms in the oxygen molecule, O_2, are held together by

       a. a single covalent bond
!   b. a double covalent bond
       c. a triple covalent bond
       d. an ionic bond
       e. a magnetic dipole bond

19. The atoms in the hydrogen fluoride molecule are held together by

!   a. a single covalent bond
       b. a double covalent bond
       c. a triple covalent bond
       d. an ionic bond
       e. a magnetic dipole bond

20. The Lewis symbol for the carbon atom shows __ valence electrons. The number of bonds which carbon usually forms in order to complete its valence shell and obey the octet rule is ___

       a. 4, 1
       b. 4, 2
       c. 2, 4
       d. 4, 3
!   e. 4, 4

21. The Lewis symbol for the nitrogen atom shows __ valence electrons. The number of bonds which nitrogen usually forms in order to complete its valence shell and obey the octet rule is ___

       a. 5, 1
       b. 5, 2
       c. 3, 4
!   d. 5, 3
       e. 5, 4

22. An element, whose chemical symbol is illegible, had 6 electrons surrounding it in the Lewis symbol. Which element among the following could it possibly be?

       a. Cr
       b. Ni
       c. Ba
!   d. Se
       e. As

23. The structural formula for one of the heptadiene isomers can be written in abbreviated form as
$$CH_3CHCHCH_2CHCHCH_3$$
How many bonds should there be in this molecule?

      a. 16
      b. 18
      c. 19
 ! d. 20
      e. 22

24. The structural formula for a certain alcohol can be written in abbreviated form as
$$CH_2CHCH_2OH$$
How many bonds should there be in this molecule?

      a. 8
      b. 9
 ! c. 10
      d. 11
      e. 12

25. The structural formula for a certain alcohol can be written in abbreviated form as
$$CH_2CHCH_2CH_2OH$$
How many bonds should there be in this molecule?

 ! a. 13
      b. 14
      c. 15
      d. 16
      e. 17

26. The compound shown immediately below is an example of

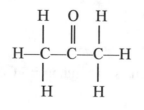

      a. an alcohol
 ! b. a ketone
      c. an acid
      d. a hydrocarbon
      e. a base

27. The compound shown immediately below is an example of

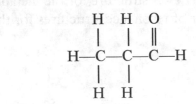

        a. an alcohol
        b. a ketone
    !   c. an aldehyde
        d. an acid
        e. a base

28. The compound shown immediately below is an example of

$$H-\underset{\underset{H}{|}}{\overset{\overset{H}{|}}{C}}-\underset{\underset{H}{|}}{\overset{\overset{H}{|}}{C}}-\overset{\overset{H}{|}}{N}-H$$

        a. an alcohol
        b. a ketone
        c. an aldehyde
        d. an acid
    !   e. a base

29. The structural formula for a hydrocarbon can be written in abbreviated form as
$$CH_3CHCHCH_2CHCH_2$$
    How many bonds should there be in this molecule?

        a. 15
        b. 16
    !   c. 17
        d. 18
        e. 19

30. Draw the "best" Lewis structure for sulfur trioxide based on formal charge considerations. The number of resonance structures for this "best" Lewis structure is

    !   a. 1 (no resonance)
        b. 2
        c. 3
        d. 4
        e. 5

31. The metaphosphate ion, PO_3^-, is the structural analog of the NO_3^- ion with respect to the geometric arrangement of the atoms in the ion. After drawing the "best" Lewis structure for the metaphosphate ion based on formal charge considerations, what is the number of resonance structures for this "best" Lewis structure?

    a. 1 (no resonance)
    b. 2
!   c. 3
    d. 4
    e. 5

32. How many resonance structures, if any, can be drawn for the O_3 molecule?

    a. 1 (no resonance)
!   b. 2
    c. 3
    d. 4
    e. 5

33. How many resonance structures, if any, can be drawn for the nitrate ion?

    a. 1 (no resonance)
    b. 2
!   c. 3
    d. 4
    e. 5

34. How many resonance structures, if any, can be drawn for the nitrite ion?

    a. 1 (no resonance)
!   b. 2
    c. 3
    d. 4
    e. 5

35. How many resonance structures, if any, can be drawn for the BF_3 molecule?

!   a. 1 (no resonance)
    b. 2
    c. 3
    d. 4
    e. 5

36. Based on the "best" Lewis structure from formal charge considerations, how many resonance structures, if any, can be drawn for the PO_4^{3-} ion?

      a. 1 (no resonance)
      b. 2
      c. 3
!   d. 4
      e. 5

37. Based on the "best" Lewis structure from formal charge considerations, how many resonance structures, if any, can be drawn for the NF_3 molecule?

!   a. 1 (no resonance)
      b. 2
      c. 3
      d. 4
      e. 5

38. Which one of the following bonds is the most polar one of the set?

      a. H—Br
      b. H—Cl
!   c. H—F
      d. H—I
      e. H—N

39. Which one of the following bonds is the most polar one of the set?

      a. H—C
!   b. H—Cl
      c. H—P
      d. H—S
      e. H—Se

40. Draw the Lewis structure for hydrogen peroxide. Based on this structure, the correct number of polar bonds and non-polar bonds is

      a. 3 polar bonds and no non-polar bonds
!   b. 2 polar bonds and 1 non-polar bonds
      c. 1 polar bonds and 2 non-polar bonds
      d. no polar bonds and 3 non-polar bonds

41. Draw the Lewis structure for the H_2CO molecule. Based on this structure, the correct number of polar bonds and non-polar bonds is

    ! a. 3 polar bonds and no non-polar bonds
    b. 2 polar bonds and 1 non-polar bonds
    c. 1 polar bonds and 2 non-polar bonds
    d. no polar bonds and 3 non-polar bonds

42. Draw the Lewis structure for the F_2CO molecule. Based on this structure, the correct number of polar bonds and non-polar bonds is

    ! a. 3 polar bonds and no non-polar bonds
    b. 2 polar bonds and 1 non-polar bond
    c. 1 polar bonds and 2 non-polar bonds
    d. no polar bonds and 3 non-polar bonds

43. The formal charge on the oxygen atom in the carbon monoxide molecule is

    a. -2
    b. -1
    c. 0
    ! d. +1
    e. +2

44. The formal charge on the nitrogen atom in the nitrate ion is

    a. -3
    b. 0
    ! c. +1
    d. +3
    e. +5

45. The formal charge on the carbon atom in the carbonate ion is

    a. -2
    ! b. 0
    c. +1
    d. +2
    e. +4

46. Based on the "best" Lewis structure after applying formal charge considerations, how many non-bonding valence electrons are there around the carbon atom in the CO molecule?

    a. 0
    ! b. 2
    c. 4
    d. 6
    e. 8

47. The metaphosphate ion, PO_3^-, is the structural analog of the NO_3^- ion with respect to the geometric arrangement of the atoms in the ion. After drawing the "best" Lewis structure for the metaphosphate ion based on formal charge considerations, what is the formal charge on the phosphorus atom?

      a. -1
  !   b. 0
      c. +1
      d. +2
      e. +5

48. Based on the "best" Lewis structure after applying formal charge considerations, how many non-bonding valence electrons are there around the nitrogen atom in the nitrate ion?

  !   a. 0
      b. 2
      c. 4
      d. 6
      e. 8

49. Based on the "best" Lewis structure after applying formal charge considerations, how many non-bonding valence electrons are there around the nitrogen atom in the nitrite ion?

      a. 0
  !   b. 2
      c. 4
      d. 6
      e. 8

50. Based on the position in the periodic table, which one of the following atoms would you expect to be the most electronegative?

      a. Ba
      b. Ga
      c. Mn
  !   d. N
      e. Si

51. Based on the position in the periodic table, which one of the following atoms would you expect to be the most electronegative?

  !   a. Cl
      b. Ge
      c. P
      d. Se
      e. Sn

52. Which one of the following is the least electronegative element of the set presented?

   a. F
   b. N
   c. C
   d. O
! e. H

53. Which one of the following is the least electronegative element of the set presented?

   a. N
   b. S
! c. C
   d. P
   e. O

54. Which one of the following is the least electronegative element of the set presented?

   a. N
   b. O
   c. Cl
   d. Br
! e. I

55. Based on electronegativity considerations, which one of the following listed species should be the strongest oxidizing agent?

   a. Ne
   b. Kr
   c. Br_2
! d. Cl_2
   e. S

56. Based on electronegativity considerations, which one of the following listed species should be the strongest oxidizing agent?

   a. Xe
   b. As
! c. Br_2
   d. I_2
   e. Sb

57. Based on electronegativity considerations, which one of the following listed species should be the strongest oxidizing agent?

        a. O_2
!   b. F_2
        c. N_2
        d. Cl_2
        e. S

58. Some possible skeletons for the Lewis structure of sulfurous acid, H_2SO_3 are shown below. Which one of the following is the correct skeleton?

    a.
```
                O

      H   H   S   O

                O
```

    b.
```
          O

      H   S   H   O   O
```

!   c.
```
                O

      H   O   S   O   H
```

    d.   H   O   S   O   O   H

    e.
```
                H

      H   O   S   O

                O
```

151

59. Complete the Lewis structure for $HClO_2$ from the skeletal template presented below by filling in the bonds and the remaining valence electrons (those which are not in the bonds). If the valence shells are filled to the *usual* limit, how many of these non-bonding valence electrons are there in the molecule?

H   O   Cl   O

!   a. 14
     b. 16
     c. 18
     d. 20
     e. 26

60. Complete the Lewis structure for H_2SeO_3 from the skeletal template presented below by filling in the bonds and the remaining valence electrons (those which are not in the bonds). If the valence shells are filled to the *usual* limit, how many of these non-bonding valence electrons are there in the molecule?

O

H   O   Se   O   H

     a. 14
!   b. 16
     c. 18
     d. 20
     e. 28

61. Complete the Lewis structure for $HClO_3$ from the skeletal template presented below by filling in the bonds and the remaining valence electrons (those which are not in the bonds). If the valence shells are filled to the *usual* limit (maximum of 8), what is the formal charge on the chlorine atom?

O

H   O   Cl   O

     a. -1
     b. 0
     c. +1
!   d. +2
     e. +3

62. Complete the Lewis structure for H_2SeO_4 from the skeletal template presented below by filling in the bonds and the remaining valence electrons (those which are not in the bonds). If the valence shells are filled to the **usual** limit (maximum of 8), what is the sum of the absolute values of all the formal charges in the molecule?

$$
\begin{array}{ccccc}
 & & O & & \\
H & O & Se & O & H \\
 & & O & &
\end{array}
$$

    a. 0
    b. 1
    c. 2
    d. 3
! e. 4

63. A student drew four possible Lewis structures for $HBrO_4$

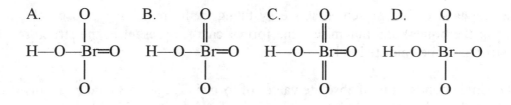

Complete these Lewis structures presented above by filling in the remaining valence electrons (those which are not in the bonds). Based on these structures, the preferred structure would be the structure shown as ____ in which the sum of the absolute values of the formal charges on all the atoms is ____, ____

    a. A, 4
    b. B, 2
! c. C, 0
    d. D, 6
    e. D, 0

64. The Lewis structure for SF_5^- ion when completed, should include ____ bonds and ____ non-bonding valence electrons (the valence electrons which are not in any bond).

    a. 5, 30
    b. 6, 28
! c. 5, 32
    d. 5, 42
    e. 5, 31

65. Complete the Lewis structure for $HClO_3$ from the skeletal template presented below by filling in the bonds and the remaining valence electrons (those which are not in the bonds). If the valence shells are filled to the *usual* limit (maximum of 8), what is the sum of the absolute values of all the formal charges in the molecule?

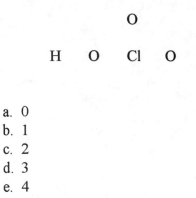

    a. 0
    b. 1
    c. 2
    d. 3
! e. 4

66. The chlorite ion has a Lewis structure which is based on the structural template shown below.

O   Cl   O

Complete the Lewis structure presented above by filling in the remaining valence electrons (those which are not in the bonds) and minimizing the formal charges present in the structure. Based on this "tuned" structure, the chlorite ion has

    a. two single bonds, sum of absolute values of formal charges = 3, and no resonance hybrids
    b. one single and one double bond, sum of absolute values of formal charges = 5, and there are two contributing resonance hybrids
    c. one single and one double bond, sum of absolute values of formal charges = 3, and there are two contributing resonance hybrids
    d. two double bonds, sum of absolute values of formal charges = 1, and no resonance hybrids
! e. one single and one double bond, sum of absolute values of formal charges = 1, and there are two contributing resonance hybrids

67. Draw a correct Lewis structure for CH_2Cl_2. Based on this Lewis structure, the calculated value for the formal charge on the carbon atom is

! a. 0
    b. +4
    c. +2
    d. -2
    e. -4

68. Draw a correct Lewis structure for $H_3C—NH_2$. Based on this Lewis structure, the calculated value for the formal charge on the nitrogen atom is

    a. -2
    b. +3
    c. -3
    d. +2
!   e. 0

69. Draw a Lewis structure for $H_3C—NO_2$. Both oxygen atoms are directly attached to the nitrogen atom. What is the formal charge on the nitrogen atom?

    a. -3
!   b. +1
    c. +3
    d. -1
    e. 0

70. When the fluoride ion reacts with a BF_3 molecule (a molecule in which there are no multiple bonds) an ion is formed in which the boron atom in the central atom. The bond between the boron trifluoride and the fluoride ion is

    a. an ionic bond
    b. a regular covalent bond, where both species contribute 1 electron to the bond.
!   c. a coordinate covalent bond
    d. a resonance hybrid bond
    e. a bond where two atoms share one electron instead of two

71. Complete the Lewis structures for $COCl_2$ and $SOCl_2$ using the structural templates shown below, being sure to follow the procedure for minimizing the sum of the absolute values for the formal charges, where valence shell size restrictions permit. Based on the structures you have completed, which statement below is true?

    a. The $COCl_2$ exhibits residual formal charges but no resonance hybrids, while the $SOCl_2$ exhibits both residual formal charges and resonance hybrids.
    b. The $COCl_2$ exhibits both residual formal charges and resonance hybrids, while the $SOCl_2$ exhibits residual formal charges but no resonance hybrids.
    c. The $COCl_2$ exhibits residual formal charges but no resonance hybrids, while the $SOCl_2$ exhibits resonance hybrids but no residual formal charges
    d. The $COCl_2$ exhibits residual both formal charges and resonance hybrids, while the $SOCl_2$ exhibits resonance hybrids but no residual formal charges.
!   e. Neither of the two compounds have residual formal charges or resonance hybrids.

72. The carbonate ion has the skeletal structure as shown below. Complete the Lewis structure by filling in the bonds and the remaining valence electrons which are not involved in bonds. Which assertion made about the carbonate ion below is true?

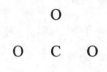

Based on the structure the carbonate ion should have ___ resonance hybrids and ___ atoms with residual formal charges on them in its structure.

    a. 2, 2
    b. 3, 1
 ! c. 3, 2
    d. 2, 1
    e. no, 2

73. When the fluoride ion reacts with a BF$_3$ molecule (a molecule in which there are no multiple bonds) an ion is formed in which the boron atom is the central atom. In this reaction,

 ! a. the fluoride ion behaves as a Lewis base and the BF$_3$ behaves as a Lewis acid.
    b. the fluoride ion behaves as a Lewis acid and the BF$_3$ behaves as a Lewis base.
    c. the fluoride ion behaves as an Arrhenius base and the BF$_3$ behaves as an Arrhenius acid.
    d. the fluoride ion behaves as a Brönsted acid and the BF$_3$ behaves as a Brönsted base.
    e. the fluoride ion behaves as an Arrhenius acid and the BF$_3$ behaves as an Arrhenius base.

74. The structural template for the Lewis structure of nitromethane, CH$_3$NO$_2$, is shown below. Complete the Lewis structure by filling in the bonds and the remaining valence electrons which are not involved in bonds. Which assertion made about the nitromethane below is true?

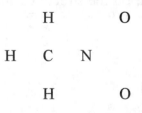

Based on the structure of the nitromethane molecule, it should have ___ resonance hybrids and ___ atoms with residual formal charges on them.

    a. no, 2
    b. no, 3
 ! c. 2, 2
    d. 2, 3
    e. 3, 2

75. How many coordinate covalent bonds are there in the product of the reaction between H^+ and NH_3 which gives NH_4^+ as the only product?

    a. 0
! b. 1
    c. 2
    d. 3
    e. 4

76. How many coordinate covalent bonds are there in the product of the reaction between F^- and BF_3 which gives BF_4^- as the only product?

    a. 0
! b. 1
    c. 2
    d. 3
    e. 4

Fill in the Blanks

77. The sulfide ion can react with the sulfur trioxide molecule to produce a thiosulfate ion, as shown below.

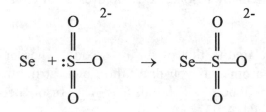

Complete the Lewis structures by filling in the bonds and the remaining valence electrons which are not involved in bonds. Which reagent is the Lewis base, if any? _____ (! S^{2-})

78. Selenium atoms can react with the sulfite ion to produce a selenosulfate ion, as shown below

$$Se + :\!\overset{\displaystyle O \atop \|}{\underset{\displaystyle \| \atop O}{S}}\!-\!O^{2-} \quad \rightarrow \quad Se\!-\!\overset{\displaystyle O \atop \|}{\underset{\displaystyle \| \atop O}{S}}\!-\!O^{2-}$$

Complete the Lewis structures by filling in the bonds and the remaining valence electrons which are not involved in bonds. Which reagent is the Lewis base, if any? _____ (! SO_3^{2-})

79. The oxide ion can react with the carbon dioxide molecule to produce a carbonate ion, as shown below.

$$O^{2-} + \begin{matrix} O \\ \| \\ C \\ \| \\ O \end{matrix} \quad \rightarrow \quad \begin{matrix} O \\ \| \\ O-C \\ | \\ O \end{matrix}^{2-}$$

Complete the Lewis structures by filling in the bonds and the remaining valence electrons which are not involved in bonds. Which reagent, if any, is the Lewis acid? _____ (! CO_2)

80. Lattice energies of ionic compounds are proportional (to a significant degree) to the product of the charge on the ions in the lattice. This means that a CaO sample in which there are Ca^{3+} and O^{3-} ions should have much greater lattice energies than the case where the ions are Ca^{2+} and O^{2-}. Why is the lattice with the Ca^{2+} and O^{2-} the one which is actually found in nature?

_____

_____

(! The ionization energies and electron affinity for removal or acquisition of a third electron are so high that the increased lattice energy still does not make it energetically favorable.)

81. What is the electronic configuration of the metal ion in chromium(III) sulfate? _____
(! [Ar] $3d^3$)

82. The total number of bonds in the nitrogen trifluoride molecule is _____ (! 3)

83. In the covalent bond between the atoms in the S—Cl bond, which atom carries the partial negative charge? _____ (! Cl)

84. In the covalent bond between the atoms in the O—H bond, which atom carried the partial negative charge? _____ (! O)

85. Draw the Lewis structure for the sulfite ion. When formal charge considerations are fully taken into account and adjustments made, if necessary, how many resonance structures, if any, can be drawn for this ion (1 for no resonance) ? _____ (! 3)

86. Thionyl chloride, $SOCl_2$, has a Lewis structure related to that of sulfur trioxide, wherein two of the oxygen atoms have been replaced with chlorine atoms. If you draw the Lewis structure, and take formal charge considerations into account, there will be _____ bonds and _____ resonance structures (1 for no resonance) in the molecule. _____ (! 4, 1)

87. A compound has the same carbon skeleton as the benzene molecule, but its formula is C_6H_8 instead of C_6H_6. How many bonds are there in this molecule? _____ (! 16)

True and False

88. The H—Cl bond is more polar than the H—O bond. (! F)

89. The maximum number of electrons that can be shared by a given pair of atoms to form bonds in a molecule which has two or more atoms is 4. (! F)

90. The number of electrons in the Lewis symbol for the arsenic atom is 3. (! F)

91. There are two covalent bonds in the Lewis structure for magnesium fluoride. (! F)

92. There are two covalent bonds in the Lewis structure for calcium chloride. (! F)

93. When the Lewis structure for the nitrite ion is drawn, and optimized ("fine tuned") based on formal charge considerations, there are four bonds in this optimized Lewis structure . (! F)

94. A compound which has the formula, C_4H_8O, should have 12 bonds in its Lewis structure. (! F)

95. The energy of the bond holding two covalently bound atoms together is independent of the distance between the two atoms. (! F)

96. A good rule of thumb is: the higher the atomic number, the greater the electronegativity of the atom. (! F)

Critical Thinking

97. Complete, with modifications as needed, the Lewis structures of the following species:

$$CO_2, \quad CH_3—C—O^-, \quad CO, \quad CO_3^{2-}, \quad H—C—H$$
$$\quad\quad\quad\quad\quad O \quad\quad\quad\quad\quad\quad\quad\quad\quad\quad O$$

Which one of the species has the longest carbon oxygen bond(s)?

  a. CO_2
  b. HCHO
 ! c. CO_3^{2-}
  d. CH_3COO^-
  e. CO

98. A molecule has the formula, C_4H_8. How many different Lewis structures are possible for this molecule? _____ (! 5)

159

99. Complete, with modifications as needed, the Lewis structures of the following species:

$$CO_2, \quad CH_3\!-\!C\!-\!O^-, \quad CO, \quad CO_3{}^{2-}, \quad H\!-\!C\!-\!H$$
$$\qquad\qquad\quad O \qquad\qquad\qquad\qquad\qquad\quad O$$

Which one(s) of the species has (have) the weakest carbon oxygen bond(s)?

     a. CO_2
     b. HCHO
  ! c. $CO_3{}^{2-}$
     d. CH_3COO^-
     e. CO

100. Complete, with modifications as needed, the Lewis structures of the following species:

$$CO_2, \quad CH_3\!-\!C\!-\!O^-, \quad CO, \quad CO_3{}^{2-}, \quad H\!-\!C\!-\!H$$
$$\qquad\qquad\quad O \qquad\qquad\qquad\qquad\qquad\quad O$$

Which one of the species has (have) the strongest carbon oxygen bond(s)?

     a. CO_2
     b. HCHO
     c. $CO_3{}^{2-}$
     d. CH_3COO^-
  ! e. CO

101. The chlorosulfonate ion, $ClSO_3{}^-$, has a structure similar to that of the sulfate ion, the difference being that one of the oxygen atoms has been replaced by a chlorine atom. Draw the Lewis structure for this ion, optimized for formal charge considerations, showing all resonance structures that should exist.

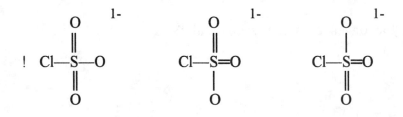

102. The fluorophosphonate ion, $FPO_3{}^{2-}$, has a structure similar to that of the orthophosphate ion, the difference being that one of the oxygen atoms has been replaced by a fluorine atom. Draw the Lewis structure for this ion, optimized for formal charge considerations, showing all resonance structures that should exist.

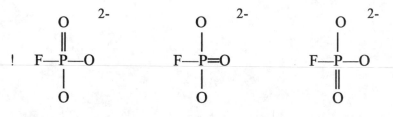

160

Chapter 9 Chemical Bonding and Molecular Structure

Multiple Choice

1. All of the geometries listed below are examples of the five basic geometries for molecules with more than 3 atoms except

   a. planar triangular
   b. octahedral
   c. tetrahedral
   ! d. trihedral
   e. trigonal bipyramidal

2. The concept that electron pairs located in the valence shell of an atom bonded to other atoms tend to stay as far apart as possible so as to minimize repulsions between them is incorporated in the

   a. Pauli principle
   b. Heisenberg uncertainty principle
   ! c. **v**alence **s**hell **e**lectron **p**air **r**epulsion theory
   d. electronegativity and polar bonds theory
   e. Aufbau principle

3. Which one of the following arrangements would best accommodate three electron pairs in the valence shell of a covalently bonded atom?

   ! a. planar triangular
   b. octahedral
   c. tetrahedral
   d. trihedral
   e. trigonal bipyramidal

4. Three different values can be observed for the bond angles in which of the following basic molecular structures for simple molecules:

   a. linear
   b. planar triangular
   c. tetrahedral
   ! d. trigonal bipyramidal
   e. octahedral

5. Application of the concepts of VSEPR theory leads us to conclude that the shape of the SO_3 molecule is

       a. trigonal pyramidal
       b. square planar
       c. regular tetrahedral
 !   d. triangular planar
       e. distorted tetrahedral

6. The geometric structure of the SF_4 molecule is best described as

       a. trigonal pyramidal
       b. square planar
       c. regular tetrahedral
       d. triangular planar
 !   e. distorted tetrahedral

7. Application of the concepts of VSEPR theory leads to the prediction that the shape of the PCl_3 molecule is

       a. bent
       b. linear
       c. tetrahedral
       d. triangular planar
 !   e. trigonal pyramidal

8. Application of the concepts of VSEPR theory leads to the prediction that the shape of the PH_3 molecule is

       a. bent
       b. linear
       c. tetrahedral
       d. triangular planar
 !   e. trigonal pyramidal

9. The geometry of the CS_2 molecule is best described as

       a. bent
 !   b. linear
       c. tetrahedral
       d. triangular planar
       e. trigonal pyramidal

10. The geometry of the ClF_3 molecule is best described as

    a. distorted tetrahedral
    b. tetrahedral
    ! c. T-shaped
    d. trigonal pyramidal
    e. triangular planar

11. Application of the concepts of the VSEPR theory suggests that the geometric arrangement of the atoms in the carbonate ion, CO_3^{2-} is

    a. octahedral
    b. square planar
    c. tetrahedral
    ! d. triangular planar
    e. trigonal pyramidal

12. Based on conclusions from application of the VSEPR theory, which one of the following species is linear?

    a. BF_3
    ! b. HCN
    c. H_2CO
    d. H_2S
    e. SO_2

13. Based on conclusions from application of the VSEPR theory, which one of the following molecules is trigonal bipyramidal?

    ! a. AsF_5
    b. NF_3
    c. SF_4
    d. SF_6
    e. IF_5^-

14. Based on conclusions from application of the VSEPR theory, which one of the following molecules is bent (nonlinear)?

    a. CO_2
    b. CS_2
    c. KrF_2
    d. C_2H_2
    ! e. SO_2

15. Based on conclusions from application of the VSEPR theory, which one of the following molecules or ions is bent (nonlinear)?

   ! a. Cl_2O
      b. CO_2
      c. HCN
      d. CO
      e. NO_2^+

16. Based on conclusions from application of the VSEPR theory, which one of the following molecules or ions is tetrahedral?

      a. BF_3
   ! a. CF_4
      c. NH_3
      d. SF_4
      e. XeF_4

17. The bond angle in Cl_2O is expected to be approximately:

      a. 90 degrees
   ! b. 109.5 degrees
      c. 120 degrees
      d. 145 degrees
      e. 180 degrees

18. The Se=C=Se molecule is a non-polar molecule because

      a. the bonds in the molecule are all non-polar
      b. the bonds in the molecule are polar but their effect on the overall polarity is canceled by the effect of lone pairs in the valence shell of the carbon atom
   ! c. the bonds in the molecule are polar but their effect on the overall polarity is canceled by the fact that they are equal in magnitude and oppositely directed
      d. the bonds in the molecule are polar but the polar effect is canceled by the resonance hybrids which distribute the charge evenly
      e. the bonds in the molecule are polar but only slightly so and this is not enough to affect the polarity of the molecule as a whole

19. The smallest F—S—F bond angle in SF_6, in degrees, is:

   ! a. 90 degrees
      b. 109.5 degrees
      c. 120 degrees
      d. 145 degrees
      e. 180 degrees

20. The F—Cl—F bond angles in ClF_3, in degrees, are:

    a. 90, only
    b. 109.5, only
    c. 120, only
    d. 90, 120 and 180
  ! e. 90 and 180

21. Based on conclusions from application of the VSEPR theory, the expected bond angles in the AsF_4^- ion should be:

    a. 90, only
    b. 109.5, only
    c. 120, only
  ! d. 90, 120 and 180
    e. 90 and 180

22. Based on observed periodic trends, arrange the following species, HBr, HCl, HF, HI, in order of increasing dipole moment.

    a. HF < HCl < HBr < HI
    b. HBr < HCl < HF < HI
    c. HI < HF < HCl < HBr
  ! d. HI < HBr < HCl < HF
    e. HCl < HBr < HI < HF

23. Which of the following molecules CO_2, CS_2, NO_2, COS is/are polar?

    a. NO_2 only
    b. CS_2, NO_2, and COS
    c. CO_2 only
  ! d. COS and NO_2
    e. COS only

24. Based on conclusions from application of the VSEPR theory, which one of the following molecules should be nonpolar?

    a. CH_3Cl
  ! b. CSe_2
    c. H_2O
    d. NH_3
    e. OF_2

25. Which one of the molecules below is a polar molecule?

   a. Br_2
   b. BF_3
   c. CO_2
   d. CS_2
 ! e. IBr

26. Which one of the molecules below has no permanent dipole moment?

 ! a. SO_3
   b. SO_2
   c. CO
   d. NH_3
   e. CH_2Cl_2

27. Which one of the following is a polar molecule?

   a. XeF_2
 ! b. BrF_5
   c. XeF_4
   d. CCl_4
   e. PBr_5

28. Determine the expected molecular geometry and polarity of the SO_2 molecule by applying VSEPR theory.

   a. linear, nonpolar
   b. linear, polar
   c. bent, 109.5° angle, polar
 ! d. bent, 120° angle, polar
   e. bent, 109.5° angle, nonpolar

29. Predict the molecular geometry and polarity of the O—C—S molecule.

   a. linear, nonpolar
   b. bent, nonpolar
 ! c. linear, polar
   d. tetrahedral, nonpolar
   e. bent, polar

166

30. Bonding in the hydrogen chloride molecule can be explained by the valence bond theory in terms of an overlap between

      a. the 1s orbital of the hydrogen and the 1s orbital of the chlorine
      b. the 1s orbital of the hydrogen and the 2s orbital of the chlorine
      c. the 1s orbital of the hydrogen and the 2p orbital of the chlorine
      d. the 1s orbital of the hydrogen and the 3s orbital of the chlorine
!   e. the 1s orbital of the hydrogen and the 3p orbital of the chlorine

31. Bonding in the chlorine molecule can be explained by the valence bond theory in terms of an overlap between

      a. the 1s orbital of a chlorine atom and the 1s orbital of the other chlorine atom
      b. the 2s orbital of a chlorine atom and the 2s orbital of the other chlorine atom
      c. the 2p orbital of a chlorine atom and the 2p orbital of the other chlorine atom
      d. the 3s orbital of a chlorine atom and the 3s orbital of the other chlorine atom
!   e. the 3p orbital of a chlorine atom and the 3p orbital of the other chlorine atom

32. Bonding in the water molecule can be explained by the valence bond theory in terms of an overlap between

      a. the 1s orbital of the hydrogen and the 1s orbital of the oxygen
      b. the 1s orbital of the hydrogen and the 2s orbital of the oxygen
!   c. the 1s orbital of the hydrogen and the 2p orbital of the oxygen
      d. the 1s orbital of the hydrogen and the 3s orbital of the oxygen
      e. the 1s orbital of the hydrogen and the 3p orbital of the oxygen

33. Bonding in the nitrogen trifluoride molecule can be explained by the valence bond theory in terms of an overlap between

      a. the 2s orbital of the nitrogen and the 2s orbital of the fluorine
      b. the 2s orbital of the nitrogen and the 2p orbital of the fluorine
!   c. the 2p orbital of the nitrogen and the 2p orbital of the fluorine
      d. the 1s orbital of the nitrogen and the 2p orbital of the fluorine
      e. the 2p orbital of the nitrogen and the 3p orbital of the fluorine

34. Draw a Lewis structure for $H_3C\text{—}NO_2$. Both oxygen atoms are directly attached to the nitrogen atom. What is the hybrid orbital set used by the nitrogen atom for bonding?

      a. sp^3d^2
      b. sp
      c. sp^3d
      d. sp^3
!   e. sp^2

35. The central atom in BrF_5 uses sp^3d^2 hybridization. It must therefore have _____ σ-bonds and _____ lone pair(s) of electrons in the valence shell of the central atom of the molecule.

      a. 1, 5
      b. 3, 3
      c. 5, 0
  ! d. 5, 1
      e. 6, 0

36. The central atom in SF_4 has _____ σ-bonding pair(s) and _____ lone pair(s) of electrons in the valence shell of the central atom.

      a. 3, 2
      b. 4, 0
  ! c. 4, 1
      d. 5, 0
      e. 5, 1

37. Which one of the following hybrid orbital sets is used by the central atom for σ-bonding in the PCl_3 molecule?

      a. sp
      b. sp^2
  ! c. sp^3
      d. sp^3d
      e. sp^3d^2

38. Which one of the following hybrid orbital sets is used by the central atom for σ-bonding in the PCl_4^- ion?

      a. sp
      b. sp^2
      c. sp^3
  ! d. sp^3d
      e. sp^3d^2

39. Which one of the following hybrid orbital sets is used by the central atom for σ-bonding in the SF_6 molecule?

      a. sp
      b. sp^2
      c. sp^3
      d. sp^3d
  ! e. sp^3d^2

40. Which one of the following hybrid orbital sets is used by the central atom for σ-bonding in the AsF_5 molecule?

    a. sp
    b. sp^2
    c. sp^3
! d. sp^3d
    e. sp^3d^2

41. Which one of the following hybrid orbital sets is used by the central atom for σ-bonding in the NO_3^- ion?

    a. sp
! b. sp^2
    c. sp^3
    d. sp^3d
    e. sp^3d^2

42. Which one of the following molecules uses an sp^2 hybrid orbital set on the central atom for σ-bonding?

    a. CS_2
    b. N_2O
! c. SO_2
    d. NF_3
    e. PF_5

43. Which one of the following hybrid orbital sets is used by the As atom for σ-bonding in the AsF_4^- ion?

    a. sp
    b. sp^2
    c. sp^3
! d. sp^3d
    e. sp^3d^2

44. Which one of the following hybrid orbital sets is used by the central atom for σ-bonding in the ClO_3^- ion?

    a. sp
    b. sp^2
! c. sp^3
    d. sp^3d
    e. sp^3d^2

45. The skeleton for the Lewis structure of thionyl chloride, SOCl$_2$, is shown below. Complete the Lewis structure by filling in the bonds and the remaining valence electrons which are not involved in bonds.

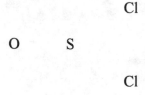

After adjusting for formal charges, what type of orbitals are predicted to lie around the sulfur atom by the valence bond theory?

     a. 5 sp^{3}d hybrid orbitals and no π-orbitals
! b. 4 sp^3 hybrid orbitals and one localized π-orbital
     c. 4 sp^3 hybrid orbitals and one delocalized π-orbital
     d. 3 sp^{3}d hybrid orbitals and one localized π-orbital
     e. 3 sp^{3}d hybrid orbitals and one delocalized π-orbital

46. Thionyl chloride, SOCl$_2$, has a Lewis structure related to that of sulfur trioxide, wherein two of the oxygen atoms have been replaced with chlorine atoms. If you draw the Lewis structure, and take formal charge considerations into account, there will be _____ π-bond(s) and the _____ hybrid orbital set would be used for σ-bonding in the molecule.

     a. 1, sp^{3}d
! b. 1, sp^3
     c. 2, sp^3
     d. 2, sp^{3}d
     e. 3, sp^3

47. The chlorosulfonate ion, ClSO$_3^-$, has a structure similar to that of the sulfate ion, the difference being that one of the oxygen atoms has been replaced by a chlorine atom. If you draw the Lewis structure, and take formal charge considerations into account, there will be _____ π-bond(s) and the _____ hybrid orbital set would be used for σ-bonding in the molecule.

     a. 1, sp^{3}d
     b. 1, sp^3
! c. 2, sp^3
     d. 2, sp^{3}d
     e. 3, sp^3

48. In the carbon monoxide molecule, there will be there will be _____ π-bond(s) and the _____ hybrid orbital set on the carbon would be used for σ-bonding in the molecule.

     a. 2, sp
     b. 2, sp^2
! c. 3, sp
     d. 3, sp^2
     e. 1, sp^2

49. The fluorophosphonate ion, FPO_3^{2-}, has a structure similar to that of the orthophosphate ion, the difference being that one of the oxygen atoms has been replaced by a fluorine atom. If you draw the Lewis structure, and take formal charge considerations into account, there will be _____ π-bond(s) and the _____ hybrid orbital set would be used for σ-bonding in the molecule.

      a. 1, sp^3d
!   b. 1, sp^3
      c. 2, sp^3
      d. 2, sp^3d
      e. 3, sp^3

50. Draw a Lewis structure for H_3C—NO_2. Both oxygen atoms are directly attached to the nitrogen atom. How many σ-bonds are there in the molecule?

      a. 7
!   b. 6
      c. 1
      d. 5
      e. 2

51. How many σ-bonds and π-bonds, respectively, are there in a CO_2 molecule?

      a. 1 σ-bonds and 2 π-bonds
      b. 2 σ-bonds and 0 π-bonds
!   c. 2 σ-bonds and 2 π-bonds
      d. 2 σ-bonds and 4 π-bonds
      e. 4 σ-bonds and 0 π-bonds

52. How many σ-bonds and π-bonds, respectively, are there in a N_2H_2 molecule?

      a. 2 σ-bonds and 2 π-bonds
      b. 4 σ-bonds and 0 π-bonds
      c. 3 σ-bonds and 0 π-bond
!   d. 3 σ-bonds and 1 π-bond
      e. 2 σ-bonds and 1 π-bond

53. Which one of the following statements about the ammonia molecule is true?

      a. The N—H bonds are polar, but the molecule is non-polar.
      b. The molecule has both σ- and π-bonds in it.
!   c. The nitrogen atom can be said to utilize sp^3 hybrid orbitals for σ-bonding.
      d. The H—N—H bond angles are greater than 109.5 degrees.
      e. The molecular geometry is planar triangular.

54. How many π-bonds are there in the CN$^-$ ion?

      a. 0
      b. 1
      c. 1.5
!   d. 2
      e. 3

55. Draw a Lewis structure for H_3C—NO_2. Both oxygen atoms are directly attached to the nitrogen atom. If you take formal charge considerations into account, how many π-bonds are there in the molecule?

      a. 0
!   b. 1
      c. 2
      d. 3
      e. 4

56. Draw a Lewis structure for H_3C—PO_2. Both oxygen atoms are directly attached to the phosphorus atom. If you take formal charge considerations into account, how many π-bonds are there in the molecule?

      a. 0
      b. 1
!   c. 2
      d. 3
      e. 4

57. Ozone (O_3) is an allotropic form of oxygen. Based on VSEPR theory, which statement below would you expect to be true for this molecule?

      a. The molecule is linear, and has no lone pairs in the valence shell on the center atom.
      b. The molecule is linear, and has two π-bonds.
      c. The molecule is T-shaped.
      d. The molecule is bent, and has two lone pairs in the valence shell on the center atom.
!   e. The molecule is bent, and has one π-bond.

58. What is the average bond order for the N—O bonds in the nitrite ion?

      a. 1.0
      b. 1.333
!   c. 1.5
      d. 2.0
      e. 2.5

59. When we compare the carbon monoxide molecule with the carbon dioxide molecule, from VSEPR theory we find

        a. CO_2 is polar and CO is non-polar
        b. the bond in CO is weaker than the ones in CO_2
        c. CO_2 has shorter bonds than CO
 !   d. the bond order in CO is higher than the bond order in CO_2
        e. Both CO and CO_2 are non-polar

60. What is the bond order for the carbon-carbon bond in the C_2H_2 molecule?

        a. 1.0
        b. 1.5
        c. 2.0
        d. 2.5
 !   e. 3.0

61. What is the bond order for the carbon-carbon bond in the C_2F_4 molecule?

        a. 1.0
        b. 1.5
 !   c. 2.0
        d. 2.5
        e. 3.0

62. Which statement below is true for the BrF_5 molecule?

        a. There are two lone pairs in the valence shell of the bromine atom.
        b. The molecule is non-polar.
 !   c. Some of the F—Br—F bond angles are close to 90 degrees.
        d. At least one of the bond angles, F—Br—F, is about 109.5 degrees.
        e. Some of the F—Br—F bond angles are close to 120 degrees.

63. A comparison of the two molecules, SbF_5 and IF_5, using VSEPR theory reveals that

 !   a. the IF_5 is polar and the SbF_5 is non-polar
        b. both molecules are non-polar
        c. the SbF_5 is polar and the IF_5 is non-polar
        d. both molecules are polar
        e. both molecules have lone pairs in the valence shell of the central atom

64. Application of the bonding theories and other concepts to the NCl_3 molecule leads to the prediction that

    ! a. the molecule should have trigonal pyramidal geometry
    b. the molecule should have delocalized valence electrons
    c. the molecule should be non-polar
    d. the formal charge on the center atom is +3
    e. the molecule should have a planar triangular geometry

65. Which statement below is true about the BF_3 molecule?

    a. The molecule can function as a Lewis base.
    b. The molecule has one σ-bond and three π-bonds.
    c. The B—F bond order is 1.33.
    ! d. The boron atom is electron deficient in its valence shell.
    e. The boron atom uses sp^3 hybridization.

66. The restrictions placed on the assignment of electrons to molecular orbitals in the ground state electronic configuration of multinuclear species

    a. must obey the Pauli principle but not Hund's rule or the Aufbau principle
    b. must obey the Pauli principle and the Aufbau principle but not Hund's rule
    c. must obey the Aufbau principle but the Pauli principle or Hund's rule
    d. are not governed by either the Aufbau principle, Hund's rule, or the Pauli principle
    ! e. must obey the Aufbau principle, Hund's rule, and the Pauli principle

67. The energy level scheme for the valence orbitals of 2nd period homonuclear diatomic molecules lists the valence molecular orbitals in the following order of increasing energy
$$\sigma_{2s} < \sigma^*_{2s} < \sigma_{2p(x)} < \pi_{2p(y)}, \pi_{2p(z)} < \pi^*_{2p(y)}, \pi^*_{2p(z)} < \sigma^*_{2p(x)}$$
Based on this energy level scheme, the bond order for the bond in the N_2^+ ion is

    a. 1.0
    b. 1.5
    c. 2.0
    ! d. 2.5
    e. 3.0

68. The energy level scheme for the valence orbitals of 2nd period homonuclear diatomic molecules lists the valence molecular orbitals in the following order of increasing energy
$$\sigma_{2s} < \sigma^*_{2s} < \sigma_{2p(x)} < \pi_{2p(y)}, \pi_{2p(z)} < \pi^*_{2p(y)}, \pi^*_{2p(z)} < \sigma^*_{2p(x)}$$
Based on this energy level scheme, the bond order for the bond in the O_2^+ ion in its ground state is

    a. 1.0
    b. 1.5
    c. 2.0
    ! d. 2.5
    e. 3.0

69. The energy level scheme for the valence orbitals of 2nd period homonuclear diatomic molecules lists the valence molecular orbitals in the following order of increasing energy

$$\sigma_{2s} < \sigma^*_{2s} < \sigma_{2p(x)} < \pi_{2p(y)}, \pi_{2p(z)} < \pi^*_{2p(y)}, \pi^*_{2p(z)} < \sigma^*_{2p(x)}$$

Based on this energy level scheme, the bond order for the bond in the O_2^- ion in its ground state is

     a. 1.0
! b. 1.5
     c. 2.0
     d. 2.5
     e. 3.0

70. The energy level scheme for the valence orbitals of 2nd period homonuclear diatomic molecules lists the valence molecular orbitals in the following order of increasing energy

$$\sigma_{2s} < \sigma^*_{2s} < \sigma_{2p(x)} < \pi_{2p(y)}, \pi_{2p(z)} < \pi^*_{2p(y)}, \pi^*_{2p(z)} < \sigma^*_{2p(x)}$$

Based on this energy level scheme, how many electrons are there in all of the antibonding molecular orbitals of the O_2 molecule in its ground state?

     a. 1
     b. 2
     c. 3
! d. 4
     e. 5

71. The energy level scheme for the valence orbitals of 2nd period homonuclear diatomic molecules lists the valence molecular orbitals in the following order of increasing energy

$$\sigma_{2s} < \sigma^*_{2s} < \sigma_{2p(x)} < \pi_{2p(y)}, \pi_{2p(z)} < \pi^*_{2p(y)}, \pi^*_{2p(z)} < \sigma^*_{2p(x)}$$

Based on this energy level scheme, how many electrons are there in all of the antibonding molecular orbitals of the F_2^+ ion in its ground state?

     a. 1
     b. 2
     c. 3
     d. 4
! e. 5

72. The energy level scheme for the valence orbitals of 2nd period homonuclear diatomic molecules lists the valence molecular orbitals in the following order of increasing energy

$$\sigma_{2s} < \sigma^*_{2s} < \sigma_{2p(x)} < \pi_{2p(y)}, \pi_{2p(z)} < \pi^*_{2p(y)}, \pi^*_{2p(z)} < \sigma^*_{2p(x)}$$

Based on this energy level scheme, how many unpaired electrons are there in all of the antibonding molecular orbitals of the O_2 molecule in its ground state?

     a. 1
! b. 2
     c. 3
     d. 4
     e. 5

73. The energy level scheme for the valence orbitals of 2nd period homonuclear diatomic molecules lists the valence molecular orbitals in the following order of increasing energy

$$\sigma_{2s} < \sigma^*_{2s} < \sigma_{2p(x)} < \pi_{2p(y)}, \pi_{2p(z)} < \pi^*_{2p(y)}, \pi^*_{2p(z)} < \sigma^*_{2p(x)}$$

Based on this energy level scheme, how many unpaired electrons are there in all of the antibonding molecular orbitals of the O_2^- ion in its ground state?

!　a. 1
　　b. 2
　　c. 3
　　d. 4
　　e. 5

74. The energy level scheme for the valence orbitals of 2nd period homonuclear diatomic molecules lists the valence molecular orbitals in the following order of increasing energy

$$\sigma_{2s} < \sigma^*_{2s} < \sigma_{2p(x)} < \pi_{2p(y)}, \pi_{2p(z)} < \pi^*_{2p(y)}, \pi^*_{2p(z)} < \sigma^*_{2p(x)}$$

Based on this energy level scheme, which one of the following species has the *largest* number of unpaired electrons in its ground state?

　　a. N_2^+
　　b. O_2^+
　　c. O_2^-
!　d. O_2
　　e. F_2^+

75. The energy level scheme for the valence orbitals of 2nd period homonuclear diatomic molecules lists the valence molecular orbitals in the following order of increasing energy

$$\sigma_{2s} < \sigma^*_{2s} < \sigma_{2p(x)} < \pi_{2p(y)}, \pi_{2p(z)} < \pi^*_{2p(y)}, \pi^*_{2p(z)} < \sigma^*_{2p(x)}$$

Based on this energy level scheme, how many unpaired electrons are there in all of the antibonding molecular orbitals of the O_2^{2-} ion in its ground state?

!　a. 0
　　b. 1
　　c. 2
　　d. 3
　　e. 4

76. The energy level scheme for the valence orbitals of 2nd period homonuclear diatomic molecules lists the valence molecular orbitals in the following order of increasing energy

$$\sigma_{2s} < \sigma^*_{2s} < \sigma_{2p(x)} < \pi_{2p(y)}, \pi_{2p(z)} < \pi^*_{2p(y)}, \pi^*_{2p(z)} < \sigma^*_{2p(x)}$$

Based on this energy level scheme, which statement below is true about the bonds in the set, O_2, O_2^+, O_2^-, O_2^{2-}?

　　a. O_2^- has the shortest bond.
　　b. O_2^{2-} has the shortest bond.
　　c. O_2 has the shortest bond.
!　d. O_2^+ has the shortest bond.
　　e. Actually, the bonds in all these species are of equal length.

77. The H_2^- molecular ion, in its ground state electronic configuration, should have a bond order of

       a. 0
!   b. 0.5
       c. 1.0
       d. 1.5
       e. 2.0

78. Which one of the sets below includes all those from the list, NO_3^-, NO_2^-, O_3, that have delocalized molecular orbitals?

       a. NO_3^- and NO_2^-
       b. NO_2^- and O_3
!   c. NO_3^-, NO_2^- and O_3
       d. NO_3^- only
       e. NO_3^- and O_3

79. What is the total number of π-bonds in the benzene molecule?

       a. 0
       b. 1
       c. 2
!   d. 3
       e. 4

80. Metallic magnesium is a good conductor of electricity. The conduction is explained by

       a. the presence of a delocalized 3s band which extends throughout the solid and is fully populated by electrons which can move freely in this 3s band
       b. the presence of a localized 3s band which extends throughout the solid and is fully populated by electrons which can move freely in this 3s band
       c. the presence of a delocalized 3p band which extends throughout the solid and is fully populated by electrons which can move freely in this 3p band
       d. the presence of a delocalized 3p band which extends throughout the solid and is partially populated (half filled) by electrons which can move freely in this 3p band
!   e. the presence of a delocalized 3p band which extends throughout the solid, is empty, and overlaps the fully delocalized 3s valence band which is fully populated by electrons. This provides easy access for electrons to move freely throughout the metal.

81. In which one of the elements below (when in the solid state) is overlap between the 3s and 3p bands which are fully delocalized throughout the solid most important in the mechanism which allows high electrical conductivity?

       a. Al
!   b. Mg
       c. Na
       d. P
       e. S

82. Metallic sodium is a good conductor of electricity. The conduction is explained by

    a. the presence of a delocalized 3s band which extends throughout the solid and is fully populated by electrons which can move freely in this 3s band

    b. the presence of a localized 3s band which extends throughout the solid and is partially populated by electrons which can move freely in this 3s band

  ! c. the presence of a delocalized 3s band which extends throughout the solid and is partially populated by electrons which can move freely in this 3s band

    d. the presence of a delocalized 3p band which extends throughout the solid and is partially populated (half filled) by electrons which can move freely in this 3p band

    e. the presence of a delocalized 3p band which extends throughout the solid, is empty, and overlaps the fully delocalized 3s valence band which is fully populated by electrons. This provides easy access for electrons to move freely throughout the metal.

Fill in the Blanks

83. The PCl_5 molecule has (polar)(non-polar) bonds and is a (polar)(non-polar) molecule._____, _____ (! polar, non-polar)

84. The shape of dichlorophosphine, $PHCl_2$, would be best described as _____ (! trigonal pyramidal)

85. The shape of the ammonium ion would be best described as _____ (! tetrahedral)

86. The butane molecule, C_4H_{10}, should have ___ σ-bonds. (! 13)

87. The hybrid orbital set used for σ-bonding in the PO_3^- ion (metaphosph**ate**) is the _____ set. (! sp^2)

88. If we use the same molecular orbital energy level scheme for the valence orbitals in the CO molecule as we use for homonuclear diatomic molecules,

$$\sigma_{2s} < \sigma^*_{2s} < \sigma_{2p(x)} < \pi_{2p(y)}, \pi_{2p(z)} < \pi^*_{2p(y)}, \pi^*_{2p(z)} < \sigma^*_{2p(x)}$$

how many valence electrons are there in the antibonding orbitals of the system? _____ (! 2)

89. If we use the same molecular orbital energy level scheme for the valence orbitals in the NO^- ion as we use for homonuclear diatomic molecules,

$$\sigma_{2s} < \sigma^*_{2s} < \sigma_{2p(x)} < \pi_{2p(y)}, \pi_{2p(z)} < \pi^*_{2p(y)}, \pi^*_{2p(z)} < \sigma^*_{2p(x)}$$

how many unpaired electrons are there in the antibonding orbitals of the system? _____ (! 2)

90. In the NO^+ ion, there will be _____ π-bond(s) and the ____ hybrid orbital set on the nitrogen atom would be used for σ-bonding in the ion. (! 3, sp)

91. A triple bond is (shorter, longer, the same length) and (stronger, the same strength, weaker) than a double bond between the same two atoms. _____, _____ (! shorter, stronger)

True and False

92. When two atoms interact so as to form a bond, an s orbital in either atom can never be employed for π-bonding. (! T)

93. A covalent bond is formed when two atoms position themselves so that maximum overlap of the atomic orbitals occurs with an increase in the potential energy of the system. (! F)

94. When two hydrogen interact so that their valence orbitals form a bonding molecular orbital and an antibonding molecular orbital, the formation of these molecular orbitals lowers the potential energy of the system. (! T)

95. The numerical restrictions placed on the number of electrons that can occupy an orbital by the Pauli principle applies to atomic orbitals but not to molecular orbitals. (! F)

96. The molecular orbital energy level scheme for the He_2 molecule (generated by using the valence orbitals) employs two atomic valence orbitals to form 4 molecular orbitals. (! F)

97. The ground state electronic configuration for the He_2^+ molecular ion is $(\sigma_{1s})^2 (\sigma^*_{1s})^1$. (! T)

98. The conductivity of some metalloids can be modified. The modified materials derive their conductivity from impurities that affect the population of the valence band (which would ordinarily be filled if the material were pure and thus be considerably lower in conductivity). (!T)

Critical Thinking

99. Consider these species: ClO_2^-, NO_2^-, ClO_2, NO_2, ClO_2^+, NO_2^+. Determine the molecular geometry using VSEPR theory, then list them in order of *increasing* bond angle.

    _____ (! $ClO_2^- < ClO_2 < ClO_2^+ \approx NO_2^- < NO_2 < NO_2^+$)

100. The commonly used energy level scheme for the valence orbitals of 2nd period homonuclear and heteronuclear diatomic molecules lists the valence molecular orbitals in the following order of increasing energy:

$$\sigma_{2s} < \sigma^*_{2s} < \sigma_{2p(x)} < \pi_{2p(y)}, \pi_{2p(z)} < \pi^*_{2p(y)}, \pi^*_{2p(z)} < \sigma^*_{2p(x)}$$

Other considerations, backed by experimental evidence, suggest that modified scheme below is a true description in some cases.

$$\sigma_{2s} < \sigma^*_{2s} < \pi_{2p(y)}, \pi_{2p(z)} < \sigma_{2p(x)} < \pi^*_{2p(y)}, \pi^*_{2p(z)} < \sigma^*_{2p(x)}$$

Based on this energy level scheme, how many valence electrons are there in π-type orbitals of the N_2^+ ion in its ground state? (! 4)

101. The commonly used energy level scheme for the valence orbitals of 2nd period homonuclear and heteronuclear diatomic molecules lists the valence molecular orbitals in the following order of increasing energy:

$$\sigma_{2s} < \sigma^*_{2s} < \sigma_{2p(x)} < \pi_{2p(y)}, \pi_{2p(z)} < \pi^*_{2p(y)}, \pi^*_{2p(z)} < \sigma^*_{2p(x)}$$

Other considerations, backed by experimental evidence, suggest that the modified scheme below is a true description in some cases.

$$\sigma_{2s} < \sigma^*_{2s} < \pi_{2p(y)}, \pi_{2p(z)} < \sigma_{2p(x)} < \pi^*_{2p(y)}, \pi^*_{2p(z)} < \sigma^*_{2p(x)}$$

Based on this energy level scheme, how many valence electrons are there in π-type orbitals of the C_2^+ ion in its ground state? (! 3)

102. Two adjacent atoms, a and b, can form bonds by overlap of their atomic orbitals. Using the axis system immediately below, if the internuclear axis is labeled as the x axis, which pair of orbitals will overlap correctly to form a σ-bond?

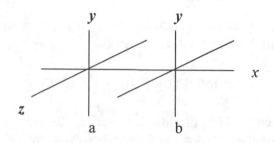

   a. the d_{xz} on atom a with the d_{xz} on atom b
   b. the d_{xy} on atom a with the d_{xy} on atom b
   c. the p_z on atom a with the p_z on atom b
   d. the p_y on atom a with the p_y on atom b
!   e. the p_x on atom a with the p_x on atom b

103. Two adjacent atoms, a and b, can form bonds by overlap of their atomic orbitals. Using the axis system immediately below, if the internuclear axis is labeled as the x axis, which pair of orbitals will overlap correctly to form a π-bond?

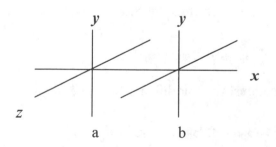

   a. the d_{xz} on atom a with the p_x on atom b
   b. the d_{yz} on atom a with the d_{xz} on atom b
   c. the p_x on atom a with the p_y on atom b
!   d. the p_y on atom a with the d_{xy} on atom b
   e. the p_x on atom a with the d_{x2-y2} on atom b

104. Kevin Vitellan is trying to come up with a scheme for making a compound which contains neon as one of its elements. He figured that the difference in electron affinity between oxygen and neon is too small for them to form an ionic bond, so he is considering a feasibility study on the NeO molecule. He tried the same molecular orbital energy level scheme for the valence orbitals in the the proposed NeO system as we used for homonuclear diatomic species like O_2 and heteronuclear diatomic species like CO and CN^-.

$$\sigma_{2s} < \sigma^*_{2s} < \sigma_{2p(x)} < \pi_{2p(y)}, \pi_{2p(z)} < \pi^*_{2p(y)}, \pi^*_{2p(z)} < \sigma^*_{2p(x)}$$

Based on his proposal, a) what would be the bond order of this molecule; b) how many unpaired electrons would there be in the antibonding orbitals of the system? _____, _____ (! 1, 0)

Chemicals in Our World 5 Good Ozone—Where Is It?

105. Which one of the following statements concerning ozone is false?

    a. There is a significant and important presence of ozone in the stratosphere.

    b. Ozone performs the useful function on converting UV energy into heat, contributing to the temperature balance between the earth and cold outer space.

!   c. Massive amounts of unburned HC's released from internal combustion engines are a threat to the ozone layer because they react rapidly with ozone in the presence of UV radiation.

    d. Chlorofluorocarbons, such as those used in the refrigeration industry and as propellants for aerosols are a major player in the progressive destruction of the ozone layer.

    e. Ozone can absorb UV radiation, preventing it from reaching the planetary surface and causing severe health problems.

106. The reaction which Cl atoms undergo with ozone molecules, $Cl + O_3 \rightarrow ClO_2 + O$, followed by $O + O \rightarrow O_2$ clearly shows that each chlorine atom consumes only one ozone molecule. This still causes serious depletion because the ozone concentration is not very high in unpolluted atmospheres. (! F)

107. The reaction sequence of chlorine atoms with ozone molecules is such that one chlorine atom is capable of consuming hundreds of ozone molecules before some reaction occurs to terminate its reactive state. (! T)

108. Atmospheric ozone is consumed by

    a. the bromine atoms produced by chlorine induced displacement reactions from bromine containing compounds in industrial waste gases present in the atmosphere

    b. the iodine atoms produced by chlorine induced displacement reactions from iodine containing compounds in industrial waste gases present in the atmosphere

!   c. the chlorine atoms produced by action of ultraviolet light on chlorine containing compounds in industrial waste gases present in the atmosphere

    d. the fluorine atoms produced by action of ultraviolet light on fluorine containing compounds in industrial waste gases present in the atmosphere

    e. the nitrogen chlorides, like N_2Cl, produced by reaction of irradiated nitrogen molecules with chlorine containing compounds in industrial waste gases. These nitrogen chlorides react with ozone and quickly consume it.

Chapter 10   Properties of Gases

Multiple Choice

1. An open end manometer constructed from a U-shaped tube was operated using an oil which has a density of 1.088 g ml^{-1}. In a particular measurement, the level in the end connected to the gas manifold, on which the experiment was being conducted, measured 76.2 cm above the U-neck, while the level in the open end (to the atmosphere) was 23.8 cm above the U-neck. The outside air pressure in the laboratory was measured as 754 torr. What is the pressure in the gas manifold? For reference, the density of mercury is 13.533 g ml^{-1} at room temperature.

    a. 42.0 torr
    b. 230 torr
    c. 272 torr
    d. 516 torr
!   e. 712 torr

2. An open end manometer constructed from a U-shaped tube was operated using an oil which has a density of 1.164 g ml^{-1}. In a particular measurement, the level in the end connected to the gas manifold, on which the experiment was being conducted, measured 82.8 cm above the U-neck, while the level in the open end (to the atmosphere) was 17.2 cm above the U-neck. The outside air pressure in the laboratory was measured as 764 torr. What is the pressure in the gas manifold? For reference, the density of mercury is 13.533 g ml^{-1} at room temperature.

    a. 200 torr
    b. 563 torr
    c. 706 torr
!   d. 708 torr
    e. 738 torr

3. A closed end manometer which utilizes an oil having a density of 0.820 g ml^{-1} is being used to measure gas pressure in a manifold designed for studies on the gaseous state. In a particular experiment, the oil in the closed end of this manometer was 62.2 cm above the U-neck, while the level in the open end (connected to the manifold) was measured as 25.2 cm above the U-neck. By way of comparison, the density of mercury at room temperature is 13.533 g ml^{-1}. What is the pressure, in atmospheres, in the gas collection manifold?

    a. 2.66 x 10^{-2} atm
!   b. 2.95 x 10^{-2} atm
    c. 0.345 atm
    d. 0.784 atm
    e. 1.16 atm

4. A closed end manometer was constructed from a U-shaped glass tube which was 80.5 cm high. It was loaded with mercury so that the closed side was filled all the way to the top (80.0 cm above the neck) while the open end was at a level 18.0 cm above the neck. It was taken into a chamber used for training astronauts. What is the highest pressure, in torr, that can be read on this manometer?

   a. 62.0 torr
   b. 62.5 torr
   c. 98.0 torr
   d. 98.5 torr
   ! e. 620 torr

5. A properly designed Torricelli barometer (the simplest type of barometer) should be at least

   a. 50 cm tall
   ! b. 80 cm tall
   c. 2.50 meters tall
   d. 100 in tall
   e. 76 mm tall

6. A sample of a gas in a cylindrical chamber with a movable piston occupied a volume of 6.414 liters when the pressure was 850 torr and the temperature was 27.2 °C. The pressure was readjusted to 5.82 atm by moving the piston. What was the volume occupied by the sample under the later conditions if the temperature remained constant throughout?

   a. 0.837 liters
   b. 0.937 liters
   ! c. 1.23 liters
   d. 1.53 liters
   e. 3.34 liters

7. A sample of a gas in a cylindrical chamber with a movable piston occupied a volume of 2.86 cubic meters when the pressure was 9.85×10^4 Pa and the temperature was 25.8 °C. The pressure was readjusted to 1.08×10^5 Pa by moving the piston. What was the volume occupied by the sample under the later conditions if the temperature remained constant throughout?

   a. 0.383 m^3
   ! b. 2.61 m^3
   c. 3.14 m^3
   d. 8.23 m^3
   e. 26.1 m^3

8. A sample of a gas in a cylindrical chamber with a movable piston occupied a volume of 1.40 liters when the pressure was 762 torr and the temperature was 26.9 °C. The volume of the system was readjusted to 0.150 liters by moving the piston. What was the pressure exerted on the surface of the piston, in atmospheres, by the gas if the temperature of the system remained constant?

    a. 0.107 atm
    b. 2.89 atm
    c. 9.30 atm
!   d. 9.36 atm
    e. 9.38 atm

9. A sample of a gas in a cylindrical chamber with a movable piston occupied a volume of 8.50 liters when the pressure was 9.85×10^4 Pa and the temperature was 24.9 °C. The volume of the system was readjusted to 11.6 liters by moving the piston. What was the pressure exerted on the surface of the piston, in pascals, by the gas if the temperature of the system remained constant?

    a. 7.22 Pa
    b. 2.66×10^4 Pa
!   c. 7.22×10^4 Pa
    d. 1.34×10^5 Pa
    e. 3.90×10^5 Pa

10. The standard reference conditions for studies of the gaseous state of matter has the values

    a. temperature: 0.00 K; pressure: 1.000 standard atmosphere
!   b. temperature: 0.00 °C; pressure: 1.000 standard atmosphere
    c. temperature: 273.15 K; pressure: 1.000 Pascal
    d. temperature: 298.15 K; pressure: 1.000 standard atmosphere
    e. temperature: 298.15 K; pressure: 1.000 Pascal

11. A sample of a gas in a cylindrical chamber with a movable piston occupied a volume of 6.414 liters when the pressure was 850 torr and the temperature was 27.2 °C. The temperature was readjusted to 65.5 °C while the load on the piston was kept constant to keep the pressure constant in the system. What was the volume occupied by the sample at the new temperature?

    a. 2.66 liters
    b. 5.689 liters
    c. 7.21 liters
!   d. 7.232 liters
    e. 15.4 liters

12. A sample of a gas in a cylindrical chamber with a movable piston occupied a volume of 2.86 cubic meters when the pressure was 9.85 x 10⁴ Pa and the temperature was 25.8 °C. The temperature was readjusted to -20.5 °C while the load on the piston was kept constant to keep the pressure constant in the system. What was the volume occupied by the sample under the later conditions?

     a. 2.27 m^3
! b. 2.42 m^3
     c. 3.38 m^3
     d. 3.60 m^3
     e. 15.2 m^3

13. A sample of a gas in a cylindrical chamber with a movable piston occupied a volume of 1.40 liters when the pressure was 768 torr and the temperature was 26.9 °C. The volume of the system was readjusted to 2.16 liters by changing the temperature while the load on the piston was kept constant to keep the pressure in the system constant. What was the temperature in the system at this point?

     a. 41.5 °C
     b. 41.9 °C
! c. 189.8 °C
     d. 194.7 °C
     e. 288.6 °C

14. A sample of a gas in a cylindrical chamber with a movable piston occupied a volume of 0.00256 cubic meters when the pressure was 1.20 x 10⁵ Pa and the temperature was 77.8 °C. The volume of the system was readjusted to 1.88 liters by changing the temperature while the load on the piston was kept constant to keep the pressure in the system constant. What was the temperature in the system at this point?

! a. -15.4 °C
     b. +36.1 °C
     c. +57.1 °C
     d. +204.7 °C
     e. +571 °C

15. A sample of an unknown gas was isolated in a gas containment bulb on a manifold used in this type work. The volume of the bulb was 1.425 liters. The temperature was 25.40 °C, and the manifold pressure was 583.0 torr. What volume, in liters, would this gas sample occupy at STP?

! a. 1.000 liters
     b. 1.195 liters
     c. 1.700 liters
     d. 2.030 liters
     e. 11.76 liters

16. A sample of a gas was isolated in a gas containment bulb on a manifold used in this type work. The volume of the bulb was 1.524 liters. The temperature was 28.40 °C, and the manifold pressure was 85.00 kPa. What volume, in liters, would this gas sample occupy at STP?

    a. 1.069 liters
! b. 1.158 liters
    c. 1.412 liters
    d. 1.645 liters
    e. 2.006 liters

17. A sample of a gas was isolated in a gas containment chamber used in this type work. The volume of the chamber was 1.245 cubic meters. The temperature was 22.80 °C, and the pressure in the chamber was 88.26 kPa. What volume, in cubic meters, would this gas sample occupy at STP?

! a. 1.001 m^3
    b. 1.007 m^3
    c. 1.175 m^3
    d. 1.319 m^3
    e. 1.549 m^3

18. A sample of a gas occupies a volume of 1.820 liters at STP. What pressure, in atmospheres, would it exert if transferred to a 1.425 liter vessel in which the temperature is maintained at 25.2 °C?

    a. 0.7168 atm
    b. 0.8552 atm
    c. 1.169 atm
    d. 1.278 atm
! e. 1.395 atm

19. A sample of a gas occupies a volume of 1.664 liters at STP. What pressure, in kilopascals, would it exert if it is transferred to a 1.524 liter vessel if the temperature in the vessel is maintained at 29.5 °C?

    a. 83.75 kPa
    b. 99.85 kPa
    c. 102.8 kPa
    d. 112.3 kPa
! e. 122.6 kPa

20. A sample of a gas occupies a volume of 1.566 cubic meters at STP. What pressure, in kilopascals, would it exert if it is transferred to a gas chamber with a volume of 1.824 cubic meters if the temperature in the chamber is maintained at 22.5 °C?

    a. 80.37 kPa
    b. 86.26 kPa
! c. 94.16 kPa
    d. 109.0 kPa
    e. 127.7 kPa

21. A sample of a gas occupies a volume of 185.5 ml at STP. What pressure, in torr, would it exert if it is transferred to a gas bulb with a volume of 255.5 ml in which the temperature is maintained at 34.5 °C?

    a. 489.9 torr
    b. 569.4 torr
! c. 621.5 torr
    d. 929.4 torr
    e. 1179 torr

22. A sample of a gas occupies a volume of 1.462 liters at STP. It was placed in a different vessel in which the pressure was measured as 722.5 torr when the temperature was 25.20 °C. What was the volume of this new vessel, in liters?

    a. 1.272 liters
    b. 1.408 liters
    c. 1.518 liters
    d. 1.539 liters
! e. 1.680 liters

23. A sample of a gas occupies a volume of 1.524 cubic meters at STP. It was placed in a different gas chamber in which the pressure was measured as 88.95 kPa when the temperature was 29.60 °C. What was the volume of this new gas chamber, in cubic meters?

    a. 1.207 m^3
    b. 1.483 m^3
    c. 1.566 m^3
    d. 1.763 m^3
! e. 1.924 m^3

24. A sample of a gas occupies a volume of 1.624 liters at STP. It was placed in a different vessel in which the pressure was measured as 106.3 kPa when the temperature was 28.6 °C. What was the volume of this new vessel, in liters?

    a. 1.401 liters
    b. 1.542 liters
    c. 1.567 liters
! d. 1.710 liters
    e. 1.882 liters

25. A sample of a gas occupies a volume of 1.462 liters at STP. It was placed in a different vessel with a volume of 1.601 liters, in which the pressure was measured as 722.0 torr. What was the temperature in the vessel at measurement time?

      a. -32.6 °C
      b. -10.6 °C
  ! c. +11.0 °C
      d. +37.0 °C
      e. +41.7 °C

26. A sample of a gas occupies a volume of 1.246 liters at STP. It was placed in a different vessel with a volume of 1.410 liters, in which the pressure was measured as 108.5 kPa. What was the temperature in the vessel at measurement time?

      a. -47.7 °C
      b. -14.7 °C
      c. +15.5 °C
  ! d. +57.8 °C
      e. +88.1 °C

27. A sample of a gas occupies a volume of 122.4 ml at STP. It was placed in a different vessel with a volume of 164.2 ml, in which the pressure was measured as 0.9915 atm. What was the temperature in the vessel at measurement time?

  ! a. 90.2 °C
      b. 96.4 °C
      c. 123.4 °C
      d. 201.9 °C
      e. 205.4 °C

28. A cylinder fitted with a movable piston and filled with a gas has a volume of 188.5 ml at 26.7 °C when the applied pressure is 755.2 torr. The temperature of the oil bath surrounding the cylinder was increased to 165.2 °C, and the load on the piston was changed. Careful measurement now gave a value of 210.5 ml for the volume. What was the final pressure in the system, in torr?

      a. 462.6 torr
      b. 576.9 torr
      c. 715.5 torr
  ! d. 988.6 torr
      e. 1233 torr

29. A cylinder fitted with a movable piston and filled with a gas has a volume of 16.44 liters at 22.4 °C when the applied pressure is 772.2 torr. The temperature of the oil bath surrounding it was increased to 184.4 °C, and the load on the piston was changed. Careful measurement now gave a value of 16.60 liters for the volume. What is the final pressure in the system, in torr?

    a. 494.0 torr
    b. 503.6 torr
! c. 1184 torr
    d. 1207 torr
    e. 6295 torr

30. A cylinder fitted with a movable piston and filled with a gas has a volume of 1.466×10^{-2} cubic meters when the temperature is 24.2 °C and the applied pressure is 97.03 kPa. The temperature of the oil bath surrounding it was increased to 146.4 °C. Careful measurement now gave a value of 1.479×10^{-2} cubic meters for the volume. What is the final pressure in the system, in kilopascals?

    a. 68.16 kPa
    b. 69.38 kPa
! c. 135.7 kPa
    d. 138.1 kPa
    e. 581.8 kPa

31. A gas sample occupies volume of 18.86 liters when the temperature is 35.2 °C and the pressure is 735.5 torr. How many moles of gas are there in the sample?

! a. 0.7214 moles
    b. 0.7702 moles
    c. 1.298 moles
    d. 5.411 moles
    e. 6.319 moles

32. A gas sample containing 0.2820 moles of a compound is trapped in a vessel on a manifold at a temperature of 25.2 °C and a pressure of 642.0 torr. What is the volume of the vessel, in liters?

    a. 0.01075 liters
    b. 0.6903 liters
! c. 8.173 liters
    d. 12.72 liters
    e. 92.99 liters

33. A gas sample containing 0.3250 moles of a compound is confined in a glass vessel on a manifold at a temperature of 28.4 °C and a pressure of 112.8 kPa. What is the volume of the vessel, in m^3?

! a. $7.224 \times 10^{-3} \ m^3$
    b. $7.369 \times 10^{-1} \ m^3$
    c. $7.722 \times 10^{-2} \ m^3$
    d. $7.722 \times 10^{-2} \ m^3$
    e. $7.824 \times 10^{-3} \ m^3$

34. A gas sample containing 0.2820 moles of a compound is trapped in a 2.461 liter vessel on a manifold at a temperature of 25.2 °C. What is the pressure in the vessel, in atmospheres, if it behaves as an ideal gas?

    a. 0.2369 atm
    b. 0.3740 atm
 ! c. 2.805 atm
    d. 4.112 atm
    e. 24.01 atm

35. A gas sample containing 0.3525 moles of a compound is trapped in a 2.641 liter vessel on a manifold at a temperature of 28.4 °C. What is the pressure in the vessel, in torr, if the gas behaves as an ideal gas?

    a. 334.6 torr
    b. 2007 torr
 ! c. 2510 torr
    d. 2513 torr
    e. 2694 torr

36. A gas sample containing 0.3250 moles of a compound is trapped in a chamber with a volume of 0.002460 cubic meters. If the temperature in the chamber is 26.8 °C, what is the pressure in the chamber, in kPa? Assume the gas exhibits ideal gas behavior.

    a. 29.44 kPa
    b. 307.0 kPa
 ! c. 329.5 kPa
    d. 356.9 kPa
    e. 3251 kPa

37. A gas sample occupies a volume of 1.662 liters when the temperature is 150.0 °C and the pressure is 842.0 torr. How many molecules are there in the sample?

    a. 1.516×10^{22}
    b. 2.602×10^{22}
 ! c. 3.194×10^{22}
    d. 9.009×10^{22}
    e. 9.419×10^{21}

38. A gas sample occupies a volume of 1.446 liters when the temperature is 185.0 °C and the pressure is 83.19 kPa. How many molecules are there in the sample?

 ! a. 1.902×10^{22}
    b. 2.821×10^{22}
    c. 4.710×10^{22}
    d. 9.095×10^{21}
    e. 9.095×10^{22}

39. A gas sample occupies a volume of 1.264×10^{-3} cubic meters when the temperature is 168.0 °C and the pressure is 126.2 kPa. How many molecules are there in the sample?

    a. 2.072×10^{22}
!   b. 2.619×10^{22}
    c. 2.654×10^{23}
    d. 2.654×10^{24}
    e. 6.877×10^{22}

40. A gas sample weighing 4.480 grams occupies a volume of 2.150 liters at STP. What is the apparent molecular weight of the sample?

    a. 9.632 g mol^{-1}
    b. 10.76 g mol^{-1}
!   c. 46.70 g mol^{-1}
    d. 112.8 g mol^{-1}
    e. 215.9 g mol^{-1}

41. A student doing a laboratory study on determination of molecular weight of gases obtained the following data for one of his unknowns: 6.155 grams of the gaseous substance occupy a volume of 1,484 ml when the temperature was held at 27.3 °C and the pressure in the measurement system was recorded as 747.2 torr. Calculate the molecular weight of the substance, assuming ideal gas behavior.

    a. 13.87 g mol^{-1}
    b. 30.40 g mol^{-1}
!   c. 104.0 g mol^{-1}
    d. 106.7 g mol^{-1}
    e. 110.0 g mol^{-1}

42. A specially designed gas containment vessel has a volume of 5.604 liters. It was charged with carbon monoxide gas at 28.2 °C. The pressure in the vessel now measured 868.5 torr. If the gas behaves as an ideal gas, how much should the gas sample weigh, in grams?

    a. 0.7651 g
    b. 1.289 g
    c. 5.555 g
    d. 6.286 g
!   e. 7.254 g

43. A mixture of 5.00 moles of neon and 3.00 moles of nitrogen occupy a volume of 36.0 liters in a vessel where the total pressure is 6.00 atm. The partial pressure of the neon in the container is

    a. 0.375 atm
    b. 0.625 atm
    c. 0.833 atm
!   d. 3.75 atm
    e. 43.2 atm

191

44. A chemical reaction, A(s) $\rightarrow$ B(s) + C(g) occurs when substance A is strongly heated. The molecular weight of the gaseous substance was to be determined from the following experimental data. Mass of A: 4.962 g ; Mass of residue (B) after cooling and weighing when no more gas was evolved: 3.684 g. When collected and stored in a 658.5 ml glass vessel on a manifold at 30.4 °C, the gas exerted a pressure of 748.5 torr. From this data, determine the apparent molecular weight of C, assuming it behaves as an ideal gas.

    a. 6.544 g mol^{-1}
    b. 47.58 g mol^{-1}
! c. 49.08 g mol^{-1}
    d. 71.68 g mol^{-1}
    e. 141.5 g mol^{-1}

45. A specially designed gas containment vessel has a volume of 6.504 liters. When filled with propane gas, C_3H_8, at 28.3 °C, the pressure measured 486.3 torr. How much should the gas sample weigh?

    a. 4.674 g
! b. 7.419 g
    c. 7.528 g
    d. 18.12 g
    e. 263.6 g

46. What is the total pressure exerted by a gaseous mixture that consists of 8.00 g of methane and 12.00 g of ethane, C_2H_6, in a 3.50 liter container maintained at 35.20 °C?

    a. 0.400 atm
    b. 0.741 atm
    c. 3.13 atm
! d. 6.49 atm
    e. 16.5 atm

47. What is the total pressure exerted by a gaseous mixture that consists of 1.00 g of hydrogen and 8.00 g of neon in a 2.80 liter container maintained at 44.10 °C?

    a. 1.15 atm
    b. 3.77 atm
    c. 3.95 atm
! d. 8.30 atm
    e. 12.9 atm

48. What is the total pressure exerted by a gaseous mixture that consists of 8.00 g of methane and 8.00 g of ethane, C_2H_6, in a 3.50 liter container maintained at 35.20 °C?

    a. 0.286 atm
    b. 0.631 atm
    c. 2.51 atm
! d. 5.53 atm
    e. 30.7 atm

49. What is the mole fraction of methane in a gaseous mixture that consists of 8.00 g of methane and 12.00 g of ethane, C_2H_6, in a 3.50 liter container maintained at 35.20°C?

  a. 0.400
  b. 0.434
  ! c. 0.555
  d. 0.800
  e. 1.50

50. What is the mole fraction of hydrogen in a gaseous mixture that consists of 8.00 g of hydrogen and 12.00 g of neon in a 3.50 liter container maintained at 35.20°C?

  a. 0.150
  b. 0.400
  c. 0.660
  ! d. 0.870
  e. 0.930

51. A sample gas mixture occupies a volume of 1.662 liters when the temperature is 185.0 °C and the pressure is 624.4 torr. The mole fraction of oxygen in this sample is 0.3500. How many oxygen molecules are there in the sample?

  a. 1.134×10^{22}
  b. 1.896×10^{22}
  c. 2.262×10^{22}
  d. 5.803×10^{24}
  ! e. 7.656×10^{21}

52. A sample gas mixture has a volume of 1.288×10^{-2} cubic meters when the temperature is 168.0 °C and the pressure is 109.7 kPa. The mole fraction of helium in this sample is 0.5224. How many helium molecules are there in the sample?

  a. 1.212×10^{20}
  ! b. 1.212×10^{23}
  c. 3.182×10^{24}
  d. 4.441×10^{23}
  e. 8.167×10^{23}

53. A sample of oxygen gas was collected by downward displacement of water in a large gas collection apparatus. The total pressure in the collection vessel was 744.2 torr, the temperature was 26.0 °C, and the vessel contained 522 ml of the collected gas. How many moles of oxygen were collected? At 26.0 °C, the vapor pressure of water is 25.2 torr.

  ! a. 0.0201 moles
  b. 0.0215 moles
  c. 0.0842 moles
  d. 0.151 moles
  e. 0.231 moles

54. A sample of hydrogen gas was collected by downward displacement of water in a very large gas buret. The total pressure in the buret was measured as 764.2 torr, the temperature was 23.0 °C, and the buret contained 511 ml of the collected gas. How many moles of hydrogen were collected? At 23.0 °C, the vapor pressure of water is 21.1 torr.

   a. 0.0191 moles
 ! b. 0.0206 moles
   c. 0.0211 moles
   d. 0.0215 moles
   e. 0.0217 moles

55. A sample of nitrogen gas was collected by downward displacement of water in a gas collection flask. The total pressure in the collection flask was measured as 754.2 torr, the temperature was 20.0 °C, and the measured volume of gas collected was 516 ml. How many grams should the nitrogen weigh? At 20.0 °C, the vapor pressure of water is 17.5 torr.

   a. 0.291 g
   b. 0.305 g
 ! c. 0.582 g
   d. 0.596 g
   e. 0.610 g

56. A sample of methane gas was collected by downward displacement of water in a gas collection flask. The total pressure in the collection flask was measured as 758.2 torr, the temperature was 25.0 °C, and the measured volume of gas in the flask was 526.0 ml. How many grams should the methane weigh? At 25.0 °C, the vapor pressure of water is 23.8 torr.

   a. 0.01080 g
 ! b. 0.3333 g
   c. 0.3441 g
   d. 0.3549 g
   e. 8.438 g

57. The reaction, $MnO_2(s) + 4 HCl(aq) \rightarrow MnCl_2(aq) + Cl_2(g) + H_2O(l)$ was being studied. 12.2 g of MnO_2 were reacted with 70.0 ml of 2.50 M HCl solution. The chlorine produced was collected in a vessel. The pressure measured 0.971 atm at a temperature of 78.2 °C. Determine the volume of chlorine produced if the theoretical yield was obtained.

   a. 0.289 l
   b. 1.22 l
 ! c. 1.30 l
   d. 4.17 l
   e. 5.20 l

58. When $KClO_3$ is strongly heated, it decomposes to give KCl and oxygen gas. When 4.902 g of $KClO_3$ are heated until no more gas is evolved, how many liters of oxygen gas (measured at 25.0 °C and 771.0 torr) are produced, if the oxygen behaves as an ideal gas?

    a. 0.6431 liters
    b. 0.8314 liters
    c. 0.9647 liters
 ! d. 1.447 liters
    e. 1.925 liters

59. When $KClO_3$ is strongly heated, is decomposes to give KCl and oxygen gas. When 4.289 g of $KClO_3$ are heated until no more gas is evolved, how many liters of oxygen gas (measured at 22.4 °C and 754.0 torr) are produced, if the oxygen behaves as an ideal gas?

    a. 0.8555 liters
    b. 0.9625 liters
 ! c. 1.283 liters
    d. 1.668 liters
    e. 1.925 liters

60. When Ag_2O is strongly heated, it decomposes to produce silver and oxygen gas. If a 6.894 g sample of Ag_2O is heated until no more gas is evolved and all the oxygen is recovered, what volume of space, measured at 25.0 °C and 754.0 torr, should it occupy if it exhibits ideal gas behavior?

    a. 0.2934 liters
 ! b. 0.3668 liters
    c. 0.5502 liters
    d. 0.7336 liters
    e. 1.100 liters

61. When Ag_2O is strongly heated, it decomposes to produce silver and oxygen gas. If a 8.964 g sample of Ag_2O is heated until no more gas is evolved and all the oxygen is recovered, what volume of space, measured at 22.4 °C and 771.0 torr, should it occupy if it exhibits ideal gas behavior?

 ! a. 0.4624 liters
    b. 0.6935 liters
    c. 0.9247 liters
    d. 1.156 liters
    e. 1.387 liters

62. A gas mixture is 50.00% helium and 50.00% methane, by *volume*. What is the mole fraction of methane in the mixture?

    a. 0.1997
    b. 0.2005
    c. 0.2500
 ! d. 0.5000
    e. 0.8003

63. Silver oxide, Ag₂O, when heated strongly decomposes to yield silver and oxygen gas. A 4.262 g sample was heated to decompose it completely. What volume, in ml, should the gas collected occupy at 28.3 °C and 749.0 torr if it behaves as an ideal gas?

   ! a. 230.8 ml
     b. 346.2 ml
     c. 461.6 ml
     d. 615.5 ml
     e. 923.2 ml

64. A student prepared hydrogen gas by the reaction,
$$Zn(s) + 2\,HCl(aq) \rightarrow ZnCl_2(aq) + H_2(g)$$
The gas evolved was collected over water by downward displacement in a large gas collection tube. The volume of the saturated gas collected was 135.5 ml and the pressure measured 752.5 torr. The temperature of the collection system was measured as 25.8 °C, at which temperature the saturation vapor pressure of water is 24.9 torr. If a large excess of the HCl solution was used, how many milli-grams of zinc were there in the sample?

     a. 4.60 mg
   ! b. 346 mg
     c. 358 mg
     d. 359 mg
     e. 377 mg

65. How many liters of pure oxygen gas, measured at STP, are required for the complete combustion of 11.2 liters of methane gas, also measured at STP?

     a. 11.2 liters
     b. 16.8 liters
   ! c. 22.4 liters
     d. 32.0 liters
     e. 33.6 liters

66. How many liters of pure oxygen gas, measured at STP, are required for the complete combustion of 16.6 liters of ethylene gas (C₂H₄), also measured at STP?

     a. 16.6 liters
     b. 22.4 liters
     c. 24.9 liters
     d. 33.2 liters
   ! e. 49.8 liters

67. How many liters of pure oxygen gas, measured at 45.2 °C and 104.0 kPa, are required for the complete combustion of 5.60 liters of acetaldehyde gas (C_2H_4O), measured under the same conditions of temperature and pressure?

      a. 4.93 liters
      b. 12.3 liters
  ! c. 14.0 liters
      d. 14.8 liters
      e. 16.8 liters

68. According to the kinetic theory of gases, the average kinetic energy of the gas particles in a gas sample is directly proportional to the

      a. pressure
      b. volume
  ! c. temperature
      d. molar mass
      e. number of moles of gas

69. A gaseous substance diffuses twice as rapidly as sulfur dioxide gas. The gas could be

      a. carbon monoxide
      b. helium
      c. hydrogen
  ! d. methane
      e. oxygen

70. The average speed at which a nitrogen molecule effuses at 30.0 °C is 480 meters per second. The average speed at which a butene molecule (C_4H_8) effuses at this same temperature should then be

      a. 120 m s^{-1}
      b. 170 m s^{-1}
      c. 240 m s^{-1}
  ! d. 339 m s^{-1}
      e. 679 m s^{-1}

71. The average speed at which a methane molecule effuses at 28.5 °C is 631 meters per second. The average speed at which a krypton molecule effuses at this same temperature should therefore be

      a. 121 m s^{-1}
  ! b. 276 m s^{-1}
      c. 315 m s^{-1}
      d. 417 m s^{-1}
      e. 631 m s^{-1}

72. If container "A" is occupied by 1.00 mole of oxygen gas while container "B" is occupied by 20.0 grams of nitrogen gas and both containers are maintained at 0.00 °C and 650 torr then,

    a. container "B" must be larger than container "A"

    b. the average speed of the molecules in container "A" is greater than that of the molecules in container "B"

    c. container "A" must have a volume of 22.4 L

!   d. the average kinetic energy of the molecules in "A" is equal to the average kinetic energy of the molecules in "B"

    e. the number of atoms in container "B" is greater than the number of atoms in container "A"

73. If container "A" is occupied by 1.00 mole of oxygen gas while container "B" is occupied by 20.0 grams of nitrogen gas and both containers are maintained at 0.00 °C and 650 torr then,

    a. container "B" must be larger than container "A"

!   b. the average speed of the molecules in container "B" is greater than that of the molecules in container "A"

    c. container "A" must have a volume of 22.4 L

    d. the average kinetic energy of the molecules in "B" is greater than the average kinetic energy of the molecules in "A"

    e. the number of atoms in container "B" is greater than the number of atoms in container "A"

74. If container "A" is occupied by 1.00 mole of nitrogen gas while container "B" is occupied by 20.0 grams of oxygen gas and both containers are maintained at 0.00 °C and 650 torr then,

    a. container "B" must be larger than container "A"

    b. the average speed of the molecules in container "B" is greater than that of the molecules in container "A"

    c. container "A" must have a volume of 22.4 L

!   d. the average kinetic energy of the molecules in "A" is equal to the average kinetic energy of the molecules in "B"

    e. the number of atoms in container "B" is greater than the number of atoms in container "A"

75. If container "A" is occupied by 1.00 mole of nitrogen gas while container "B" is occupied by 20.0 grams of oxygen gas and both containers are maintained at 0.00 °C and 650 torr then,

    a. container "B" must be larger than container "A"

    b. container "A" must have a volume of 22.4 L

    c. the average kinetic energy of the molecules in "B" is less than the average kinetic energy of the molecules in "A"

    d. the number of atoms in container "B" is greater than the number of atoms in container "A"

!   e. the average speed of the molecules in container "B" is less than that of the molecules in container "A"

76. The average speed at which a methane molecule effuses at 28.5 °C is 631 meters per second. The average speed at which an argon molecule effuses at this same temperature should therefore be

    a. 253 m s^{-1}
    b. 315 m s^{-1}
! c. 400 m s^{-1}
    d. 502 m s^{-1}
    e. 631 m s^{-1}

77. A mixture contains sand and $KClO_3$. The sand is not affected by heating, while the $KClO_3$ is decomposed to KCl and oxygen by heating. A 5.000 g sample, when heated until no further reaction occurred, gave off a gas which occupied a volume of 1.157 liters at 27.2 °C and 748.0 torr pressure. How many grams of sand are there in the mixture?

    a. 0.6125 g
    b. 0.817 g
! c. 1.225 g
    d. 1.838 g
    e. 3.775 g

78. A mixture contains sand and $KClO_3$. The sand is not affected by heating, while the $KClO_3$ is decomposed to KCl and oxygen by heating. A 5.000 g sample, when heated until no further reaction occurred, gave off a gas which occupied a volume of 0.9605 liters at 24.2 °C and 768.0 torr pressure. What is the percent, by weight, of sand in the mixture?

    a. 2.50 %
    b. 12.73 %
    c. 22.50 %
    d. 25.46 %
! e. 35.00 %

79. A gas mixture is 50.00% helium and 50.00% methane, by *volume*. What is the percent, *by weight*, of methane in the mixture?

    a. 19.97 %
    b. 20.05 %
    c. 50.00 %
    d. 75.00 %
! e. 80.03 %

80. The van der Waals equation of state for a real gas is

$$\left(p + \frac{n^2 a}{V^2}\right)\left(\frac{V - nb}{1}\right) = nRT$$

In this equation, the van der Waals constant, a, represents a correction for

     a. a positive deviation in the value of PV from that for an ideal gas due to the finite volume of space occupied by molecules of a real gas
     b. a negative deviation in the value of PV from that for an ideal gas due to the finite volume of space occupied by molecules of a real gas
     c. a positive deviation in the value of PV from that for an ideal gas due to the attractive forces between the molecules of a real gas
!   d. a negative deviation in the value of PV from that for an ideal gas due to the attractive forces between the molecules of a real gas
     e. a positive deviation in the value of PV from that for an ideal gas due to the finite mass of the molecules of a real gas

Fill in the Blanks

81. Air pressure at the top of a very high mountain was measured as 250 mm Hg. How many standard atmospheres is this? _____ (! 0.329 atm)

82. A mercury containing torricelli barometer is located in a controlled atmosphere chamber used for training astronauts. The chamber is maintained at an air pressure of 1.20×10^4 Pa. What height, in mm of mercury, should the mercury containing torricelli barometer in the chamber register? _____ (! 90.0 mm Hg)

83. A mixture of ethylene gas, C_2H_4, and methane is trapped in a container maintained at a pressure of 73.9 kPa and a temperature of 55.2 °C. If the mole fraction of methane in the mixture is 0.240, what is the partial pressure of methane in the mixture? _____ (! 17.7 kPa)

84. A gas sample has a volume of 12.42 liters at STP. How many moles of gas are there in the sample? _____ (! 0.5541 moles)

85. A gas sample has a volume of 1.424 cubic meters at STP. How many moles of gas are there in the sample? _____ (! 63.53 moles)

86. A gas sample occupies volume of 0.01500 cubic meters at a temperature is 30.0 °C and a pressure of 94.85 kPa. How many moles of gas are there in the sample? _____ (! 0.5645 moles)

87. A gas sample weighing 8.280 grams occupies a volume of 4.260 liters at STP. What is the apparent molecular weight of the sample, in grams per mole? _____ (! 43.57 g/mole)

88. A gas sample weighing 6.480 grams occupies a volume of 3.550 liters at STP. What is the apparent molecular weight of the sample, in grams per mole? _____ (! 40.91 g/mole)

89. In a measurement carried out to determine the molecular weight of a gaseous substance the following data was obtained: 6.268 g of the gaseous sample occupied a volume of 0.01148 cubic meters when the temperature was 29.5 °C and the applied pressure was 48.55 kPa. Calculate the molecular weight, in grams per mole, of the gaseous substance, assuming ideal gas behavior. _____ (! 28.30 g mol^{-1})

90. A gas sample containing 0.3520 moles of a compound is trapped in a vessel on a manifold at a temperature of 28.4 °C and a pressure of 91.23 kPa. If the gas behaves as an ideal gas, what is the volume of the vessel, in liters? _____ (! 9.674 liters)

91. Calculate the density of oxygen gas, in g L^{-1} at 1.000 atm and 25.00 °C. _____ (! 1.308 g/liter)

92. A gaseous element has a density of 1.098 g L^{-1} when the temperature is 31.4 °C and the pressure is 744.5 torr. Which element best fits the description? _____ (! nitrogen, MW = 28.01)

93. A gaseous element has a density of 3.195 g L^{-1} when the temperature is 35.8 °C and the pressure is 734.6 torr. Which element best fits the description? _____ (! krypton, MW = 83.80)

94. Results of measurements on a gas to determine its molecular weight gave a value of 1.614 g L^{-1} for the density, at 27.2 °C and 749.4 torr. What is the molecular weight of the gas, in grams per mole? _____ (! 40.34 g mol^{-1})

95. Results of measurements on a gas to determine its molecular weight gave a density of 2.416 kg/m^3, at 22.7 °C and 105.9 kPa. What is the molecular weight of the gas, in grams per mole? _____ (! 56.12 g mol^{-1})

96. How many liters of pure oxygen gas, measured at STP, are required for the complete combustion of 6.01 grams of pentane (C_5H_{12})? _____ (! 14.9 g)

97. How many cubic feet of pure oxygen gas, measured at 35.2 °C and 0.9474 atm, are required for the complete combustion of 11.2 cubic feet of butene gas (C_4H_8), under the same conditions of temperature and pressure? _____ (! 67.2 ft^3).

98. A sample gas mixture occupies a volume of 1.446 liters when the temperature is 155.0 °C and the pressure is 714.8 torr. The mole fraction of methane in this sample is 0.2250. How many methane molecules are there in the sample? _____ (! 5.245 x 10^{21} molecules)

99. The product, $\dfrac{P_{actual}V_{container}}{nRT}$ $(<,>,or =)$ $\dfrac{P_{actual}V_{actual}}{nRT}$ for a real gas. _____ (! >)

100. The product, $\dfrac{P_{actual}V_{container}}{nRT}$ $(<,>,or =)$ $\dfrac{P_{ideal}V_{container}}{nRT}$ for a real gas. _____ (! <)

101. A piece of zinc is allowed to react with an excess quantity of sulfuric acid, and the gas produced is collected in a gas buret by downward displacement of water. If the gas buret has an on-scale capacity of 100 ml (don't go off scale unless you are good at guessing), neglecting the effect of the vapor pressure of water on the system, calculate how many mg of zinc would generate 92.0 ml of the gas at a temperature of 25.0 °C and a pressure of 1.00 atm. _____ (! 246 mg)

True and False

102. Air pressure in a deep mine shaft is the same (numerically equal) to the air pressure at the earth's surface next to the shaft opening. (! F)

103. Gases usually possess negative volumes when the temperature falls below -273.15 K. (! F)

104. A gas behaves as an ideal gas. At a temperature of 25.0 °C and a pressure of 760.0 torr, one mole of the gas occupies a volume of 22.414 liters. (! F)

105. Three 4.625 liter spheres in the same room are filled with gas at the same temperature and pressure. The gas in sphere A is pure hydrogen, the gas in sphere B is pure carbon monoxide, but the gas in sphere C is a *mixture* of hydrogen and carbon monoxide. According to the gas laws, all three spheres contain the same number of atoms. (! T)

106. The density of a pure gaseous substance is inversely related to its temperature and directly related to its molecular weight. (! T)

107. One pascal represents a greater pressure than one torr. (! F)

108. If you have a gas and do some measurements, the number of grams you obtain by weighing divided by the number of moles you calculate from the temperature--pressure--volume measurements will give the molecular weight. This will indicate to you whether it is a pure substance or not. (! F)

109. The value 8.31441 J/K-mole for the gas constant, R, can not be used in calculation involving the ideal gas law. (! F)

110. The torricelli barometer is based on Charles' Law. (! F)

111. Even though the average speed of a carbon monoxide molecule at 27.5°C is greater than that of a sulfur dioxide molecule at the same temperature, the average kinetic energy of the molecules is a sample of carbon monoxide at 27.5 °C is the same as the average kinetic energy of the molecules in a sample of sulfur dioxide gas at the same temperature. (! T)

112. The ratio, pV/nT, for a gaseous substance has a fixed and reproducible value independent of the nature of the gas or the physical conditions provided it is in the gaseous state. (! F)

Critical Thinking—Level 1

113. A gaseous mixture is 20.00 % argon, 25.00 % nitrogen, 30.00 % methane and 25.00 % ethylene, C_2H_4 *by weight*. Calculate the percent, by volume, of methane in the mixture. _____ (! 45.01 %)

114. A gas mixture being used in a diving bell is 28.50% O_2, by weight and the rest is helium. Calculate the density of this mixture at 1.000 atm and 25.00 °C. _____ (! 0.2179—0.2180 g L^{-1})

115. A gas mixture contains 31.50% CO, 22.50% argon and 46.00% oxygen, all by volume. What is the apparent molecular weight (g mol^{-1}) of the gas? _____ (! 32.53 g mol^{-1})

116. A mixture is composed of potassium chlorate, $KClO_3$, potassium chloride, and sand. The $KClO_3$, when heated strongly, decomposes to yield potassium chloride and oxygen gas, while both the potassium chloride and the sand are thermally stable and are not affected by heat. A 2.600 gram sample of the mixture was heated and the gas evolved was collected over water by downward displacement in a large gas collection tube. Heating was continued until no potassium chlorate remained, as evidenced by cessation of the evolution of bubbles of gas in the collection apparatus. The volume of the saturated gas collected was 183.5 ml and the pressure measured 757.5 torr. The temperature of the collection system was measured as 26.9 °C, at which temperature the saturation vapor pressure of water is 26.6 torr. From these data, determine the percent, by weight, of potassium chlorate in the sample. _____ (! 22.52%)

117. In a gas mixture containing oxygen, neon, and argon, the mole fractions are:
$$X_{oxygen} = 0.250 \quad X_{neon} = 0.500 \quad X_{argon} = 0.250$$
If this mixture behaves as an ideal gas, what is the density of this mixture, in g/liter, at 37.0 °C and 765 torr? If someone gave a sample of the mix described above to a student and had them determine the molar mass of the "gas" without telling the student it was a mixture, what value should the student report if the measurement and the calculations were correctly performed? _____ , _____
(! 1.11 g L^{-1}, 28.1 g mol^{-1})

118. A gas mixture contains CH_4, C_2H_4, and C_3H_8. Mole fractions of each component in the mixture are, CH_4: 0.3150; C_2H_4: 0.4750; C_3H_8: 0.2100. Calculate how many liters of O_2, measured at 25.0 °C and 742.5 torr, will be required for the complete combustion of 8.000 liters of the gas mixture, which is also at 25.0 °C and 742.5 torr. _____ (! 24.84 liters)

Critical Thinking—Level 2

119. Air can be purified by the reaction, $MgO(s) + CO_2(g) \rightarrow MgCO_3(s)$. If the air to be recycled has a density of 1.185 g/liter at 25.0°C and 1.000 atm pressure, and contains 0.320% CO_2, by weight, how many cubic meters of air can be purified by 1.000 kg of MgO if the process is conservatively rated as 60.0% efficient? _____ (! 173 m^3)

120. A freshman laboratory room has the general shape of a rectangular box. Its dimensions are: 11.5 meters x 6.50 meters x 3.20 meters. Most young people can detect a concentration of H_2S (the gas with the rotten egg smell) of 0.15 ppb (parts per billion) v/v. At 25.0 °C and 1.0 atm, how many g of thioacetamide(TA, $CH_3C(S)NH_2$) would have to be consumed in the reaction,

$$CH_3C(S)NH_2) + H_2O \xrightarrow{H^+} CH_3C(O)NH_2) + H_2S$$

to produce 500 times as much H_2S in the laboratory room as the threshold quantity? This is only the case if the room is tightly sealed and the fume hoods are shut off. _____ (! 0.055 g)

121. An alloy contains zinc and magnesium as its only components. Both elements react with hydrochloric acid solution to produce hydrogen gas and the chloride salt of the metal cation. An alloy sample weighing 452 milligrams was treated with excess hydrochloric acid solution and the gas evolved was collected over water by downward displacement in a large gas collection tube. The volume of the saturated gas collected was 287.5 ml and the pressure measured 761.5 torr. The temperature of the collection system was measured as 26.9 °C, at which temperature the saturation vapor pressure of water is 26.6 torr. From these data, determine the percent, by weight, of magnesium in the alloy. _____ (! 37.5%)

122. A mixture is composed of potassium chlorate, $KClO_3$, potassium chloride, and sand. The $KClO_3$, when heated strongly, decomposes to yield potassium chloride and oxygen gas, while both the potassium chloride and the sand are thermally stable and are not affected by heat. A 2.600 gram sample of the mixture was heated and the gas evolved was collected over water by downward displacement in a large gas collection tube. Heating was continued until no potassium chlorate remained, as evidenced by cessation of the evolution of bubbles of gas in the collection apparatus. The volume of the saturated gas collected was 183.5 ml and the pressure measured 757.5 torr. The temperature of the collection system was measured as 26.9 °C, at which temperature the saturation vapor pressure of water is 26.6 torr. The solid residue remaining after the heating was treated with water to remove all soluble material, and the soluble material treated with excess silver nitrate solution. The precipitate, silver chloride, when dried was found to have a mass of 3.009 grams. From this data determine the percent by weight of potassium chloride in the original mixture. _____ (! 46.50%)

Chapter 11 Intermolecular Attractions and the Properties of Liquids and Solids

Multiple Choice

1. It is now generally thought that the strongest intermolecular forces between molecules of HCl are

        a. covalent bonds
        b. dipole-dipole interactions
        c. ionic bonds
        d. hydrogen bonds
    !   e. London forces

2. Which one of the following molecules is most polarizable, and subject to significant instantaneous dipole-induced dipole forces?

        a. H_3C—Br
        b. H_3C—Cl
        c. H_3C—F
        d. H_3C—H
    !   e. H_3C—I

3. For a series of small molecules of comparable molecular weight, which one of following choices lists the intermolecular forces in the correct increasing order?

        a. hydrogen bonds < dipole-dipole forces < London forces
        b. dipole-dipole forces < hydrogen bonds < London forces
        c. London forces < hydrogen bonds < dipole-dipole forces
        d. hydrogen bonds < London forces < dipole-dipole forces
    !   e. London forces < dipole-dipole forces < hydrogen bonds

4. What one of the following covalent compounds will not exhibit hydrogen bonding in the liquid state?

    !   a. CH_3—CH_2—Br
        b. CH_3—CH_2—NH_2
        c. CH_3—CH_2—CH_2—OH
        d. CH_3—NH—CH_3
        e. NH_2—O—H

5. Which one of the following covalent compounds will exhibit hydrogen bonding in the liquid state?

        a. CH_2F_2
    !   b. Cl_2NH
        c. H_2PCl
        d. HBr
        e. NCl_3

205

6. Which one of the following covalent compounds will exhibit hydrogen bonding in the liquid state?

    a. CCl_2F_2
    b. H_2PCl
    c. HCl
!   d. NH_2OH
    e. NF_3

7. Which compound is expected to have the strongest intermolecular forces?

    a. CH_3—CH_2—H
!   b. CH_3—CH_2—O—H
    c. CH_3—CH_2—PH_2
    d. CH_3—CH_2—S—H
    e. CH_3—CH_2—Se—H

8. Which compound is expected to have the weakest intermolecular forces?

!   a. CH_3—CH_2—H
    b. CH_3—CH_2—O—H
    c. CH_3—CH_2—PH_2
    d. CH_3—CH_2—S—H
    e. CH_3—CH_2—Se—H

9. Which compound is expected to exhibit hydrogen bonding forces?

    a. CH_3—CH_2—H
!   b. CH_3—CH_2—O—H
    c. CH_3—CH_2—PH_2
    d. CH_3—CH_2—S—H
    e. CH_3—CH_2—Se—H

10. The property that measures or describes the magnitude of resistance to flow in a liquid is called

    a. London forces
    b. malleability
    c. surface tension
    d. vapor pressure
!   e. viscosity

11. Which one of the following is not a property or phenomenon associated with the liquid state?

    a. fluidity
    b. meniscus
!   c. sublimation
    d. surface tension
    e. viscosity

12. The ability of capillary tubing to draw liquids up against the action of gravity is an example of

    a. fluidity
    b. meiosis
!   c. wetting and surface tension
    d. osmosis
    e. viscosity

13. The vapor pressure of a liquid increases with increasing temperature. The temperature at which this vapor pressure is equal to the prevailing outside atmospheric pressure is

!   a. the boiling point
    b. the flash point
    c. the vaporization point
    d. 100 °C
    e. the normal boiling point

14. The vapor pressure of a liquid increases with increasing temperature. The temperature at which this vapor pressure is equal 760 torr or 101,325 Pa is

    a. the boiling point
    b. the flash point
    c. the vaporization point
    d. 100 °C
!   e. the normal boiling point

15. When a liquid undergoes a phase change to a gas, the process is called

    a. condensation
    b. deposition
    c. fusion
    d. sublimation
!   e. vaporization

16. A liquid which is at room temperature is in equilibrium with its vapor, because there is a cover on the container. If the cover is removed, what is the immediate result?

    a. the average kinetic energy increases
    b. the evaporation rate decreases
    c. the evaporation rate increases
!   d. the re-condensation rate decreases
    e. the re-condensation rate increases

17. Which one of the following listed compounds should have the lowest vapor pressure at a given temperature at which all these substances are in the liquid state?

    a. CH_3—CH_2—F
    b. CH_3—CH_2—CH_3
    c. CH_3—CH_2—CH_2—CH_3
! d. CH_3—CH_2—O—H
    e. CH_3—O—CH_3

18. Which one of the following listed compounds should have the highest vapor pressure at a given temperature at which all these substances are in the liquid state?

! a. CH_3—CH_2—H
    b. CH_3—O—CH_3
    c. CH_3—CH_2—CH_2—CH_3
    d. CH_3—CH_2—CH_3
    e. CH_3—CH_2—S—H

19. Which one of the following listed compounds should have the highest vapor pressure at a given temperature?

    a. CH_3—Hg—CH_3
! b. CH_3—O—CH_3
    c. CH_3—S—CH_3
    d. CH_3—Se—CH_3
    e. CH_3—Te—CH_3

20. Which one of the following listed compounds should have the lowest boiling point temperature?

    a. CH_3—Br
    b. CH_3—Cl
    c. CH_3—F
! d. CH_3—H
    e. CH_3—I

21. Which one of the compounds listed below should have the highest boiling point temperature?

    a. CH_3—Br
    b. CH_3—Cl
    c. CH_3—F
    d. CH_3—H
! e. CH_3—I

22. Given the following substances and their normal boiling points, in °C:
    C: 43.8 °C   D: 93.7 °C   M: 56.7 °C   T: 83.5 °C   R: 63.6 °C
    Which set below correctly lists some of these substances in order of **decreasing** vapor pressure at 20 °C?

    ! a. C > R > D
    b. D > T > R
    c. R > M > D
    d. C > D > M
    e. D > R > M

23. Given the following substances and their normal boiling points, in °C:
    C: 43.8 °C   D: 93.7 °C   M: 56.7 °C   T: 83.5 °C   R: 63.6 °C
    Which set below correctly lists some of these substances in order of **increasing** vapor pressure at 20 °C?

    a. C < R < D
    ! b. T < R < C
    c. R < T < D
    d. C < D < M
    e. D < M < R

24. Given the following substances and their normal boiling points, in °C:
    C: 43.8 °C   D: 93.7 °C   M: 56.7 °C   T: 83.5 °C   R: 63.6 °C
    Which set below correctly lists some of these liquids in order of **decreasing** intermolecular forces at 20 °C?

    a. C > R > D
    b. D > C > R
    c. R > T > D
    d. C > D > M
    ! e. D > R > M

25. Given the following substances and their normal boiling points, in °C:
    C: 43.8 °C   D: 93.7 °C   M: 56.7 °C   T: 83.5 °C   R: 63.6 °C
    Which set below correctly lists some of these liquids in order of **increasing** intermolecular forces at 20 °C?

    ! a. C < R < D
    b. D < T < R
    c. R < T < C
    d. C < D < M
    e. D < R < M

26. Which one of the following factors has an effect on the value of the normal boiling point of a liquid?

    a. atmospheric pressure
    b. rate of condensation
    c. rate of evaporation
! d. strength of the intermolecular forces
    e. the external temperature

27. Substance A has a normal fusion point of -25.0 °C, an enthalpy of fusion = 1200 J g^{-1}; specific heats for the solid and the liquid are 3.00 and 6.20 J g^{-1} °C^{-1}, respectively. To change 150 grams of A from a solid at –40.0 °C to a liquid at +70.0 °C

    a. will require 1.52 x 10^5 joules
    b. will require 1.81 x 10^5 joules
    c. will require 2.21 x 10^3 joules
    d. will require 2.29 x 10^5 joules
! e. will require 2.75 x 10^5 joules

28. A substance, A, has a normal fusion point of +25.0 °C, an enthalpy of fusion = 1200 J g^{-1}; specific heats for the solid and the liquid are 3.00 and 6.20 J g^{-1} °C^{-1}, respectively. To change 150 grams of A from a solid at –40.0 °C to a liquid at +70.0 °C

    a. will require 2.27 x 10^5 joules
    b. will require 2.29 x 10^5 joules
! c. will require 2.51 x 10^5 joules
    d. will require 2.75 x 10^5 joules
    e. will require 2.83 x 10^5 joules

29. A substance, B, has a normal boiling point of +89.3 °C, an enthalpy of vaporization = 2600 J g^{-1}; specific heats for the liquid and the gas are 6.20 and 3.20 J g^{-1} °C^{-1}, respectively. To change 150 grams of B from a liquid at –10.0 °C to gas at +129.0 °C

    a. will require 4.83 x 10^5 joules
! b. will require 5.01 x 10^5 joules
    c. will require 5.49 x 10^5 joules
    d. will require 5.58 x 10^5 joules
    e. will require 6.81 x 10^5 joules

30. A substance, C, has a normal boiling point of +89.3 °C, an enthalpy of vaporization = 2600 J g^{-1}; specific heats for the liquid and the gas are 6.20 and 3.20 J g^{-1} °C^{-1}, respectively. To change 150 grams of C from +10.0 °C to gas at +129.0 °C

! a. will require 4.83 x 10^5 joules
    b. will require 5.01 x 10^5 joules
    c. will require 5.49 x 10^5 joules
    d. will require 5.58 x 10^5 joules
    e. will require 6.81 x 10^5 joules

31. For substance A, the melting point is 16.61 °C and the specific heats of the solid and the liquid form are 2.662 and 5.188 J g^{-1} °C^{-1}, respectively. It required 38,600 joules to move 120.0 g of A from 0.00 °C to 32.50 °C.

    a. The enthalpy of fusion is 6.550 J g^{-1}.
    b. The enthalpy of fusion is 151.3 J g^{-1}.
! c. The enthalpy of fusion is 195.0 J g^{-1}.
    d. The enthalpy of fusion is 238.6 J g^{-1}.
    e. The enthalpy of fusion is 321.7 J g^{-1}.

32. If 34.0 g of a solid with a molecular weight of 174.0 g/mole requires 21.3 kJ of heat to melt it, what is the molar enthalpy of fusion, in kJ mol^{-1}?

! a. $(21.3)(174.0/34.0)$ kJmol^{-1}
    b. $(21.3)(174.0)(34.0)$ kJmol^{-1}
    c. $(21.3/174.0)(34.0)$ kJmol^{-1}
    d. $(21.3/174.0)/34.0$ kJmol^{-1}
    e. $(174.0/21.3)/34.0$ kJmol^{-1}

33. A liquid has a normal boiling point of 78.0 °C and its vapor pressure is 400 torr at 50.0 °C. To calculate the molar enthalpy of vaporization, one needs, in addition:

! a. nothing; enough information is given
    b. the molecular weight of the substance
    c. the specific heat of the substance
    d. the vapor pressure at another temperature below the boiling point
    e. the enthalpy of fusion

34. The normal boiling point of acetic acid, $HC_2H_3O_2$, is 117.9 °C, and its molar enthalpy of vaporization is 39,690 J mol^{-1}. What is its vapor pressure, at 100.0 °C?

! a. 423.2 torr
    b. 479.7 torr
    c. 586.6 torr
    d. 616.2 torr
    e. 694.4 torr

35. The normal boiling point of 2,3,4-trimethypentane, C_8H_{18}, is 113.47 °C, and its molar enthalpy of vaporization is 37,600 J mol^{-1}. What is its vapor pressure, at 105.5 °C?

    a. 479.7 torr
    b. 586.6 torr
! c. 594.1 torr
    d. 616.2 torr
    e. 694.4 torr

36. The normal boiling point of 2,2,3-trimethypentane, C_8H_{18}, is 109.84 °C, and its molar enthalpy of vaporization is 37,070 J mol^{-1}. What is its vapor pressure, at 102.5 °C?

    a. 586.6 torr
    b. 594.1 torr
!   c. 605.4 torr
    d. 616.2 torr
    e. 694.4 torr

37. Find the normal boiling point temperature of an isomer of octane, C_8H_{18}, if its enthalpy of vaporization is 38,210 J mol^{-1} and its vapor pressure at 110.0 °C is 638.43 torr and its vapor pressure at 125.0 °C is 1003.1 torr.

    a. 111.52 °C
    b. 113.22 °C
    c. 115.00 °C
!   d. 115.65 °C
    e. 118.30 °C

38. Given the phase changes: condensation, deposition, freezing, fusion, sublimation, vaporization. Which (set) of these phase changes is (are) endothermic?

    a. deposition, condensation, and freezing **only**
    b. fusion **only**
    c. fusion and vaporization **only**
    d. fusion, deposition and sublimation **only**
!   e. sublimation, fusion, and vaporization **only**

39. At 1.0 atm pressure, ice (solid H_2O) floats in water instead of sinking. The reason for this is

!   a. when water freezes, it expands instead of contracting
    b. the fusion process is endothermic, therefore the solid will float
    c. the triple point has a lower temperature than the freezing point for water
    d. the critical temperature has a higher temperature than the normal boiling point
    e. the triple point corresponds to a pressure below 1 standard atmosphere

40. Supercooling is defined as

    a. the extremely rapid cooling of a vapor to form a liquid
    b. the use of extremely cold refrigerants to achieve smaller crystal size when liquids are frozen
    c. the extremely rapid cooling of a liquid to form a softer crystalline solid
!   d. the cooling of a liquid to a temperature below its melting point without solidification
    e. the cooling of a substance to absolute zero

41. As we vary temperatures along isobars (lines of constant pressure) which lie below the triple point on a phase diagram for a substance, which one of the processes below would **never** be observed to occur?

        a. decrease in volume
        b. deposition
        c. expansion
  ! d. fusion
        e. sublimation

42. As we vary temperatures along isobars (lines of constant pressure) which lie above the critical point pressure on a phase diagram for a substance, which one of the processes below would **never** be observed to occur?

  ! a. condensation
        b. deposition
        c. expansion
        d. scattering
        e. sublimation

43. As we vary temperatures along isobars which lie above the critical point pressure on a phase diagram for a substance, which of the processes below would **never** be observed to occur?

        a. deposition
        b. expansion
  ! c. fusion
        d. sublimation

44. The critical temperature of a substance is

  ! a. always higher than the triple point temperature
        b. the temperature below which it cannot exist in the liquid state
        c. the temperature which is always higher than the Kelvin point
        d. the temperature below which it cannot be liquefied by increasing the pressure
        e. the temperature below which it cannot be supercooled

45. Which one of the following noble gas elements will have the lowest critical point temperature?

        a. Ar
  ! b. Ne
        c. Kr
        d. Rn
        e. Xe

46. The triple point of a substance is the temperature and pressure at which

      a. all three physical states cease to exist
!   b. sublimation, fusion, and condensation are taking place simultaneously
      c. the solid will always float on the liquid for all substances
      d. the vapor pressure of the liquid is higher than the vapor pressure of the solid
      e. the vapor pressure of the solid is higher than the vapor pressure of the liquid

Questions 47 through 50 refer to the phase diagram immediately below

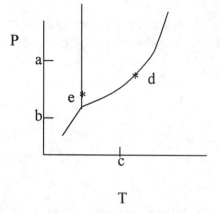

47. At the temperature and pressure of point d, which statement below is true?

      a. The substance will sublime.
      b. There will be an equilibrium between the solid phase and the gaseous phase.
      c. Vaporization and deposition will take place simultaneously.
!   d. Condensation and evaporation will take place simultaneously.
      e. The substance will be a superfluid.

48. At the temperature and pressure of point e, which statement below is true?

      a. The substance will sublime.
      b. There will be an equilibrium between the solid phase and the gaseous phase.
      c. Vaporization and deposition will take place simultaneously.
!   d. Fusion and freezing will take place simultaneously.
      e. Fusion and vaporization will take place simultaneously.

49. Starting at the temperature and pressure of point b, if the temperature is increased, ultimately

!   a. the substance will sublime
      b. the substance will undergo fusion
      c. the substance will undergo deposition
      d. the substance will freeze
      e. the substance will be a superfluid

50. Starting at the temperature and pressure of point c, if the pressure is increased, ultimately

    a. the substance will sublime
    b. the substance will undergo fusion
    c. the substance will undergo deposition
    d. the substance will freeze
!   e. the substance will undergo condensation

51. Which one of the following cannot be liquefied by compression at temperature of 25.0 °C?

!   a. C_2H_4, critical point data: 9.9 °C, 50.5 atm
    b. CH_3Cl, critical point data: 144.0 °C, 66.0 atm
    c. C_2H_2, critical point data: 35.5 °C, 61.6 atm
    d. C_2H_6, critical point data: 32.2 °C, 48.2 atm
    e. SO_2, critical point data: 158.0 °C, 78.0 atm

52. Which one of the following cannot be liquefied by compression at temperature of 25.0 °C?

    a. CH_3Cl, critical point data: 144.0 °C, 66.0 atm
    b. C_2H_2, critical point data: 35.5 °C, 61.6 atm
    c. C_2H_6, critical point data: 32.2 °C, 48.2 atm
!   d. SiF_4, critical point data: -14.1 °C, 36.7 atm
    e. SO_2, critical point data: 158.0 °C, 78.0 atm

53. A technique used for determination of the structure of a crystalline substance and obtaining information from which the unit cell data can be obtained is

    a. magnetic resonance imaging (MRI)
    b. microwave spectroscopy
    c. infrared spectroscopy
    d. ultraviolet laser scattering
!   e. x-ray diffraction

54. How many lattice points does it require to fully define a body centered cubic unit cell?

    a. 2
    b. 4
    c. 8
!   d. 9
    e. 14

55. How many lattice points does it require to fully define a face centered cubic unit cell?

    a. 2
    b. 4
    c. 8
    d. 9
!   e. 14

56. How many atoms are there per unit cell in metallic tungsten if it forms a face centered cubic unit cell?

    a. 2
!   b. 4
    c. 8
    d. 9
    e. 14

57. How many atoms are there per unit cell in metallic lanthanum if it forms a body centered cubic unit cell?

!   a. 2
    b. 4
    c. 8
    d. 9
    e. 14

58. Gold crystallizes in a face centered cubic lattice. How many unit cells are there in a gold sample whose mass is 1.50 grams? The atomic weight of gold is 196.97 g mol^{-1}.

!   a. 1.15×10^{21} unit cells
    b. 2.29×10^{21} unit cells
    c. 3.28×10^{20} unit cells
    d. 3.86×10^{21} unit cells
    e. 9.17×10^{21} unit cells

59. A unit cell of sodium chloride (face centered cubic) was chosen so that the face centered cube was formed from sodium ions. How many chloride ions lie on the faces of this unit cell?

!   a. 0
    b. 4
    c. 6
    d. 8
    e. 12

60. A unit cell of sodium chloride (face centered cubic) was chosen so that the face centered cube was formed from sodium ions. A certain number of sodium ion lattice points and a certain number of chloride ion lattice points are required. How many chloride ion lattice points are there in the unit cell as described above?

    a. 1
    b. 4
    c. 9
    d. 12
!   e. 13

61. A unit cell of sodium chloride (face centered cubic) was chosen so that the face centered cube was formed from sodium ions. What lies in the geometric center of this cube?

      a. a sodium ion
!   b. a chloride ion
      c. neither a sodium ion nor a chloride ion

62. How many grams would a sample of silver which has 5.00×10^{22} unit cells weigh, if it crystallizes in a face centered cubic lattice?

      a. 8.96 g
      b. 14.2 g
!   c. 35.8 g
      d. 71.6 g
      e. 128.8 g

63. Which set of properties below is associated with ionic crystalline substances?

      a. broad range of melting points, soft to hard, conductors in liquid and solid states
!   b. high melting point, brittle, non-conductor
      c. high melting point, hard, not brittle, non-conductor
      d. low melting point, soft, non-conductor
      e. low melting point, soft, conductor in liquid and solid states

64. Which set of properties below is associated with molecular crystalline substances?

      a. broad range of melting points, soft to hard, conductors in liquid and solid states
      b. high melting point, brittle, non-conductor
      c. high melting point, hard, not brittle, non-conductor
!   d. low melting point, soft, non-conductor
      e. low melting point, soft, conductor in liquid and solid states

65. Paradichlorobenzene is a white crystalline solid which is very soft, has a low melting point, and is a non-conductor of electricity. Which category of substance does it most likely fit under?

      a. ionic
!   b. molecular
      c. metallic
      d. covalent (network)
      e. amorphous

66. Which one of the following types of substance shows poorly defined fusion point temperatures?

      a. ionic
      b. molecular
      c. metallic
      d. covalent (network)
!   e. amorphous

67. Which one of the following substances is most likely composed of ions rather than distinct molecules when it is in the solid state?

 ! a. Al_2O_3, m.p. 2000 °C, very hard substance
 b. CrO_3, m.p. 196 °C, very soft substance
 c. Mn_2O_7, m.p. 5.9 °C, soft in solid state
 d. OsO_4, m.p. 40 °C, soft substance
 e. SeO_3, m.p. 118 °C, relatively soft

68. Which one of the following substances is most likely composed of ions rather than distinct molecules when it is in the solid state?

 ! a. $CaCl_2$, m.p. +772 °C
 b. $SnCl_4$, m.p. -33 °C
 c. $SbCl_5$, m.p. +2.8 °C
 d. $TiCl_4$, m.p. -25 °C
 e. VCl_4, m.p. -28 °C

69. A particular solid crystalline substance has a high melting point and is very hard. It is a non-conductor of electricity, even in the molten state. What type of solid is this substance most likely?

 a. an ionic crystal
 b. an amorphous crystal
 c. a molecular crystal
 ! d. a covalent network crystal
 e. a metallic crystal

Fill in the Blanks

70. A solid chemical substance whose triple point pressure is 4.60 atmospheres will normally _____ when it is heated to a sufficiently high temperature in the open laboratory. (! sublime)

71. The basic building block of a crystalline ionic compound is called the _____ (! unit cell)

72. A liquid which is kept in a pressure container at a temperature which is above the critical temperature is called a _____ (! superfluid)

73. The pressure below which the liquid state of matter does not exist regardless of the temperature is described as or called _____ (! the triple point pressure)

74. The temperature above which only a solid state and a non-solid exists for a substance is called _____ (! critical temperature)

75. Solid carbon dioxide never forms a liquid, instead it always sublimes when left out in the open. Why? _____
(! The triple point pressure of carbon dioxide is much greater than 1 atmosphere)

218

76. In terms of kinetic theory, why would the coffee purchased in a container at the fast food takeout shop remain hot much longer than the coffee you pour into your ceramic cup at home?

_____

_____

(! the cover on the fast food variety prevents the most energetic molecules from leaving through evaporation, and the composite material of the cup is a better insulator than a ceramic material)

77. Arrange, in order of increasing intermolecular attractive forces: CCl_4, $GeCl_4$, $SiCl_4$, $SnCl_4$.
_____ (! CCl_4 < $SiCl_4$ < $GeCl_4$ < $SnCl_4$)

78. Arrange, in order of increasing ΔH_{vap}: CBr_4, CCl_4, CF_4, CH_4, CI_4.
_____ (! CH_4 < CF_4 < CCl_4 < CBr_4 < CI_4)

79. Arrange, in order of increasing vapor pressure at 20 °C: CCl_4, $GeCl_4$, $SiCl_4$, $SnCl_4$.
_____ (! $SnCl_4$ < $GeCl_4$ < $SiCl_4$ < CCl_4)

80. Arrange, in order of increasing vapor pressure at 20 °C: CBr_4, CCl_4, CF_4, CH_4, CI_4.
_____ (! CI_4 < CBr_4 < CCl_4 < CF_4 < CH_4)

True and False

81. The change in resistance to flow with temperature that many liquids exhibit is a chemical property which is based on intermolecular attractive forces. (! F)

82. A cylinder contains a liquid which is in equilibrium with its vapor at 45.0 °C. If the piston is moved down to constrict the volume of the cylinder without changing the temperature, the vapor pressure of the liquid will increase. (! F)

83. When a substance decomposes before it vaporizes, it is an indication that the intermolecular bonds between the molecules are stronger than the covalent bonds within the molecule. (!T)

84. Network covalent substances exhibit characteristically high melting points and are usually very hard. (! T)

85. Metallic substances are good conductors of electricity because the do not have a definite structure with unit cells and thus their atoms are free to move around. (! F)

Critical Thinking

86. The potassium ion has a *radius* of 133 picometers, while the bromide ion has a radius of 195 picometers. Potassium bromide crystallizes in the rock salt crystal structure (same as sodium chloride, similar unit cell, etc.). From this data, determine the unit cell volume in cubic picometers.
_____ (! 2.82 x 10^{-28} cubic picometers)

87. Some temperatures (in °C) and the vapor pressure for water are:
    20.0 °C 17.4 torr   25.0 °C 23.8 torr   30.0 °C 31.6 torr   35 °C 42.2 torr
    If the temperature is 35.0 °C and the relative humidity is 50.0% (50.0% of the saturation value), estimate the dew point temperature (temperature below which the moisture would begin to condense).

      a. 20.0 °C
!   b. 22.5 °C
      c. 25.0 °C
      d. 27.5 °C
      e. 30.0 °C

88. Some temperatures (in °C) and the vapor pressure for water are:
    20.0 °C 17.4 torr   25.0 °C 23.8 torr   30.0 °C 31.6 torr   35 °C 42.2 torr
    If the temperature is 35.0 °C and the relative humidity is 50.0% (50.0 % of the saturation value), calculate the actual vapor pressure.

      a. 17.5 torr
!   b. 21.1 torr
      c. 25.0 torr
      d. 27.5 torr
      e. 84.4 torr

89. Some temperatures (in °C) and the vapor pressure for water are:
    20.0 °C 17.4 torr   25.0 °C 23.8 torr   30.0 °C 31.6 torr   35 °C 42.2 torr
    If the temperature is 35.0 °C and the relative humidity is 41.0% (41.1% of the saturation value), estimate the dew point temperature (temperature below which the moisture would begin to condense).

!   a. 20.0 °C
      b. 22.5 °C
      c. 25.0 °C
      d. 27.5 °C
      e. 30.5 °C

90. Brian W. has found an equation which gives the relation between the air pressure at sea level, p_0, and the air pressure, p_1, at a height, h_1, above sea level:

$$h_1 = +4405 \ln \frac{p_0}{p_1}$$

where the height is given in meters. He also hunted and found a value for ΔH_{vap} of water, 41,108 J mol^{-1}. Brian has now challenged two other whiz kids in the class with this problem. The radio announcer has broadcast the weather, and gave the barometric pressure at sea level as 30.18 inches of mercury. What would you calculate is the temperature, in °C, of the boiling water in a teapot at a mountain camp which is 2200 meters (about 7220 feet) above sea level? _____ °C (! 86.7)

91. A metal, element X, crystallizes in a face centered cubic lattice. It has a density of 16.654 g cm^{-3} and the unit cell measured 416 picometers along the edge as determined by crystallographic studies. From this data and Avogadro's number determine the atomic weight of the element. _____
(! 180—181)

Chemicals in Our World 6 Bad Ozone—How Does It Get into Smog?

92. What bad health and/or environmental effect does the presence of ozone in the surface atmosphere produce

       a. attacks iron in hemoglobin and hemoglobin is a critical component of the transport mechanism in respiration
       b. it oxidizes CO_2 to CO_3 which causes respiration problems
       c. it selectively deactivates magnesium ions in chlorophyll molecules which has a severe effect on growth of green plants
  ! d. it attacks molecules with double bonds and many living organisms have critical chemical components which contain double bonds
       e. it reacts with CO_2 and N_2 in the atmosphere to produce deadly cyanide ions which affect hemoglobin and thus affect respiration

93. Oxygen, an abundant component in the surface atmosphere, can be converted to ozone by

       a. direct reaction with O atoms
       b. direct reaction with SO_2 pollutant in the surface atmosphere
       c. direct reaction with NO_2 molecules produced in exhaust emissions from high temperature engines
  ! d. direct reaction with O atoms produced by breakdown of NO_2 molecules produced in turn from exhaust emissions of high temperature engines
       e. reaction with other oxygen molecules in the presence of ultraviolet radiation

94. One reaction which produces $NO_2(g)$ in the upper atmosphere is,
$$N_2(g) + O_2(g) \xrightarrow{hv} N(g) + NO_2(g) \qquad (! F)$$

95. Write equations for the reactions which produce harmful NO_2 present in smog.

_____

$$(! \ N_2 + O_2 \xrightarrow{hightemp, pressure} 2\ NO \qquad 2\ NO + O_2 \longrightarrow 2\ NO_2)$$

221

Chapter 12 Solutions

Multiple Choice

1. Concerning the process of separation of a solid substance into its component units (molecules or ions) where the interparticle distances are large compared to the particle sizes,

    a. the process is exothermic and the potential energy increases
    b. the process is exothermic and the potential energy decreases
    ! c. the process is endothermic and the potential energy increases
    d. the process is endothermic and the potential energy decreases
    e. the process is endothermic and occurs with no change in potential energy

2. Concerning the solvation step of the solution process,

    a. the process is exothermic and the potential energy increases
    ! b. the process is exothermic and the potential energy decreases
    c. the process is endothermic and the potential energy increases
    d. the process is endothermic and the potential energy decreases
    e. the process is endothermic and occurs with no change in potential energy

3. A solution in a beaker has some undissolved solute lying on the bottom of the beaker. If the rate of crystallization exceeds the rate of dissolution of the excess solute, the solution is described as

    a. dilute
    b. concentrated
    c. unsaturated
    d. saturated
    ! e. supersaturated

4. A solution in a beaker has some undissolved solute lying on the bottom of the beaker. If the rate of crystallization is equal to the rate of dissolution of the excess solute, the solution is described as

    a. dilute
    b. concentrated
    c. unsaturated
    ! d. saturated
    e. supersaturated

5. A solution in a beaker has some undissolved solute lying on the bottom of the beaker. If the rate of crystallization is exceeded by the rate of dissolution of the excess solute, the solution is described as

    a. dilute
    b. concentrated
    ! c. unsaturated
    d. saturated
    e. supersaturated

6. A solution is sitting undisturbed on a side shelf in the laboratory. A small crystal of the same solute of which the solution is made was gently dropped into the quiet solution. Suddenly, a mass of crystals formed and settled to the bottom of the container. The solution is, or must have been

    a. dilute
    b. concentrated
    c. unsaturated
    d. saturated
!   e. supersaturated

7. Wax is a solid mixture of hydrocarbon compounds consisting of molecules with long chains of carbon atoms. Which solvent below would you expect to be most capable of dissolving wax by loosening the molecules in the solid and separating them?

    a. CH_3—C—CH_3
            $\|$
            O
    b. CH_3—O—H
    c. CH_3—C—H
           $\|$
           O
    d. H—O—CH_2—CH_2—O—H
!   e. CH_3—CH_2—CH_2—CH_2—CH_2—CH_2—CH_2—CH_3

8. Wax is a solid mixture of hydrocarbon compounds consisting of molecules with long chains of carbon atoms. Which solvent below would you expect to be most capable of dissolving wax by loosening the molecules in the solid and separating them?

    a. H—O—H
    b. CH_3—O—H
    c. CF_3—O—H
    d. H—O—CH_2—CH_2—O—H
!   e. CH_3—CH_2—CH_2—CH_2—CH_2—CH_2—CH_2—CH_3

9. Which one of the following causes an increase in the solubility of a gas in a given solvent in the situation in which the gas does not react with the solvent to form a new substance?

    a. increasing the temperature of the solvent and simultaneously decreasing the partial pressure of the gas in the space above the solvent
!   b. decreasing the temperature of the solvent and simultaneously increasing the partial pressure of the gas in the space above the solvent
    c. increasing the temperature of the solvent and simultaneously increasing the partial pressure of the gas in the space above the solvent
    d. decreasing the temperature of the solvent and simultaneously decreasing the partial pressure of the gas in the space above the solvent
    e. increasing the temperature of the solvent while maintaining the partial pressure of the gas in the space above the solvent at a set value

10. The solubility of O_2 in water is approximately 0.00380 grams per liter of water when the temperature is 25.0 °C and the partial pressure of gaseous oxygen is 760 torr. What should the solubility of oxygen be if the oxygen pressure is readjusted to 1000 torr?

     a. 0.00289 g L^{-1}
!   b. 0.00500 g L^{-1}
     c. 1.49 g L^{-1}
     d. 2.89 x 10^3 g L^{-1}
     e. 3.46 x 10^3 g L^{-1}

11. The solubility of O_2 in water is approximately 0.00380 grams per liter of water when the temperature is 25.0 °C and the partial pressure of gaseous oxygen is 760 torr. The oxygen gas above the water is replaced by air at the same temperature and pressure, in which the mole fraction of oxygen is 0.210. What should the solubility of oxygen in water be under these new conditions?

     a. 1.05 x 10^{-6} g L^{-1}
!   b. 7.98 x 10^{-4} g L^{-1}
     c. 1.33 x 10^{-3} g L^{-1}
     d. 0.606 g L^{-1}
     e. 1.01 g L^{-1}

12. A carbonated beverage is bottled and capped in a CO_2 atmosphere in which the pressure is maintained at 3.750 atm. At this pressure, the solubility of CO_2 in water is 0.65 g CO_2/100 g H_2O. If the bottle is opened, as the gas in the space above the liquid escapes, the partial pressure of the CO_2 falls to 0.30 torr, the value in the surrounding atmosphere of the room. What is the solubility of CO_2 in the beverage at this new pressure?

     a. 5.2 x 10^{-2} g/100 g beverage
     b. 5.0 x 10^{-4} g/100 g beverage
     c. 6.7 x 10^{-5} g/100 g beverage
!   d. 6.8 x 10^{-5} g/100 g beverage
     e. 9.6 x 10^{-4} g/100 g beverage

13. Which one of the following is a concentration unit whose value will be altered if the temperature of an aqueous solution is changed, even if the solution remains unsaturated over the entire temperature range of the investigation?

     a. mole fraction
!   b. molarity
     c. molality
     d. mass fraction
     e. percent by weight

14. A solution is made by mixing 138.2 grams of ethanol, C_2H_6O, (46.069 g mol^{-1}), 103.6 grams of water (18.015 g mol^{-1}), and 80.11 grams of methanol, CH_4O (32.042 g mol^{-1}). What is the mole fraction of methanol in the mixture?

    a. 0.02504
! b. 0.2222
    c. 0.2493
    d. 0.3333
    d. 0.4490

15. Consider a 0.900 M $Al(NO_3)_3$ solution. This solution has a nitrate ion concentration of:

    a. 0.300 M
    b. 0.900 M
! c. 2.70 M
    d. 3.60 M
    e. 8.10 M

16. A solution of potassium nitrate is prepared by mixing 3.50 g of KNO_3 with 12.0 g of water. The percent, by mass, of KNO_3 is

! a. 22.6 %
    b. 23.3 %
    c. 28.0 %
    d. 29.2 %
    e. 41.8 %

17. A solution of sodium nitrite is prepared by mixing 3.25 g of $NaNO_2$ with 12.0 g of water. The percent, by mass, of $NaNO_2$ is

    a. 28.0 %
    b. 23.3 %
    c. 27.0 %
! d. 21.3 %
    e. 37.1 %

18. A solution of sodium hydroxide is prepared by mixing 2.00 g of LiOH with 10.0 g of water. The percent, by mass, of LiOH is

    a. 10.7 %
    b. 12.0 %
! c. 16.7 %
    d. 20.0 %
    e. 80.0 %

19. How many grams of $NaC_2H_3O_2$ (M = 82.034 g mol^{-1}) should be dissolved in 400.0 g of water to prepare a solution which is 11.28 % $NaC_2H_3O_2$ by mass?

      a. 3.146 g
      b. 7.558 g
      c. 21.17 g
!   d. 50.86 g
      e. 127.15 g

20. A glucose solution is prepared by dissolving 5.10 g of glucose, $C_6H_{12}O_6$, in 110.5 g of water. What is the molality of the glucose solution?

      a. 0.283 m
      b. 0.000256 m
      c. 0.245 m
!   d. 0.256 m
      e. 0.351 m

21. A glucose solution is prepared by dissolving 15.2 g of glucose, $C_6H_{12}O_6$, in 250.0 g of water. A student wants to make a sucrose solution ($C_{12}H_{22}O_{11}$) with the same molality. How many grams of sucrose should she use with 150.0 g of water, if that's how much solution she needs to prepare?

      a. 4.80 g
      b. 13.3 g
!   c. 17.3 g
      d. 18.0 g
      e. 48.1 g

22. When 10.0 liters of a saturated aqueous solution of $CaSO_4$ was evaporated to dryness, 8.52 g of the dry, solid calcium sulfate dihydrate ($CaSO_4 \cdot 2H_2O$) was recovered. The density of the solution is 1.000 g mL^{-1} at this dilution. What is the calcium content of the water, in parts per million?

      a. 19.8 ppm
      b. 67.4 ppm
!   c. 198 ppm
      d. 674 ppm
      e. 852 ppm

23. A liter of water is saturated with $PbCl_2$, which is very slightly soluble in water. When 10.0 liters of this solution was evaporated to dryness, 9.90 g of the dry, solid lead (II) chloride was recovered. The density of the solution is 1.000 g mL^{-1} at this dilution. What is the lead content of the water, in parts per million?

      a. 0.990 ppm
      b. 3.56 ppm
      c. 4.78 ppm
!   d. 738 ppm
      e. 990 ppm

24. A water solution which contains magnesium chloride as the only solute measured 232 parts per million (ppm) chloride on an analytical instrument using a specific ion electrode as the sensor unit. When converted to moles per liter, what value would you get for the chloride ion concentration?

      a. 0.00327 molar
! b. 0.00654 molar
      c. 0.01309 molar
      d. 0.0327 molar
      e. 0.654 molar

25. A water solution is saturated with MgC_2O_4 (which is only very slightly soluble in water). When 10.0 liters of this solution was evaporated to dryness, 14.8 g of the dry, solid magnesium oxalate dihydrate ($MgC_2O_4 \cdot 2H_2O$) were recovered as the only residue. The magnesium content can be expressed in parts per million (ppm). What is the magnesium content of the solution? The density of the solution is 1.000 g mL^{-1} at this dilution.

      a. 2.42 ppm
      b. 24.2 ppm
      c. 320 ppm
! d. 242 ppm
      e. 3.20×10^3 ppm

26. A solution of ethylene glycol ($C_2H_6O_2$) in water is 3.981 molar and has a density of 1.0296 g mL^{-1}. Calculate the percent, by weight, of ethylene glycol in the solution.

      a. 3.867 %
      b. 4.099 %
      c. 15.14 %
! d. 24.00 %
      e. 25.45 %

27. A solution of sodium nitrate, $NaNO_3$, in water is 5.181 molar and its density is 1.2680 g mL^{-1}. Calculate the percent, by weight, of sodium nitrate in the solution.

      a. 7.939 %
      b. 17.21 %
      c. 24.47 %
      d. 29.56 %
! e. 34.73 %

28. An aqueous solution of orthophosphoric acid, H_3PO_4, has a measured density of 1.2089 g mL^{-1} and is 5.257 molal. How many moles of H_3PO_4 are there in exactly one liter of this solution?

      a. 0.4261 moles
! b. 4.194 moles
      c. 4.349 moles
      d. 5.152 moles
      e. 6.355 moles

29. An aqueous solution of ethanol, C_2H_5OH, is 19.00% ethanol by mass and has a density of 0.9700 g mL^{-1}. Calculate the molality of the ethanol solution.

    a. 4.000 m
    b. 4.124 m
    c. 4.252 m
! d. 5.092 m
    e. 14.48 m

30. An aqueous solution of ethanol, C_2H_5OH, is 19.00% ethanol by mass and has a density of 0.9700 g mL^{-1}. Calculate the molarity of the ethanol solution.

! a. 4.001 M
    b. 4.124 M
    c. 4.252 M
    d. 5.092 M
    e. 14.48 M

31. An aqueous solution of glycerol, $C_3H_8O_3$, is 48.0% glycerol by mass and has a density of 1.120 g mL^{-1}. Calculate the molarity of the glycerol solution.

    a. 12.2 M
! b. 5.84 M
    c. 0.584 M
    d. 0.521 M
    e. 0.465 M

32. An aqueous solution of glycerol, $C_3H_8O_3$, is 48.0% glycerol by mass and has a density of 1.120 g mL^{-1}. Calculate the molality of the glycerol solution.

    a. 11.2 m
    b. 5.84 m
    c. 0.584 m
    d. 0.521 m
! e. 10.0 m

33. A solution is prepared by mixing 0.3355 moles of $NaNO_3$ (84.995 g mol^{-1}) with 235.0 g of water (18.015 g mol^{-1}). Its density is 1.0733 g mL^{-1}. The solute is completely ionized. What is the percent by weight of $NaNO_3$ in the solution?

    a. 10.16 %
! b. 10.82 %
    c. 11.61 %
    d. 14.19 %
    e. 26.56 %

34. A solution is prepared by mixing 0.3355 moles of $NaNO_3$ (84.995 g mol^{-1}) with 235.0 g of water (18.015 g mol^{-1}). Its density is 1.0733 g mL^{-1}. The solute is completely ionized. What is the molality of the solution?

    a. 0.6474 m
    b. 0.7004 m
    c. 1.320 m
!   d. 1.428 m
    e. 1.545 m

35. A solution is prepared by mixing 0.3355 moles of $NaNO_3$ (84.995 g mol^{-1}) with 235.0 g of water (18.015 g mol^{-1}). Its density is 1.0733 g mL^{-1}. The solute is completely ionized. What is the molarity of the solution?

    a. 1.186 M
    b. 1.273 M
    c. 1.350 M
!   d. 1.366 M
    e. 1.428 M

36. An aqueous solution is prepared by mixing 0.2750 moles of NaOH (40.00 g mol^{-1}) with 189.0 g of water. Its density is 1.065 g mL^{-1}. The solute is completely ionized. What is the percent by weight of NaOH in the solution?

    a. 0.001375 %
!   b. 5.500 %
    c. 5.858 %
    d. 13.75%
    d. 20.00 %

37. An aqueous solution of nitric acid has a density of 1.084 g mL^{-1} and a measured concentration of 2.580 molar. What is the percent by weight of nitric acid in the solution?

    a. 2.380 %
    b. 13.82 %
!   c. 15.00 %
    d. 22.29 %
    e. 44.38 %

38. The vapor pressure of a solution containing a nonvolatile solute is directly proportional to the

!   a. mole fraction of the solvent
    b. mole fraction of the solute
    c. molality of the solvent
    d. molarity of the solvent
    e. osmotic pressure of the solute

39. When a solute such as ammonium sulfate is dissolved in a solvent like water, one of the observed effects is

!   a. a decrease in the vapor pressure of the solvent
   b. an increase in the vapor pressure of the solute
   c. an increase in the melting point of the liquid
   d. a decrease in the boiling point of the liquid
   e. scattering of light beams by the solute particles in the solution

40. At 23.0 °C, the vapor pressure of acetonitrile, CH_3CN, is 81.0 torr while that of acetone, C_3H_6O, is 184.5 torr. What is the vapor pressure of a solution which contains 0.550 moles of acetonitrile and 0.350 moles of acetone? (Assume the mixture behaves as an ideal solution.)

   a. 109 torr
!   b. 121 torr
   c. 130 torr
   d. 144 torr
   e. 239 torr

41. At 28.0 °C, the vapor pressure of *n*-propyl mercaptan, C_3H_7SH, is 175 torr, while that of acetonitrile, CH_3CN, is 102 torr. What is the vapor pressure, at 28.0 °C, of a solution made by mixing 100.0 g of C_3H_7SH and 100.0 g CH_3CN, if Raoult's Law is obeyed?

   a. 35.7 torr
!   b. 128 torr
   c. 139 torr
   d. 149 torr
   e. 277 torr

42. At 28.0 °C, the vapor pressure of *n*-propyl mercaptan, C_3H_7SH, is 175 torr, while that of acetonitrile, CH_3CN, is 102 torr. What is the vapor pressure, at 28.0 °C, of a solution made by mixing 120.0 g of C_3H_7SH and 80.0 g CH_3CN, if Raoult's Law is obeyed?

   a. 131 torr
!   b. 135 torr
   c. 142 torr
   d. 146 torr
   e. 277 torr

43. At 28.0 °C, the vapor pressure of *n*-propyl mercaptan, C_3H_7SH, is 175 torr, while that of acetonitrile, CH_3CN, is 102 torr. What is the vapor pressure, at 28.0 °C, of a solution made by mixing 80.0 g of C_3H_7SH and 120.0 g CH_3CN, if Raoult's Law is obeyed?

!   a. 121 torr
   b. 131 torr
   c. 139 torr
   d. 146 torr
   e. 156 torr

44. At 28.0 °C, the vapor pressure of acetonitrile, CH_3CN, is 102.0 torr while that of acetone, C_3H_6O, is 228.9 torr and for CS_2 the value is 378.7 torr. A three component solution is made by adding 0.300 moles of CH_3CN and 0.400 moles of C_3H_6O to 0.350 moles of CS_2. The mixture behaves as an ideal mixture. What is the vapor pressure of the solution?

    a. 203 torr
! b. 243 torr
    c. 262 torr
    d. 275 torr
    e. 610 torr

45. At 28.0 °C, the vapor pressure of pure carbon disulfide, CS_2, is 378.7 torr, while that of acetone, C_3H_6O, is 228.9 torr. What is the vapor pressure, at 28.0 °C, of a solution made by mixing 0.250 moles of carbon disulfide and 0.450 moles of acetone, if Raoult's Law is obeyed?

    a. 198 torr
    b. 228 torr
! c. 282 torr
    d. 325 torr
    e. 425 torr

46. Which one of the following listed properties of a solution is not a colligative property?

! a. solubility, in grams of solute per 100 grams of solvent
    b. freezing-point depression
    c. boiling point elevation
    d. osmotic pressure
    e. vapor pressure lowering

47. What is the expected freezing point of an aqueous 1.00 molal CsCl solution?

    a. 0.00 °C
    b. -0.93 °C
    c. +1.86 °C
    d. -1.86 °C
! e. -3.72 °C

48. What is the expected freezing point of a solution that contains 25.0 g of fructose, $C_6H_{12}O_6$, in 250.0 g of H_2O? $K_f = 1.86$ °C m^{-1}.

    a. -0.10 °C
    b. +0.10 °C
    c. -0.186 °C
    d. +0.186 °C
! e. -1.03 °C

49. A non-ionic solute with a molecular weight of 50.0 g mol^{-1} is dissolved in 500 g of water and the resulting solution has a boiling point of 101.53 °C. How many grams of solute were in the solution?

      a. 30.0 grams
!   b. 75.0 grams
      c. 100 grams
      d. 125 grams
      e. 150 grams

50. What is the freezing point of an aqueous solution of a nonvolatile solute that has a boiling point of 102.45° C? $K_f = 1.86$ °C m^{-1} and $K_b = 0.51$ °C m^{-1}.

      a. -0.67 °C
      b. -0.99 °C
      c. -2.45 °C
      d. -2.99 °C
!   e. -8.94 °C

51. Pure benzene, C_6H_6, has a molecular weight of 78.114 g mol^{-1}, a density of 0.8765 g mL^{-1}, a freezing point of 5.45 °C, and a boiling point of 80.2 °C. Its freezing point depression and boiling point elevation constants are: $K_f = 5.07$ °C m^{-1}; $K_b = 2.53$ °C m^{-1}. A solution was made by taking 24.20 g of an unknown non-electrolyte and dissolving it in 125.0 g of benzene. The measured freezing point of the solution was -1.65 °C. Calculate the molecular weight of the unknown substance.

!   a. 138 g mol^{-1}
      b. 145 g mol^{-1}
      c. 258 g mol^{-1}
      d. 272 g mol^{-1}
      e. 595 g mol^{-1}

52. Pure cyclohexane, C_6H_{12}, has a molecular weight of 84.161 g mol^{-1}, a density of 0.7785 g mL^{-1}, a freezing point of 6.53 °C, and a boiling point of 80.72 °C. Its freezing point depression and boiling point elevation constants are: $K_f = 20.0$ °C m^{-1}; $K_b = 2.69$ °C m^{-1}. A solution was made by taking 11.40 g of an unknown non-electrolyte and dissolving it in 150.0 g of cyclohexane. The measured freezing point of the solution was -0.78 °C. Calculate the molecular weight of the unknown substance.

      a. 27.8 g mol^{-1}
      b. 46.8 g mol^{-1}
!   c. 208 g mol^{-1}
      d. 264 g mol^{-1}
      e. 1949 g mol^{-1}

53. Pure cyclohexane, C_6H_{12}, has a molecular weight of 84.161 g mol^{-1} and a density of 0.7785 g mL^{-1}, a freezing point of 6.53 °C, and a boiling point of 80.72 °C. Its freezing point depression and boiling point elevation constants are: K_f = 20.0 °C m^{-1}; K_b = 2.69 °C m^{-1}. A solution was made by taking 18.55 g of an unknown non-electrolyte and dissolving it in 150.0 g of cyclohexane. The measured freezing point of the solution was -4.28 °C. Calculate the molecular weight of the unknown substance.

    a. 61.8 g mol^{-1}
    b. 66.8 g mol^{-1}
    ! c. 229 g mol^{-1}
    d. 578 g mol^{-1}
    e. 1099 g mol^{-1}

54. Pure glacial acetic acid, $HC_2H_3O_2$, has a molecular weight of 60.052 g mol^{-1} and a density of 1.0492 g mL^{-1}, a freezing point of 16.62 °C, and a boiling point of 118.3 °C. Its freezing point depression and boiling point elevation constants are: K_f = 3.57 °C m^{-1}; K_b = 3.07 °C m^{-1}. A solution was made by taking 9.755 g of an unknown non-electrolyte and dissolving it in 90.50 g of glacial acetic acid. The measured freezing point of the solution was 8.64 °C. Calculate the molecular weight of the unknown substance.

    a. 24.4 g mol^{-1}
    b. 30.5 g mol^{-1}
    c. 45.3 g mol^{-1}
    ! d. 48.2 g mol^{-1}
    e. 174 g mol^{-1}

55. Pure benzene, C_6H_6, has a molecular weight of 78.114 g mol^{-1}, a density of 0.8765 g mL^{-1}, a freezing point of 5.45 °C, and a boiling point of 80.2 °C. Its freezing point depression and boiling point elevation constants are: K_f = 5.07 °C m^{-1}; K_b = 2.53 °C m^{-1}. A solution was made by taking 10.00 g of an unknown non-electrolyte and dissolving it in 105.0 g of benzene. The measured freezing point of the solution was -1.05 °C. Calculate the molecular weight of the unknown substance

    ! a. 74.3 g mol^{-1}
    b. 82.7 g mol^{-1}
    c. 110 g mol^{-1}
    d. 122 g mol^{-1}
    e. 460 g mol^{-1}

56. An aqueous ethylene glycol solution being considered for use as a radiator coolant is 16.0 % $C_2H_6O_2$ by weight. What would be the expected boiling point of this solution? For water, K_f is 1.86 °C m^{-1} and K_b = 0.51 °C m^{-1}.

    a. 101.3 °C
    ! b. 101.6 °C
    c. 105.1 °C
    d. 106.0 °C
    e. 156.5 °C

57. Pure chloroform, $CHCl_3$, has a molecular weight of 119.38 g mol^{-1}, a density of 1.4980 g mL^{-1}, a freezing point of -63.59 °C and a boiling point of 61.23 °C. Its boiling point elevation constant, K_b, is 3.63 °C m^{-1}. A solution was made by taking 11.25 g of an unknown non-electrolyte and dissolving it in 115.5 g of chloroform. The measured boiling point of the solution was 65.46 °C. Calculate the molecular weight of the unknown substance.

   ! a. 83.6 g mol^{-1}
     b. 113 g mol^{-1}
     c. 114 g mol^{-1}
     d. 120 g mol^{-1}
     e. 158 g mol^{-1}

58. A solution contains 221 g of glycerol ($C_3H_8O_3$) in 600 grams of water. The K_f is 1.86 °C m^{-1} and K_b = 0.51 °C m^{-1}. What should the boiling point of the solution be?

     a. 100.02 °C
     b. 100.73 °C
     c. 101.65 °C
   ! d. 102.04 °C
     e. 103.62 °C

59. A solution, which was made by dissolving 62.07 g of a non-electrolyte in 500 g of water, exhibits a freezing point of -1.86 °C. What is the molecular weight of this nonelectrolyte compound? For water, K_f is 1.86 °C m^{-1} and K_b = 0.51 °C m^{-1}.

     a. 57.7 g mol^{-1}
     b. 62.07 g mol^{-1}
     c. 115 g mol^{-1}
   ! d. 124 g mol^{-1}
     e. 231 g mol^{-1}

60. How many moles of the nonelectrolyte, propylene glycol ($C_3H_8O_2$) should be dissolved in 800.0 g of water to prepare a solution whose freezing point is -3.72 °C? For water, K_f is 1.86 °C m^{-1} and K_b = 0.51 °C m^{-1}.

   ! a. 1.60 moles
     b. 2.00 moles
     c. 2.50 moles
     d. 2.98 moles
     e. 4.65 moles

61. Which one of the following can be applied to calculation of osmotic pressure in solutions?

     a. de Broglie equation
     b. Tyndall factor
     c. Peters equation
     d. van der Waals equation
   ! e. van't Hoff factor

62. How many grams of glycerol ($C_3H_8O_3$, a nonelectrolyte) should be dissolved in 600 g of water to prepare a solution whose freezing point is -4.65 °C? For water, K_f is 1.86 °C m^{-1} and $K_b = 0.51$ °C m^{-1}.

      a. 22.1 grams
      b. 93.6 grams
!   c. 138 grams
      d. 384 grams
      e. 478 grams

63. During osmosis:

!   a. pure solvent diffuses through a membrane but solutes do not
      b. pure solutes diffuse through a membrane but solvent does not
      c. pure solvent moves in one direction through the membrane while the solution moves through the membrane in the other direction
      d. pure solvent moves in one direction through the membrane while the solute moves through the membrane in the other direction
      e. pure solute moves in one direction through the membrane while the solution moves through the membrane in the other direction

64. A very dilute solution contains 116 mg of fructose (M = 180.16 g mol^{-1}) in 1.000 liter of solution. It is placed in a semipermeable membrane bladder, which is then suspended by a support in some pure water. What osmotic pressure would develop across the membrane if the temperature is 26.0 °C?

      a. 3.36 torr
!   b. 12.0 torr
      c. 151 torr
      d. 475 torr
      e. 1217 torr

65. An aqueous solution made by dissolving 168 mg of an unknown compound (a nonelectrolyte) in enough water to make 500.0 mL of solution, registered an osmotic pressure of 5.22 torr when the temperature was 23.5 °C. What is the molecular weight of this unknown compound?

      a. 94.3 g mol^{-1}
      b. 124 g mol^{-1}
      c. 943 g mol^{-1}
!   d. 1.19 x 10^3 g mol^{-1}
      e. 1.57 x 10^3 g mol^{-1}

66. Which one of the following aqueous solutions will have the lowest freezing point temperature?

      a. 0.100 molal NaBr(aq)
      b. 0.100 molal $MgSO_4$(aq)
      c. 0.150 molal $KClO_3$(aq)
!   d. 0.150 molal $MgCl_2$(aq)
      e. 0.250 molal sucrose(aq)

67. A solution is prepared by mixing 0.3355 moles of $NaNO_3$ (84.995 g mol^{-1}) with 235.0 g of water (18.015 g mol^{-1}). Its density is 1.0733 g mL^{-1}. The solute is completely ionized. If $K_f = 1.86$ °C m^{-1}, what is the expected freezing point of the solution?

    a. -2.65 °C
    b. -2.87 °C
! c. -5.31 °C
    d. -5.75 °C
    e. -7.97 °C

68. Which one of the following aqueous solutions will have the highest freezing point temperature?

    a. 0.100 molal $MgBr_2(aq)$
! b. 0.100 molal $MgSO_4(aq)$
    c. 0.150 molal $KClO_3(aq)$
    d. 0.150 molal $MgCl_2(aq)$
    e. 0.250 molal sucrose(aq)

69. Which one of the following aqueous solutions will have the highest boiling point temperature?

    a. 0.100 molal $NiBr_2(aq)$
    b. 0.100 molal $MgSO_4(aq)$
    c. 0.150 molal $NH_4NO_3(aq)$
! d. 0.150 molal $Na_2SO_4(aq)$
    e. 0.250 molal methanol, $CH_3OH(aq)$

70. Which one of the following aqueous solutions will have the lowest boiling point temperature?

    a. 0.100 molal $NiBr_2(aq)$
    b. 0.200 molal $MgSO_4(aq)$
    c. 0.150 molal $NH_4NO_3(aq)$
    d. 0.150 molal $Na_2SO_4(aq)$
! e. 0.250 molal methanol, $CH_3OH(aq)$

71. Which one of the following aqueous solutions has the highest boiling point? $K_f = 0.51$ °C m^{-1}.

    a. 0.200 m $KCl(aq)$
    b. 0.200 m $Na_2SO_4(aq)$
    c. 0.200 m $Ca(NO_3)_2(aq)$
    d. 0.200 m glycerol ($C_3H_8O_3$) (aq)
! e. 0.200 m $Na_3PO_4(aq)$

72. Which one of the following solutions has the highest osmotic pressure at 25 °C?

      a. 0.200 M $(NH_4)_2SO_4$
      b. 0.200 M $KClO_3$
      c. 0.200 M ethanol (C_2H_6O)
      d. 0.200 M NiF_2
  ! e. 0.200 M $Fe(NO_3)_3$

73. Arrange the following aqueous solutions in order of increasing boiling points:
          0.100 m $Mg(NO_3)_2$ 0.200 m ethylene glycol, $C_2H_6O_2$ 0.175 m LiCl.

  ! a. ethylene glycol < $Mg(NO_3)_2$ < LiCl
      b. $Mg(NO_3)_2$ < LiCl < ethylene glycol
      c. ethylene glycol < LiCl < $Mg(NO_3)_2$
      d. LiCl < ethylene glycol < $Mg(NO_3)_2$
      e. $Mg(NO_3)_2$ < ethylene glycol < LiCl

74. A solution was made by mixing 24.40 g of NaCl, 19.77 g of $MgCl_2$, 38.22 g of Na_2SO_4 and 1.665 kg of water. It had a measured density of 1.042 g mL^{-1}. What is the colligative molality (moles of particles per kilogram of solvent) of the solution?

      a. 0.5371 molal
  ! b. 1.360 molal
      c. 1.418 molal
      d. 1.452 molal
      e. 4.297 molal

75. A solution was made by mixing 24.40 g of NaCl, 19.77 g of $MgCl_2$, 38.22 g of Na_2SO_4 and 1.665 kg of water. It had a measured density of 1.042 g mL^{-1}. What is the expected freezing point of the solution?

      a. -1.00 °C
  ! b. -2.53 °C
      c. -2.64 °C
      d. -2.70 °C
      e. -7.99 °C

76. A solution is made by dissolving 0.840 moles of sodium hydroxide in 300.0 g of water. If the i factor for this particular concentration is 1.70, what is the expected freezing point of this solution? K_f = 1.86 °C m^{-1}.

      a. -0.80 °C
      b. -2.66 °C
      c. -3.06 °C
  ! d. -8.85 °C
      e. -9.97 °C

77. 9.92 grams of a compound with a molecular weight of 124.0 grams/mole when dissolved in 150.0 grams of water gave a solution which had a freezing point of -2.69 °C. Calculate the experimental value of the *i* factor.

   a. 1.21
   b. 1.45
   c. 1.54
   d. 2.69
 ! e. 2.71

78. A solution is made by dissolving 1.25 moles of magnesium nitrate in 300.0 g of water. If the *i* factor for this particular concentration is 2.25, what is the expected freezing point of this solution? $K_f = 1.86 °C \, m^{-1}$.

   a. -0.45 °C
   b. -1.57 °C
   c. -3.44 °C
   d. -5.23 °C
 ! e. -17.4 °C

79. An aqueous solution which is 12.00% sodium hydroxide by weight has a freezing point of -10.40 °C. What is the observed value of the *i* factor in this solution? $K_f = 1.86 °C \, m^{-1}$.

   a. 1.59
   b. 1.86
 ! c. 1.64
   d. 1.75
   e. 1.70

80. Which one of the following aqueous solutions has the highest osmotic pressure?

   a. 0.100 molar $Al(NO_3)_3$
 ! b. 0.150 molar $Ba(NO_3)_2$
   c. 0.100 molar $CaCl_2$
   d. 0.150 molar $NaCl$
   e. 0.200 molar NH_3

81. A dilute aqueous solution of $CaCl_2$ contains 0.159 grams of solute per liter of solution. It is fully dissociated. What is the osmotic pressure, in torr, at 20.0 °C?

   a. 1.79 torr
   b. 3.49 torr
   c. 26.2 torr
 ! d. 78.6 torr
   e. 2.65 x 10^3 torr

82. An aqueous solution of calcium chloride contains 32.5 parts per million of calcium and is fully dissociated. What is its osmotic pressure, in torr, at 20.0 °C?

    a. 14.8 torr
    b. 26.2 torr
    c. 29.7 torr
 ! d. 44.5 torr
    e. 97.5 torr

83. A dilute aqueous solution of potassium sulfate contains 8.84 parts per million of sulfur. If the solution is 100% dissociated and the temperature is 25.0 °C, what is the osmotic pressure of the solution, in torr?

    a. 5.1 torr
    b. 10.3 torr
    c. 11.2 torr
 ! d. 15.4 torr
    e. 18.8 torr

84. When a liquid is dispersed in another liquid, the resulting colloid is called a(n)

    a. aerosol
 ! b. emulsion
    c. foam
    d. gel
    e. sol

85. The earliest soaps manufactured contained the functional group

$$-\overset{\displaystyle \|}{\underset{\displaystyle O}{C}}-O^{-}$$

They tend to form soap scums because this functional group is related to the carbonate ion, which forms insoluble compounds with all the ground water ions below except

    a. iron(III)
    b. calcium
 ! c. sodium
    d. magnesium
    e. aluminum

86. The Tyndall effect is not observed in one of the system types below. Which one?

       a. aerosol
       b. emulsion
  ! c. solution
       d. gel
       e. sol

87. The functional group

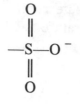

is found in certain

       a. natural soaps
  ! b. synthetic detergents
       c. liquid aerosols
       d. sols
       e. Tyndall emulsions

88. The agitating action of the washing machine and the detergent action of soap on a mixture of automobile engine oil and water produces a(n)

       a. aerosol
  ! b. emulsion
       c. solution
       d. gel
       e. sol

89. A "soap" or detergent can be classified by structure as

       a. an uncharged non-polar molecule
       b. an uncharged polar molecule
       c. an ionic molecule
  ! d. a salt
       e. an uncharged hydrogen bonding molecule

True and False

90. All soaps or detergents which contain a hydrocarbon tail are synthetic in origin. (! F)

91. A soap micelle contains a considerable number of soap units with the hydrophobic tail facing outwards. (! F)

240

92. One driving force toward formation of homogeneous gas mixtures is the spontaneity of random mixing through random motion of small molecules. (!T)

93. Liquids which are mutually miscible possess intermolecular forces of similar type and magnitude. (!T)

94. The process, $McSO_4(s) \rightarrow McSO_4(aq)$, is an endothermic process. The solubility of maclurium sulfate, $McSO_4$, in water should increase as the solvent temperature is increased. (! T)

95. Colligative properties are similar in that they all depend on the concentration of solute particles in the solution. (! T)

Fill in the Blanks

96. An aqueous solution of calcium chloride contains 420 parts per million of calcium. Calculate the molarity of this solution. (Assume the density of so dilute a solute is 1.000 g mL^{-1}) _____ (! 1.05×10^{-2} M)

97. An aqueous solution of calcium hydroxide is 2.00×10^{-2} molar. Calculate how many parts per million of calcium are present in this solution. (Assume the density of so dilute a solution is 1.000 g mL^{-1}) _____ (! 802 ppm)

98. A solution contains 25.50 grams of $NaNO_3$ (M = 84.99 g mol^{-1}) in 250.0 grams of water. Its density is 1.0620 g mL^{-1}. Calculate the molality of the solution. _____ (! 1.200 *m*)

99. What is the mole fraction of ethylene glycol, $C_2H_6O_2$, in an aqueous solution which is 50.0% ethylene glycol by mass? _____ (! 0.225)

100. A solution made by dissolving 16.25 grams of *p*-toluic acid ($C_7H_7CO_2H$, 136.15 g mol^{-1}) in 125.5 mL of benzene (f.p. = 5.45 °C, K_f = 5.07 °C m^{-1} gave a freezing point of 3.00 °C. What is the calculated molecular weight of $C_7H_7CO_2H$ from this data? _____ (! 268 g mol^{-1})

101. A solution made by dissolving 11.65 grams of butyric acid ($C_3H_7CO_2H$), 88.106 g mol^{-1}) in 110.5 mL of benzene (f.p. = 5.45 °C, K_f = 5.07 °C m^{-1}) exhibited a freezing point of 2.40 °C. What is the calculated molecular weight of $C_3H_7CO_2H$ from this data? _____ (! 175 g mol^{-1})

Critical Thinking

102. A very dilute solution contains sodium chloride and magnesium chloride as the only solutes. There are 8.05 parts per million of sodium and 6.08 parts per million of magnesium in the solution. If the solutes are fully dissociated, calculate the osmotic pressure of this solution, in torr, at 25.0 °C. _____ (! 27.0 torr)

103. An aqueous solution of fructose, $C_6H_{12}O_6$, has an osmotic pressure of 10.50 atm at 25.0 °C. What is the boiling point this solution? $K_f = 1.86$ °C m^{-1} and $K_b = 0.51$ °C m^{-1}. The density of the solution is 1.077 g mL^{-1}.

   ! a. 100.22 °C
      b. 100.41 °C
      c. 100.43 °C
      d. 100.52 °C
      e. 100.75 °C

104. A solution was made by mixing 24.40 g of NaCl, 19.77 g of $MgCl_2$, 38.22 g of Na_2SO_4, and 1.665 kg of water. It had a measured density of 1.042 g mL^{-1}. What is the chloride ion concentration, in moles per liter?

      a. 0.2476 molar
      b. 0.3728 molar
      c. 0.3755 molar
   ! d. 0.4966 molar
      e. 0.5002 molar

105. A solution was made by mixing 24.40 g of NaCl, 19.77 g of $MgCl_2$, 38.22 g of Na_2SO_4, and 1.665 kg of water. It had a measured density of 1.042 g mL^{-1}. What is the colligative molarity (moles of particles per liter of solution) of the solution?

      a. 0.5332 molar
      b. 0.5371 molar
   ! c. 1.351 molar
      d. 1.360 molar
      e. 4.266 molar

106. An aqueous solution of glycerol, $C_3H_8O_3$, in which the mole fraction of $C_3H_8O_3$ is 0.07070 was found to have a density of 1.0350 g mL^{-1} by direct measurement. What is the molarity of this solution?

   ! a. 3.147 molar
      b. 4.371 molar
      c. 4.223 molar
      d. 2.938 molar
      e. 3.651 molar

107. A solution is made by dissolving 48.07 g of $MgSO_4 \cdot 7H_2O$ in 250.0 grams of water. What is the expected freezing point of this solution if the i factor is 1.90? $K_f = 1.86$ °C m^{-1}. _____
   (-2.51 °C)

108. A solution is made by mixing acetone and methyl alcohol, whose structures are shown as I and II below. We took 0.250 moles of acetone and 0.750 moles of methyl alcohol. Which statement below describes the most probable state of affairs?

I. CH_3—$\underset{\underset{O}{\|}}{C}$—$CH_3$ II. CH_3—O—H

    a. Since the intermolecular forces for acetone—acetone, methanol—methanol, and acetone—methanol interactions are comparable, the mixture behaves as an ideal solution.

    b. Since the intermolecular forces for acetone—methanol interactions are weaker than either the acetone—acetone or methanol—methanol interactions we should observe a positive deviation from ideal solution behavior.

! c. Since the intermolecular forces for acetone—methanol and methanol—methanol interactions are stronger than the acetone—acetone interactions due to hydrogen bonding, the observed vapor pressure would be smaller than the theoretical vapor pressure and a negative deviation would be observed.

    d. Since the intermolecular forces for methanol—methanol interactions are weaker than either the acetone—acetone or acetone—methanol interactions due to hydrogen bonding, the vapor pressure would be greater than expected and we should observe a positive deviation from ideal solution behavior.

    e. Since the intermolecular forces for methanol—methanol interactions are weaker than either the acetone—acetone or acetone—methanol interactions due to hydrogen bonding, the vapor pressure would be less than expected and we should observe a negative deviation from ideal solution behavior.

243

Multiple Choice

1. Mononitrogen monoxide reacts with bromine gas at elevated temperatures according to the equation,
$$2\ NO(g)\ +\ Br_2(g)\ \rightarrow\ 2\ NOBr(g)$$
    The experimental rate law is rate = $k[NO][Br_2]$. In a certain reaction mixture the rate of formation of $NOBr(g)$ was found to be 4.50×10^{-4} mol L^{-1} s^{-1}. What is the rate of consumption of $Br_2(g)$, also in mol L^{-1} s^{-1}?

    a. 4.50×10^{-4} mol L^{-1} s^{-1}
    ! b. 2.25×10^{-4} mol L^{-1} s^{-1}
    c. 9.00×10^{-4} mol L^{-1} s^{-1}
    d. 2.12×10^{-4} mol L^{-1} s^{-1}
    e. 2.03×10^{-3} mol L^{-1} s^{-1}

2. Cyclobutane, C_4H_8, decomposes as shown: $C_4H_8(g)\ \rightarrow\ 2\ C_2H_4(g)$. In the course of a study of this reaction, the rate of consumption of C_4H_8 at a certain point was 4.50×10^{-4} mol L^{-1} s^{-1}. What is the rate at which $C_2H_4(g)$ is being generated at this point, also in mol L^{-1} s^{-1}?

    a. 4.50×10^{-4} mol L^{-1} s^{-1}
    b. 2.25×10^{-4} mol L^{-1} s^{-1}
    ! c. 9.00×10^{-4} mol L^{-1} s^{-1}
    d. 2.12×10^{-4} mol L^{-1} s^{-1}
    e. 2.03×10^{-3} mol L^{-1} s^{-1}

3. Mononitrogen monoxide reacts with chlorine gas at high temperature according to the equation,
$$2\ NO(g)\ +\ Cl_2(g)\ \rightarrow\ 2\ NOCl(g)$$
    The experimental rate law is rate = $k[NO][Cl_2]$. In a certain reaction mixture the rate of formation of $NOCl(g)$ was found to be 4.50×10^{-4} mol L^{-1} s^{-1}. What is the rate of consumption of $NO(g)$, also in mol L^{-1} s^{-1}?

    ! a. 4.50×10^{-4} mol L^{-1} s^{-1}
    b. 2.25×10^{-4} mol L^{-1} s^{-1}
    c. 9.00×10^{-4} mol L^{-1} s^{-1}
    d. 2.12×10^{-4} mol L^{-1} s^{-1}
    e. 2.03×10^{-3} mol L^{-1} s^{-1}

4. The units in which the rate of a chemical reaction in solution is measured is (could be)

    a. L^2 mol^{-1} s^{-1}
    ! b. mol L^{-1} s^{-1}
    c. s^{-2}
    d. mol s L^{-1}
    e. sec L^{-1} mol^{-1}

5. If a reaction involving a single reactant is first order with a rate constant of 4.50×10^{-2} s^{-1}, how much time is required for 75.0% initial concentration of reactant to be used up?

        a. 16.7 seconds
!   b. 30.8 seconds
        c. 23.1 seconds
        d. 25.3 seconds
        e. 11.6 seconds

6. A reaction has the rate law, rate $= k[A][B]^2$. Which one of the following will cause the greatest increase in the reaction rate?

        a. decreasing the temperature without changing the concentrations
        b. doubling the concentration of B
        c. quadrupling the concentration of A
!   d. tripling the concentration of B
        e. doubling the concentration of A

7. The reaction, $2 NO(g) + O_2(g) \rightarrow 2 NO_2(g)$, was found to be first order in each of the two reactants and second order overall. The rate law should therefore be written as

        a. rate $= k[NO]^2$
!   b. rate $= k([NO][O_2]$
        c. rate $= k[NO_2]^2[NO]^{-2}[O_2]^{-\frac{1}{2}}$
        d. rate $= k[NO]^2[O_2]^2$
        e. rate $= k([NO][O_2])^2$

8. A reaction has the rate law, rate $= k[A][B]^2$. What is the overall order of the reaction?

        a. 2
        b. 4
        c. 1
!   d. 3
        e. 0

9. For the reaction, $2 XO + O_2 \rightarrow 2 XO_2$, some data obtained from measurement of the initial rate of reaction at varying concentrations are given below.

run #	[XO]	[O$_2$]	rate, mmol L^{-1} s^{-1}
1	0.010	0.010	2.5
2	0.010	0.020	5.0
3	0.030	0.020	45.0

The rate law is therefore

!   a. rate $= k[XO]^2[O_2]$
        b. rate $= k[XO][O_2]^2$
        c. rate $= k[XO][O_2]$
        d. rate $= k[XO]^2[O_2]^2$
        e. rate $= k[XO]^2/[O_2]^2$

10. Given this data in a study on how the rate of a reaction was affected by the concentration of the reactants

run #	[A]	[B]	[C]	initial rate, mol L^{-1} hr^{-1}
1	0.200	0.100	0.600	5.0
2	0.200	0.400	0.400	80.0
3	0.600	0.100	0.200	15.0
4	0.200	0.100	0.200	5.0
5	0.200	0.200	0.400	20.0

! a. the rate constant is 2500 L^2 mol^{-2} hr^{-1}
 b. the rate constant is 208 L^2 mol^{-2} hr^{-1}
 c. the rate constant is 139 L^2 mol^{-2} hr^{-1}
 d. the rate constant is 2083 L^2 mol^{-2} hr^{-1}
 e. the rate constant is 6667 L^2 mol^{-2} hr^{-1}

11. For the reaction, 2 M + 2 N $\rightarrow$ 2 P + Q, some studies on how the initial rate of the reaction varied with concentration were carried out. Some data is given below.

run #	[M]	[N]	rate, mol L^{-1} s^{-1}
1	0.100	0.100	0.000230
2	0.100	0.200	0.000920
3	0.200	0.200	0.000920

! a. the rate law is therefore: rate = $k[N]^2$
 b. the rate law is therefore: rate = $k[M][N]^2$
 c. the rate law is therefore: rate = $k[M][N]$
 d. the rate law is therefore: rate = $k[M]^2$
 e. the rate law is therefore: rate = $k[M]^2[N]^2$

12. For the reaction, A + 2B $\rightarrow$ C + 2 D, some initial rate measurements were carried out

run #	[A]	[B]	rate, mol L^{-1} s^{-1}
1	0.100	0.200	0.000360
2	0.200	0.200	0.000720
3	0.100	0.400	0.000720

 a. the rate law is therefore: rate = $k[A][B]^2$
 b. the rate law is therefore: rate = $k[B]$
 c. the rate law is therefore: rate = $k[A]$
! d. the rate law is therefore: rate = $k[A][B]$
 e. the rate law is therefore: rate = $k[A]^2[B]$

13. For the reaction, A + 2 B → C + 2 D, some measurements of the initial rate of reaction at varying concentration gave the following data.

run #	[A]	[B]	rate, mol L^{-1} s^{-1}
1	0.100	0.200	0.000360
2	0.150	0.200	0.000540
3	0.150	0.250	0.001055

    a. The rate law is therefore: rate = $k[A]^2[B]$
    b. The rate law is therefore: rate = $k[A][B]^2$
    c. The rate law is therefore: rate = $k[A]^2[B]^2$
    d. The rate law is therefore: rate = $k[A][B]$
! e. The rate law is therefore: rate = $k[A][B]^3$

14. The reaction, A + 2 B → products, was being studied. The reagents A and B were mixed and the *time interval* until a certain *quantity* of product C accumulated was measured. The data is

run #	[A]	[B]	time, secs
1	0.100	0.140	25
2	0.050	0.140	50
3	0.100	0.070	100

From this data we can conclude that

! a. the reaction is first order with respect to substance A
    b. the reaction is zero order with respect to substance A
    c. the reaction is one-half order with respect to substance A
    d. the reaction is second order with respect to substance A
    e. the reaction is third order with respect to substance B

15. The data below was obtained in a study on how the rate of a reaction was affected by the concentration of the reactants.

run #	[A]	[B]	[C]	rate, mol L^{-1} hr^{-1}
1	0.200	0.100	0.600	5.0
2	0.200	0.400	0.400	80.0
3	0.600	0.100	0.200	15.0
4	0.200	0.100	0.200	5.0
5	0.200	0.200	0.400	20.0

From this data

    a. the order of the reaction with respect to C cannot be determined
    b. the reaction is second order with respect to C
! c. the reaction is zero order with respect to C
    d. the reaction is first order with respect to C
    e. the order of the reaction with respect to C is minus one (Rate prop to 1/[C])

16. Given these data in a study on how the rate of a reaction was affected by the concentration of the reactants,

run #	[A]	[B]	[C]	rate, mol L^{-1} hr^{-1}
1	0.200	0.100	0.600	5.0
2	0.200	0.400	0.400	80.0
3	0.600	0.100	0.200	15.0
4	0.200	0.100	0.200	5.0
5	0.200	0.200	0.400	20.0

From this data

    a. the reaction is zero order with respect to B
    b. the reaction is first order with respect to B
    c. the reaction order for B cannot be determined
! d. the reaction is second order with respect to B
    e. the reaction order for B is minus one (Rate prop to 1/[B])

17. Given these data in a study on how the rate of a reaction was affected by the concentration of the reactants,

run #	[A]	[B]	[C]	rate, mol L^{-1} hr^{-1}
1	0.200	0.100	0.600	5.0
2	0.200	0.400	0.400	80.0
3	0.600	0.100	0.200	15.0
4	0.200	0.100	0.200	5.0
5	0.200	0.200	0.400	20.0

From this data

! a. the reaction is first order with respect to A
    b. the reaction is second order with respect to A
    c. the reaction is zero order with respect to A
    d. the reaction order for A is minus one (Rate proportional to 1/[A])
    e. the reaction order for A cannot be determined from just this data alone

18. Nitric oxide reacts with bromine gas at elevated temperatures according to the equation,
$$2\ NO(g) + Br_2(g) \rightarrow 2\ NOBr(g)$$
The experimental rate law is rate = $k[NO][Br_2]$. In a certain reaction mixture the rate of formation of NOBr(g) was found to be 4.50×10^{-4} mol L^{-1} s^{-1}. Which unit below is the correct unit for the rate constant in this case?

    a. mol L^{-1} s^{-1}
    b. s^{-1}
    c. mol^2 L^{-2} s^{-1}
! d. mol^{-1} L s^{-1}
    e. mol^{-2} L^2 s^{-1}

19. For the reaction, $3 B + C \rightarrow E + 2 F$, some initial rate measurements were carried out and data for three runs are shown below

run #	[B]	[C]	rate, mol L^{-1} s^{-1}
1	0.100	0.250	0.000250
2	0.200	0.250	0.000500
3	0.100	0.500	0.00100

The rate law, therefore, is

    a. rate = $k[B]^3[C]$
    b. rate = $k[B][C]$
    c. rate = $k[B]^2[C]^2$
    d. rate = $k[B]^2[C]$
!   e. rate = $k[B][C]^2$

20. The reaction, $2 A_2X_4(g) \rightarrow 2 A_2X_3(g) + X_2(g)$, the reaction was found to be first order. The rate law, therefore, should be

    a. rate = $k([A_2X_3]^2[X_2])/[A_2X_4]^2$
    b. rate = $k[A_2X_4]^2$
    c. rate = $k([A_2X_3][X_2])/[A_2X_4]$
!   d. rate = $k[A_2X_4]$
    e. rate = $k[A_2X_4]^2/([A_2X_3]^2[X_2])$

21. For a first order reaction with a single reactant, after 230.0 seconds, 10.0% of the reactant remains. The rate constant for the reaction is therefore

    a. 0.000640 s^{-1}
!   b. 0.0100 s^{-1}
    c. 100 s^{-1}
    d. 0.0510 s^{-1}
    e. 0.0915 s^{-1}

22. In a first order reaction with only one reagent, the reaction was started with a concentration of reactant equal to 0.0800 molar. After exactly two hours, the concentration had fallen to 0.0400 molar. What is the molarity after exactly three hours?

    a. 0.0300 M
    b. 0.0267 M
    c. 0.0340 M
!   d. 0.0283 M
    e. 0.0200 M

23. The half life of a chemical reaction was found to be independent of the quantity of material which the researcher employed. The reaction is therefore

    a. possibly first order
! b. definitely first order
    c. zero order
    d. possibly second order
    e. definitely second order

24. The decomposition of an aldehyde solution in carbon tetrachloride is a first order reaction with a rate constant of 1.20×10^{-3} min^{-1}. If we start with [aldehyde] = 0.0500 molar, what will the concentration be 150 minutes later?

    a. 0.00900 M
! b. 0.0418 M
    c. 0.00926 M
    d. 0.00499 M
    e. 0.000333 M

25. The rate constant for a first order decomposition reaction is 0.0111 min^{-1}. What is the half life of the reaction?

    a. 111 min
! b. 62.4 min
    c. 5000 sec
    d. 31.25 min
    e. 27.1 min

26. Given a reaction, $2 A + B \rightarrow P$, for which the observed rate law is rate = k[A]. Which one of the following is true?

    a. [A] = 1/kt
    b. ln[A] = k/t
    c. 1/[A] = kt
! d. the half life is 0.693/k
    e. $e^{[A]}$ = -kt

27. In a first order reaction, what fraction of the material will remain after 4 half lives?

! a. 1/16
    b. 1/8
    c. 1/9
    d. 1/4
    e. 1/3

28. The initial concentration of a reactant in a first order reaction is 0.620 molar. What will be its concentration after 3 half lives?

    a. 0.0865 M
    b. 0.310 M
! c. 0.0775 M
    d. 0.103 M
    e. 0.207 M

29. For the reaction, A $\rightarrow$ B + C, the rate law is k[A]. If it takes 80.0 seconds for 70.0% of a 10.0 gram sample of A to be transformed into products, what is the value of the rate constant?

    a. 0.00450 s^{-1}
    b. 0.0290 s^{-1}
    c. 0.00530 s^{-1}
! d. 0.0150 s^{-1}
    e. 5.40 s^{-1}

30. The reaction of substance A with substance C was carefully studied under conditions where the [C] remained essentially constant. The graphs of [A] *vs* time and that of *ln*[A] *vs* time both gave curves, but the graph of 1/[A] *vs* time gave a straight line.

    a. The reaction is therefore zero order with respect to A.
    b. The reaction is therefore one-half order with respect to A.
    c. The reaction is therefore first order with respect to A.
! d. The reaction is therefore second order with respect to A.
    e. The reaction is therefore third order with respect to A.

31. The reaction of substance A with substance C was carefully studied under conditions where the [C] remained essentially constant. The graph of [A] *vs* time gave a straight line while the graph of *ln*[A] *vs* time and that of 1/[A] *vs* time both gave curves.

! a. The reaction is therefore zero order with respect to A.
    b. The reaction is therefore one-half order with respect to A.
    c. The reaction is therefore first order with respect to A.
    d. The reaction is therefore second order with respect to A.
    e. The reaction is therefore third order with respect to A.

32. A reaction is first order overall. For a given sample, if its initial rate is 0.0200 mol L^{-1} s^{-1} M/sec and 25.0 days later its rate dropped to 6.25 x 10^{-4} mol L^{-1} s^{-1}, what is its half life?

    a. 25.0 days
    b. 50.0 days
    c. 12.5 days
! d. 5.0 days
    e. 37.5 days

33. A first order reaction has a rate constant of 0.00318 min^{-1}. The half life of this reaction is therefore

    a. 94.7 minutes
    ! b. 218 minutes
    c. 31.4 minutes
    d. 5.24 seconds
    e. 68.6 minutes

34. The activation energy for a reaction can be found by finding the slope of a plot of ln(k) vs T^{-1} and

    a. adding this slope to -R
    b. multiplying this slope by 2.303
    c. dividing this slope by -R
    d. multiplying this slope by 2.303R
    ! e. multiplying this slope by -R

35. For a one step reaction, the activation energy for the forward reaction is 40.0 kJ mol^{-1}, and the enthalpy of reaction is -20.0 kJ mol^{-1}. Which statement below is true?

    a. The activation energy of the forward reaction would be affected to a greater extent than the activation energy of the reverse reaction by addition of a catalyst.
    b. The value for the enthalpy of reaction would be decreased by addition of a catalyst.
    c. The reaction is endothermic.
    ! d. The reverse reaction is slower than the forward reaction (smaller rate constant).
    e. The reaction rate would be decreased by an increase in temperature.

36. For a one step reaction, the activation energy for the forward reaction is 40.0 kJ mol^{-1}, and the enthalpy of reaction is -20.0 kJ mol^{-1}. Calculate the activation energy for the reverse reaction.

    ! a. +60.0 kJ mol^{-1}
    b. -20.0 kJ mol^{-1}
    c. -1200 kJ kJ mol^{-1}
    d. +20.0 kJ kJ mol^{-1}
    e. +1200 kJ kJ mol^{-1}

37. For a chemical reaction, the rate constant at 250.0 °C is 0.00383 s^{-1}, and the activation energy is 22.40 kilojoules. Calculate the value of the rate constant at 335.0 °C.

    a. 0.00513 s^{-1}
    b. 0.00946 s^{-1}
    ! c. 0.00787 s^{-1}
    d. 0.0224 s^{-1}
    e. 0.000640 s^{-1}

38. For a chemical reaction, the rate constant at 42.0 °C is 0.00395 s^{-1}, while the rate constant at 67.4 °C is 0.0133 s^{-1}. Calculate the value of the energy of activation, in kilojoules.

    ! a. 42.65
    b. 1.13
    c. 0.421
    d. 18.5
    e. 0.617

39. The rate constant for a certain chemical reaction is 0.00250 L mol^{-1} s^{-1} at 25.0 °C and 0.0125 L mol^{-1} s^{-1} at 50.0 °C. What is the activation energy for the reaction, expressed in kJ?

    a. 25.1 kJ
    ! b. 51.6 kJ
    c. 37.6 kJ
    d. 45.3 kJ
    e. 60.3 kJ

40. For a particular chemical reaction, the rate constant at 30.0 °C is 1.38 x 10^{-4} L mol^{-1} s^{-1}, while the value at 49.0 °C is 1.21 x 10^{-3} L mol^{-1} s^{-1}. What is the activation energy for this reaction?

    ! a. 92.8 kJ
    b. 200 kJ
    c. 40.4 kJ
    d. 343 kJ
    e. 56.4 kJ

41. A chemical reaction has been the subject of intense study, and a rate law, rate = k[A][B]^2, was developed which summarized the mechanistic findings. Which one of the following changes to the system will not cause an increase in the rate constant under any circumstances?

    a. raising the temperature by 25.0 degrees
    b. adding a positive catalyst
    c. adding a negative catalyst
    ! d. doubling the concentration of B
    e. lowering the temperature by 0.500 degrees

42. The equation, A + 2 B → C + D describes an elementary reaction, which takes place in a single step. The rate law must therefore be

    ! a. rate = k[A][B]^2
    b. rate = k([C][D])/([A][B]^2)
    c. rate = k[A]/[C]
    d. rate = k[A]^2
    e. rate = k[A][B]

43. The reaction: $A + 3B \rightarrow D + F$ was studied and the following mechanism was finally determined

$$A + B \rightleftharpoons C \qquad \text{(fast)}$$
$$C + B \rightarrow D + E \qquad \text{(slow)}$$
$$E + B \rightarrow F \qquad \text{(very fast)}$$

The step with largest activation energy is

    a. the first step
! b. the second step
    c. the third step
    d. none of the steps has an activation energy
    e. all of the steps have the same activation energy

44. Suppose the reaction: $A + B \rightarrow D$ followed the mechanism

$$A + B \rightleftharpoons C \quad \text{(fast)}$$
$$C \rightarrow D \qquad \text{(slow)}$$

The rate law for the reaction would be

    a. rate = k[A]
    b. rate = k[A]^2
! c. rate = k[A][B]
    d. rate = k[A][B]/[D]
    e. rate = k[A][B][C]

45. The reaction: $A + 3B \rightarrow D + F$ was studied carefully and the following mechanism was finally determined.

$$A + B \rightleftharpoons C \qquad \text{(fast)}$$
$$C + B \rightarrow D + E \qquad \text{(slow)}$$
$$E + B \rightarrow F \qquad \text{(very fast)}$$

The rate law for the reaction would therefore be

    a. rate = k[A]^2[B]
! b. rate = k[A][B]^2
    c. rate = k[C][B]
    d. rate = k[A][B]^3
    e. rate = k[A][B]

46. Which statement about the slow step in the mechanism for a reaction is true?

    a. It has a rate that is independent of the activation energy for the reaction.
    b. It limits the effectiveness of a catalyst.
 ! c. It controls the rate at which the products are produced.
    d. It almost always involves the breaking of hydrogen bonds.
    e. It determines the value of the standard enthalpy of reaction for the reaction.

47. The decomposition of hydrogen peroxide in solution was studied in laboratory, and the following mechanism proposed based on the experimental data.

$$H_2O_2 + I^- \rightarrow H_2O + IO^- \qquad \text{(slow)}$$
$$H_2O_2 + IO^- \rightarrow H_2O + O_2 + I^- \qquad \text{(fast)}$$

Which one of the following statements is false?

    a. The reaction is first order with respect to H_2O_2.
    b. The reaction is first order with respect to I^-.
    c. I^- is a catalyst.
    d. IO^- is an intermediate.
 ! e. The reaction is first order with respect to IO^-.

48. The reaction, $A + 3B \rightarrow D + F$ was followed and the following mechanism was finally determined.

$$A + B \rightleftharpoons C \qquad \text{(fast)}$$
$$C + B \rightarrow D + E \qquad \text{(slow)}$$
$$E + B \rightarrow F \qquad \text{(very fast)}$$

The species, E, is properly described as

 ! a. an intermediate
    b. a co-factor
    c. a catalyst
    d. an inhibitor
    e. an enzyme

49. A variable which has **no** effect on the rate of a chemical reaction under any circumstances is

    a. energy of activation
    b. catalyst
    c. concentration of the reactants
    d. temperature
 ! e. standard enthalpy of reaction for the system

50. The reaction: $A + 3B \rightarrow D + F$ was studied and the following mechanism was finally determined.

$$A + B \rightleftharpoons C \qquad \text{(fast)}$$
$$C + B \rightarrow D + E \qquad \text{(slow)}$$
$$E + B \rightarrow F \qquad \text{(very fast)}$$

The species, C, is properly described as

    a. a co-factor
    b. an inhibitor
    c. a catalyst
    d. an enzyme
!   e. an intermediate

51. The reaction mechanism that has been proposed for the decomposition of H_2O_2 is

$$H_2O_2 + I^- \rightarrow H_2O + IO^- \qquad \text{(slow)}$$
$$H_2O_2 + IO^- \rightarrow H_2O + O_2 + I^- \qquad \text{(fast)}$$

Which one of the following statements is true?

    a. The reaction is second order with respect to I^-.
    b. I^- is an intermediate.
!   c. The reaction is first order with respect to I^-.
    d. IO^- is a catalyst.
    e. The reaction is zero order with respect to I^-.

52. If the reaction, $H_2(g) + Cl_2(g) \rightarrow 2\,HCl(g)$ occurred in just two steps what would the overall order of the reaction be?

    a. 1
    b. 2
    c. 3
    d. 4
!   e. It is impossible to determine the order based on this limited information.

53. A catalyst alters the rate of a chemical reaction by

!   a. providing an alternate pathway which has a different activation energy
    b. changing the products formed in the reaction
    c. changing the frequency of collisions between molecules
    d. always providing a surface on which molecules react
    e. changing the enthalpy of reaction for the reaction

54. Which one of the following statements concerning the rate of a chemical reaction is *false*?

    ! a. It will be very rapid if the activation energy is large.
    b. It will be slow if one or more of the steps is slow.
    c. It may be inhibited sometimes by certain catalytic agents.
    d. It is dependent on temperature.
    e. It often increases when the concentrations of one of the reactants is increased.

55. Which statement below is true concerning a negative catalyst?

    a. It lowers the energy of activation of the rate determining step.
    b. It increases the enthalpy of reaction.
    c. It never undergoes a chemical change at any time during a chemical reaction.
    d. It blocks the path with the highest energy of activation for the rate determining step.
    ! e. It blocks the path with the lowest energy of activation for the rate determining step.

56. Given the reaction,

$$aA + bB \xrightarrow{\;\;C\;\;} dD + eE$$

where C is a catalyst. If we try, rate = $k[A]^q[B]^r[C]^s$ for a generic rate law statement, which one of the statements below is **false**?

    a. The exponents q, r, and s are often integers.
    b. The exponent s must be determined experimentally.
    ! c. The exponents q and r are equal to the coefficients a and b, respectively.
    d. The overall order of the reaction is q + r + s.
    e. The symbol k represents the rate constant.

57. When a positive catalyst is used in a reaction which of the statements below describes the situation which occurs?

    a. The forward reaction rate is increased while the reverse reaction rate is retarded.
    b. The enthalpy change for the reaction becomes more exothermic.
    ! c. It does not affect the final (equilibrium) amounts of reactants and products.
    d. The activation energy for the reverse reaction is increased.
    e. The activation energy for the forward reaction is not altered.

Fill in the Blanks

58. What effect does a negative catalyst have on the value of the rate constant for a particular reaction? _____ (! It causes the value to decrease)

59. What effect does the magnitude of the standard enthalpy of reaction have on the rate constant for a reaction, if the temperature is kept constant? _____ (! no effect)

60. The decomposition of a compound, A, to form B + C is known to be a first order reaction. If the half life of the reaction is 6.25 minutes at 65 °C, what is the value of the rate constant for the reaction at this temperature? _____ (! 0.1109 min^{-1})

61. The nuclear transmutation reaction, X   products, is a first order reaction. If the half life of X is 188.5 hours, how much would a sample weighing 14.55 mg today weigh at the same time tomorrow? _____ (! 13.32 mg)

62. An isomerization reaction of a substance, A, to form substance B is first order. In a laboratory class one student group found that 28.5% of A had isomerized after a period of 15.0 minutes when the temperature was maintained at 84.5 °C. What is the half life of substance A at that temperature? _____ (! 31.0 minutes)

True and False

63. In order to carry out chemical kinetics studies, all reactants must be in a catalyzed form or else they will not form products at a regular rate. (! F)

64. The half-life of a second order reaction depends on the initial concentration of the reactants. (! T)

65. Nitric oxide reacts with bromine gas at elevated temperatures according to the equation,
$$2 \, NO(g) + Br_2(g) \rightarrow 2 \, NOBr(g).$$
The experimental rate law is rate = $k[NO][Br_2]$. The half life of either of the reactant species is independent of concentration and is equal to $0.693/k$. (! F)

66. The activation energy is equal to the difference between the standard enthalpy of the reactants and the standard enthalpy of the products. (! F)

67. The final step in a multistep reaction mechanism is called the rate determining step. (! F)

68. The final step in a multistep reaction mechanism is called the net reaction step. (! F)

69. If increasing the concentration of a particular reactant in a reaction mixture by a factor of three fails to show any measurable change in the rate of a chemical reaction, the order with respect to the particular reagent is zero. (! T)

70. The activation energy is the energy required to initiate a reaction, and the reaction will continue without further outside assistance. (! F)

71. A catalyst that lowers the activation energy of the forward reaction in a system to one-half its uncatalyzed value will also lower the activation energy of the reverse reaction in the system to one-half its uncatalyzed value. (! F)

Critical Thinking

72. Suppose the reaction, $2A + 2B \rightarrow 2D + F$ followed the mechanism

$$A + B \rightleftharpoons C + D \qquad \text{(fast)}$$
$$A + C \rightarrow E \qquad \text{(slow)}$$
$$E + B \rightarrow D + F \qquad \text{(very fast)}$$

The rate law for the reaction would be

   !   a.   rate $= k[A]^2[B]$
      b.   rate $= k[A][B][C]$
      c.   rate $= k[A][B]$
      d.   rate $= k[A]^2[B]^2$
      e.   rate $= k[A][B]^2$

73. The half-life of a first order chemical reaction is 24.0 minutes at 55.0 °C and 16.4 minutes at 63.5 °C. What will be the half-life, in minutes, at 70.0 °C?_____ (! 12.4 minutes)

74. A nuclear transmutation reaction, $X \longrightarrow$ products, is a first order reaction. The mass of a sample was taken on three successive days at the same time. First day: 14.554 mg. Second day: 14.193 mg. What should the mass be at the same time on the fifth day (Friday)? _____ (! 13.163 mg)

75. The reaction, $2NO_2(g) \longrightarrow 2NO(g) + O_2(g)$, has a rate constant of 0.660 lit mol^{-1} s^{-1} when the temperature is 450 °C. How long, in seconds, would it take for a sample of NO_2 whose concentration is initially 0.355 molar to decrease to 25.0 % of its original concentration at this temperature? _____ (! 12.8 s)

Chemicals in Our World 7 Concerning Pure Water

76. Mercury in the aqueous environment enters it from

         a.   limestone and marble containing some Hg^{2+} ions in place of the Ca^{2+} ions
   !   b.   natural sources and combustion products of coal which contain mercury compounds
         c.   decomposition of algae and mold in sluiceways of industrial plants
         d.   aquatic bacteria
         e.   brain and nerve tissue in aquatic plants and animals

77. What form of mercury binds to proteins in cells rendering them incapable of carrying out their functions and thus posing a threat to humans?

   !   a. CH_3Hg^+
      b. $HgCO_3$
      c. Hg_2CO_3
      d. $Hg(NO_3)_2$
      e.   the elemental state

78. Normally, water from even the purest of natural sources is slightly acidic due to

    a. calcium carbonate which is dissolved in the water
    b. interaction of water with limestone in deep soil and wells
    c. interaction of pure ground water with aluminum containing silicate compounds in the deep water table
! d. carbon dioxide dissolved in rain water as it falls through the air
    e. interaction of the water with marble chips in the deep water table

79. Which statement is true about sulfur dioxide which eventually affects water in the environment?

    a. A principal source is the SO_2 gases trapped in oil wells which is released when oil and natural gas are pumped out.
! b. Sulfur dioxide dissolves in water by forming hydrate, $SO_2 \cdot nH_2O$.
    c. Oxygen and ozone are both capable of converting SO_3 to SO_2.
    d. SO_2 does not contribute to the acidity of rain, because it is a reducing agent.
    e. Less than a few million tons of SO_2 are produced yearly from fossil fuel combustion.

80. All of the following gases are responsible for acid rain except

    a. $CO_2(g)$
    b. $SO_2(g)$
    c. $NO_2(g)$
    d. $SO_3(g)$
! e. $NF_3(g)$

81. A general term which encompasses all methods by which acidic materials enter the surface environment of the earth is

    a. acid rain
! b. acid deposition
    c. acid hydration
    d. acid volatization
    e. acid concentration

82. Mercury persists for a very long time in the aquatic environment because

    a. mercurous chloride (formed with the chloride ion in water) is a very inert substance
    b. mercury is one of the least reactive of the metals
    c. mercury compounds are unpalatable and hence living organisms tend to ignore them as possible food
! d. once there, mercury compounds continue to be recycled into the aquatic environment by natural processes
    e. mercury compounds act as a preservative and this in turn means they will persist within the preserved tissue

Chapter 14 Chemical Equilibrium - General Concepts

Multiple Choice

1. A chemical system is considered to have reached equilibrium when

   a. the frequency of collisions between the reactant molecules is equal to the frequency of collisions between the product molecules
   b. the sum of the concentrations of each of the reactant species is equal to the sum of the concentrations of each of the product species
   c. the activation energy of the forward reaction is equal to the activation energy of the reverse reaction
   ! d. the rate of production of each of the product species is equal to the rate of consumption of each of the product species by the reverse reaction
   e. the rate of production of each of the product species is equal to the rate of consumption of each of the reactant species

2. A chemical system is considered to have reached equilibrium when

   a. the rate of consumption of each of the product species by the reverse reaction is equal to the rate of production of each of the reactant species by the reverse reaction
   b. the sum of the concentrations of each of the reactant species is equal to the sum of the concentrations of each of the product species
   ! c. the rate of production of each of the product species is equal to the rate of consumption of each of the product species by the reverse reaction
   d. the rate of production of each of the product species is equal to the rate of consumption of each of the reactant species by the reverse reaction
   e. the rate of production of each of the product species by the forward reaction is equal to the rate of production of each of the reactant species by the reverse reaction

3. All of the following statements about chemical equilibrium are true except:

   a. At equilibrium, the reactant and the product concentrations show no further change with time.
   ! b. A true chemical equilibrium can only be attained starting from the reactant side of the equation.
   c. At equilibrium, the forward reaction rate equals the reverse reaction rate.
   d. The same equilibrium state can be attained starting either from the reactant or product side of the equation.
   e. At equilibrium, the reactant and product concentrations are constant.

4. In a study of the system, $H_2(g) + I_2(g) \rightleftharpoons 2\ HI(g)$, at 699 K, several different reaction mixes, described below, were prepared, placed in a 5.00 liter container, and allowed to attain equilibrium at 699 K. Despite having different starting compositions, as shown, **four** of the five mixtures had the **identical** composition at equilibrium. Which one of the systems attains a different equilibrium composition than the others?

    a. System 1: 0.100 moles of H_2, 0.000 moles of I_2 and 0.600 moles of HI
    b. System 2: 0.175 moles of H_2, 0.075 moles of I_2 and 0.450 moles of HI
    c. System 3: 0.400 moles of H_2, 0.300 moles of I_2 and 0.000 moles of HI
    ! d. System 4: 0.150 moles of H_2, 0.100 moles of I_2 and 0.500 moles of HI
    e. System 5: 0.300 moles of H_2, 0.200 moles of I_2 and 0.200 moles of HI

5. In a study of the system, $Cl_2(g) + Br_2(g) \rightleftharpoons 2\ BrCl(g)$, at 350 K, several different reaction mixes, described below, were prepared, placed in a 5.00 liter container, and allowed to attain equilibrium at 350 K. Despite having different starting compositions, as shown, **four** of the five mixtures had the **identical** composition at equilibrium. Which one of the systems attains a different equilibrium composition than the others?

    a. System 1: 0.100 moles of Cl_2, 0.000 moles of Br_2 and 0.600 moles of BrCl
    b. System 2: 0.250 moles of Cl_2, 0.150 moles of Br_2 and 0.300 moles of BrCl
    c. System 3: 0.400 moles of Cl_2, 0.300 moles of Br_2 and 0.000 moles of BrCl
    ! d. System 4: 0.300 moles of Cl_2, 0.250 moles of Br_2 and 0.250 moles of BrCl
    e. System 5: 0.350 moles of Cl_2, 0.250 moles of Br_2 and 0.100 moles of BrCl

6. In a study of the system, $N_2O_4(g) \rightleftharpoons 2\ NO_2(g)$, at 585 K, several different reaction mixes, described below, were prepared, placed in a 5.00 liter container, and allowed to attain equilibrium at 480 K. Despite having different starting compositions, as shown, **four** of the five mixtures had the **identical** composition at equilibrium. Which one of the systems attains a different equilibrium composition than the others?

    a. System 1: 0.400 moles of N_2O_4 and 0.800 moles of NO_2
    b. System 2: 0.300 moles of N_2O_4 and 1.000 moles of NO_2
    c. System 3: 0.800 moles of N_2O_4 and 0.000 moles of NO_2
    d. System 4: 0.600 moles of N_2O_4 and 0.400 moles of NO_2
    ! e. System 5: 0.400 moles of N_2O_4 and 0.700 moles of NO_2

7. In a study of the system, $Cl_2(g) + 2\ NO(g) \rightleftharpoons 2\ NOCl(g)$, at 425 K, several different reaction mixes, described below, were prepared, placed in a 5.00 liter container, and allowed to attain equilibrium at 425 K. Despite having different starting compositions, as shown, **four** of the five mixtures had the **identical** composition at equilibrium. Which one of the systems attains a different equilibrium composition than the others?

    a. System 1: 0.100 moles of Cl_2, 0.000 moles of NO and 0.600 moles of NOCl
    b. System 2: 0.250 moles of Cl_2, 0.300 moles of NO and 0.300 moles of NOCl
    c. System 3: 0.400 moles of Cl_2, 0.600 moles of NO and 0.000 moles of NOCl
    ! d. System 4: 0.300 moles of Cl_2, 0.250 moles of NO and 0.250 moles of NOCl
    e. System 5: 0.350 moles of Cl_2, 0.500 moles of NO and 0.100 moles of NOCl

8. Given the pair of reactions shown with the equilibrium constants,

$$PCl_3(g) + Cl_2(g) \rightleftharpoons PCl_5(g) \qquad K_1$$

$$2 NO(g) + Cl_2(g) \rightleftharpoons 2 NOCl(g) \qquad K_2$$

What is the equilibrium constant for the reaction,

$$PCl_5(g + 2 NO(g) \rightleftharpoons PCl_3(g) + 2 NOCl(g)$$

    a. $K_1 K_2$
! b. K_2/K_1
    c. K_1/K_2
    d. $(K_1 K_2)^{-1}$
    e. K_2-K_1

9. Given the pair of reactions shown with the equilibrium constants,

$$PCl_3(g) + \frac{1}{2} O_2(g) \rightleftharpoons POCl_3(g) \qquad K_1$$

$$NO(g) + \frac{1}{2} O_2(g) \rightleftharpoons NO_2(g) \qquad K_2$$

What is the equilibrium constant for the reaction,

$$PCl_3(g + NO_2(g) \rightleftharpoons POCl_3(g) + NO(g)$$

    a. $K_1 K_2$
    b. K_2/K_1
! c. K_1/K_2
    d. $(K_1 K_2)^{-1}$
    e. K_2-K_1

10. The equilibrium constant for the reaction, $H_2(g) + I_2(g) \rightleftharpoons 2 HI(g)$ is 54.9 at 699.0 K. What is the equilibrium constant for $4 HI(g) \rightleftharpoons 2 H_2(g) + 2 I_2(g)$ under the same conditions?

    a. 109.8
    b. 0.00911
! c. 0.000332
    d. -109.8
    e. 0.0182

11. Using this data,

$$2 NO(g) + Cl_2(g) \rightleftharpoons 2 NOCl(g) \qquad K_c = 3.20 \times 10^{-3}$$

$$2 NO_2(g) \rightleftharpoons 2 NO(g) + O_2(g) \qquad K_c = 15.5$$

calculate a value for K_c for the reaction,

$$NOCl(g) + \frac{1}{2} O_2(g) \rightleftharpoons NO_2(g) + \frac{1}{2} Cl_2(g)$$

    a. 2.06×10^{-4}
    b. 4.84×10^{-3}
    c. 0.223
! d. 4.49
    e. 20.2

12. For the chemical reaction,

$$N_2(g) + 3 H_2(g) \rightleftharpoons 2 NH_3(g),$$

$K_c = 4.2 \times 10^2$ at some temperature which we call T_1. 4.00 moles of NH_3 were placed in a 50.0 liter container and it was brought up to T_1 and allowed to come to equilibrium. Which situation below is true, at equilibrium?

    a. $[NH_3] = 3 \times [H_2]$
! b. $[NH_3] > [H_2]$
    c. $[H_2] > [NH_3]$
    d. $[NH_3] = [H_2]$
    e. $[N_2] = [NH_3]$

13. The equilibrium constant for the reaction, $R_2 \rightleftharpoons D_2$ is 6.8×10^{-10}. Which one of the following statements is true?

    a. The equilibrium concentration of D_2 is always greater than that of R_2.
! b. The equilibrium concentration of R_2 is always greater than that of D_2.
    c. Adding more R_2 will increase the value of the equilibrium constant.
    d. Adding a catalyst will increase the equilibrium concentration of D_2.
    e. Adding a catalyst will increase the value of the equilibrium constant.

14. For the reaction, $2 SO_2(g) + O_2(g) \rightleftharpoons 2 SO_3(g)$, at 900.0 K the equilibrium constant, K_c, has a value of 13.0. Calculate the value of K_p at the same temperature.

    a. 97.3×10^3 atm^{-1}
! b. 0.176 atm^{-1}
    c. 960 atm^{-1}
    d. 0.00174 atm^{-1}
    e. 0.077 atm^{-1}

15. A student is preparing a study of the reaction, $2 CO_2(g) \rightleftharpoons 2 CO(g) + O_2(g)$, for which $K_c = 26.2$ at 827 °C. What is the value of K_p at that same temperature?

    a. 2.90×10^{-1}
    b. 3.86×10^{-1}
    c. $1.78 \times 10^{+3}$
! d. $2.36 \times 10^{+3}$
    e. $2.40 \times 10^{+5}$

16. The concentration of a pure solid or a pure liquid is left out of the expression for the equilibrium constant because

    a. solids and liquids drive the reaction in an undetermined fashion.
    b. solids and liquids do not react.
    c. their concentrations cannot be determined.
    d. solids and liquids react too slowly.
! e. their activity is constant and independent of the amount of solid or liquid present.

17. The equilibrium constant, K_c, for the system, $CaO(s) + CO_2(g) \rightleftharpoons CaCO_3(s)$, is

    a. $K_c = [CO_2]$
    b. $K_c = [CaCO_3]/([CaO] \times [CO_2])$
    ! c. $K_c = 1/[CO_2]$
    d. $K_c = [CaCO_3]/[CaO]$
    e. $K_c = ([CaO] \times [CO_2])/[CaCO_3]$

18. Given the reaction, $2 NO(g) + O_2(g) \rightleftharpoons 2 NO_2(g)$, for which the enthalpy of reaction is -118.9 kJ. Which one of the following will cause an increase in the equilibrium concentration of NO in a closed reaction chamber?

    a. adding some more $O_2(g)$ through an injection nozzle
    ! b. increasing the temperature of the system
    c. removing the NO_2 from the system by absorbing it in a species specific zeolite
    d. increasing the pressure of the system while temperature is kept constant
    e. adding a catalyst

19. For a specific reaction, which of the following statements can be made about the equilibrium constant?

    ! a. it can change with temperature
    b. it may be changed by addition of a catalyst
    c. it increases if the concentration of one of the products is increased
    d. it increases if the concentration of one of the products is decreased
    e. it always remains the same

20. For the reaction, $2 SO_2(g) + O_2(g) \rightleftharpoons 2 SO_3(g)$, at 450.0 K the equilibrium constant, K_c, has a value of 4.62. A system was charged to give these initial concentrations, $[SO_3] = 0.254$ M $[O_2] = 0.00855$ M, $[SO_2] = 0.500$ M. In which direction will it go?

    a. to the right or the left depending on the pressure
    ! b. to the left
    c. it will remain at the same concentrations
    d to the right

21. For the reaction, $2 SO_2(g) + O_2(g) \rightleftharpoons 2 SO_3(g)$, at 450.0 K the equilibrium constant, K_c, has a value of 4.62 M. A system was charged to give these initial concentrations: $[SO_3] = 0.500$ M, $[O_2] = 0.00855$ M, $[SO_2] = 0.254$ M. In which direction will it go?

    a. to the right
    b. it will remain at the same concentrations
    ! c. to the left
    d. to the right or the left depending on the pressure

22. For the reaction, $2 SO_2(g) + O_2(g) \rightleftharpoons 2 SO_3(g)$, at 450.0 K the equilibrium constant, K_c, has a value of 4.62. A system was charged to give these initial concentrations: $[SO_3] = 0.0254$, M $[O_2] = 0.00855$ M , $[SO_2] = 0.500$ M. In which direction will it go?

    ! a. to the right
       b. to the left
       c. to the right or the left depending on the pressure
       d. it will remain at the same concentrations

23. The reaction, $2 SO_3(g) \rightleftharpoons 2 SO_2(g) + O_2(g)$ is endothermic. Predict what will happen if the temperature is increased.

       a. K_c remains the same
       b. K_c decreases
       c. the pressure decreases
       d. more $SO_3(g)$ is produced
    ! e. K_c increases

24. Consider the following system, which is at equilibrium,
$$CO(g) + 3 H_2(g) \rightleftharpoons CH_4(g) + H_2O(g).$$
The result of removing some $CH_4(g)$ and $H_2O(g)$ from the system is that

    ! a. more $CH_4(g)$ and $H_2O(g)$ are produced to replace that which is removed
       b. K_c decreases
       c. more $CO(g)$ is produced
       d. more $H_2O(g)$ is consumed to restore the equilibrium
       e. more CH_4 is consumed to restore the equilibrium

25. Consider the following system, which is at equilibrium,
$$3C(s) + 3 H_2(g) \rightleftharpoons CH_4(g) + C_2H_2(g)$$
The result of removing some $CH_4(g)$ and $C_2H_2(g)$ from the system is that

       a. no further change occurs
       b. K_c increases
       c. more $C(s)$ is produced
       d. more $C_2H_2(g)$ is consumed to restore the equilibrium
    ! e. more $CH_4(g)$ and $C_2H_2(g)$ are produced to replace that which is removed

26. Consider the following system, which is at equilibrium,
$$3 C(s) + 3 H_2(g) \rightleftharpoons CH_4(g) + C_2H_2(g)$$
The result of removing some $C(s)$ from the system will be:

       a. K_c increases
       b. more $C(s)$ is produced
    ! c. no further change occurs
       d. more $CH_4(g)$ and $C_2H_2(g)$ are produced to restore the equilibrium
       e. more $C_2H_2(g)$ is consumed to restore the equilibrium

27. The system, $2 H_2O(g) + 2 Cl_2(g) \rightleftharpoons 4 HCl(g) + O_2(g)$, has a value of 8.00 atm for constant, K_p. Initially, the partial pressures of H_2O and Cl_2 are set at 0.100 atm, while those of HCl and O_2 are set at 0.250 atm. The system is allowed to come to equilibrium. Which statement below is true?

    a. $Q_p > K_p$ and the reaction proceeds to the right to reach equilibrium
    b. $Q_p < K_p$ and the reaction proceeds to the left to reach equilibrium
    c. The reaction system is already at equilibrium
!   d. $Q_p > K_p$ and the reaction proceeds to the left to reach equilibrium
    e. $Q_p < K_p$ and the reaction proceeds to the right to reach equilibrium

28. The system, $H_2(g) + X_2(g) \rightleftharpoons 2 HX(g)$ has a value of 24.4 for the constant, K_c. A system being tried in a 3.00 liter reactor was charged with 0.150 moles of H_2, 0.150 moles of X_2, and 0.600 moles of HX. The catalyst was introduced using a remote unit, and the system was allowed to come to equilibrium. Which statement below describes the situation?

!   a. The reaction goes to the right, $Q < K$.
    b. The reaction goes to the left, $Q < K$.
    c. The reaction goes to the right, $Q > K$.
    d. The reaction goes to the left, $Q > K$.
    e. It is not possible to predict in which direction the system will travel to arrive at equilibrium.

29. $NH_2CO_2NH_4(s)$ when heated to 450 K undergoes the following reaction to produce a system which reaches equilibrium:

$$NH_2CO_2NH_4(s) \rightleftharpoons 2 NH_3(g) + CO_2(g)$$

The total pressure in the closed container under these condition is found to be 0.843 atm. Calculate a value for the equilibrium constant, K_p.

    a. 0.00701 atm^3
!   b. 0.0888 atm^3
    c. 0.843 atm^3
    d. 0.599 atm^3
    c. 0.222 atm^3

30. For the reaction system , $2 SO_2(g) + O_2(g) \rightleftharpoons 2 SO_3(g)$, the equilibrium concentrations are:
              SO_3: 0.120M SO_2: 0.860M O_2: 0.330M
Calculate the value of K_c for this reaction.

    a. 1.31
    b. 2.51
    c. 0.423
    d. 0.872
!   e. 0.0590

31. For the reaction system, $H_2(g) + X_2(g) \rightleftharpoons 2\,HX(g)$, $K_c = 24.4$ at 300 K. A system made up from these components which is at equilibrium contains 0.150 moles of H_2 and 0.600 moles of HX in a 3.00 liter container. Calculate the number of moles of $X_2(g)$ present at equilibrium.

   ! a. 0.0984 mol
     b. 0.164 mol
     c. 0.197 mol
     d. 0.324 mol
     e. 0.393 mol

32. For the reaction system, $H_2(g) + X_2(g) \rightleftharpoons 2\,HX(g)$, $K_c = 24.4$ at 300 K. A system made up from these components which is at equilibrium contains 0.200 moles of X_2 and 0.600 moles of HX in a 4.00 liter container. Calculate the number of moles of $H_2(g)$ present at equilibrium.

     a. 0.059 mol
   ! b. 0.074 mol
     c. 0.123 mol
     d. 0.148 mol
     e. 0.295 mol

33. At 1500 °C the system, $2\,NO(g) \rightleftharpoons N_2(g) + O_2(g)$, was allowed to come to equilibrium. The equilibrium concentrations were: $NO(g) = 0.00035$ M, $N_2(g) = 0.040$ M, and $O_2(g) = 0.040$ M. What is the value of K_c for the system at this temperature?

     a. 1.5×10^{-6}
     b. 7.7×10^{-5}
     c. 2.2×10^{-1}
     d. 4.6
   ! e. 1.3×10^{4}

34. For the reaction sytem, $2\,SO_2(g) + O_2(g) \rightleftharpoons 2\,SO_3(g)$, K_c has a value of 4.62 at 450.0 K. A system, at equilibrium has the following concentrations: $[SO_3] = 0.254$ M, $[O_2] = 0.00855$ M. What is the equilibrium concentration of SO_2?

   ! a. 1.28 M
     b. 0.216 M
     c. 0.465 M
     d. 6.43 M
     e. 41.3 M

35. For the reaction, $H_2(g) + I_2(g) \rightleftharpoons 2\,HI(g)$, $K_c = 54.9$ at 699.0 K. A system, at equilibrium contains 2.50 moles of HI and 2.12 moles of I_2 in a 5.00 liter vessel. How many moles of H_2 should there be in the container?

> ! a. 0.0537 moles
>   b. 0.380 moles
>   c. 0.0215 moles
>   d. 0.0107 moles
>   e. 2.12 moles

36. The system, $2\,NO(g) \rightleftharpoons N_2(g) + O_2(g)$ was allowed to come to equilibrium at 1500 °C. The equilibrium concentrations were: $NO(g) = 0.00035$ M, $N_2(g) = 0.040$ M, and $O_2(g) = 0.040$ M. What is the value of K_p for the system at this temperature?

>   a. 2.2×10^{-1}
> ! b. $1.3 \times 10^{+4}$
>   c. $1.9 \times 10^{+6}$
>   d. 7.7
>   e. 1.5

37. For the reaction, $2\,BrCl(g) \rightleftharpoons Cl_2(g) + Br_2(g)$, K_p has a value of 0.140 at 350 K. In a container housing this system, the $[Cl_2(g)] = [Br_2(g)] = 0.0200$ M at equilibrium. What is the value of p_{BrCl}?

>   a. 2.86×10^{-3} atm
>   b. 5.35×10^{-2} atm
>   c. 8.21×10^{-2} atm
>   d. 1.25×10^{-5} atm
> ! e. 1.54 atm

38. A study of the system, $4\,NH_3(g) + 7\,O_2(g) \rightleftharpoons 2\,N_2O_4(g) + 6\,H_2O(g)$, was carried out. A system was prepared with $[NH_3] = [O_2] = 3.60$ M as the only components initially. At equilibrium, $[N_2O_4]$ is 0.60 M. Calculate the equilibrium concentration of NH_3.

>   a. 3.00 M
>   b. 2.10 M
>   c. 3.30 M
>   d. 1.80 M
> ! e. 2.40 M

39. A study of the system, $4 NH_3(g) + 7 O_2(g) \rightleftharpoons 2 N_2O_4(g) + 6 H_2O(g)$, was carried out. A system was prepared with $[NH_3] = [O_2] = 3.60$ M as the only components initially. At equilibrium, $[N_2O_4]$ is 0.60 M. Calculate the equilibrium concentration of O_2.

     a, 3.00 M
     b. 2.40 M
 ! c. 1.50 M
     d. 2.10 M
     e. 3.30 M

40. A study of the system, $4 NH_3(g) + 7 O_2(g) \rightleftharpoons 2 N_2O_4(g) + 6 H_2O(g)$, was carried out. A system was prepared with $[NH_3] = [O_2] = 3.60$ M as the only components initially. At equilibrium, $[N_2O_4]$ is 0.60 M. Calculate the value of the equilibrium constant, K_c, for the reaction.

     a. 8.10
     b. 0.00000930
     c. 0.300
 ! d. 0.0216
     e. 3.33

41. A study of the system, $4 NH_3(g) + 7 O_2(g) \rightleftharpoons 2 N_2O_4(g) + 6 H_2O(g)$, was carried out. A system was prepared with $[N_2O_4] = [H_2O] = 3.60$ M as the only components initially. At equilibrium, $[H_2O]$ is 0.60 M. Calculate the equilibrium concentration of NH_3.

     a. 1.50
     b. 0.90 M
     c. 3.00 M
     d. 2.40 M
 ! e. 2.00 M

42. A study of the following system, $4 NH_3(g) + 7 O_2(g) \rightleftharpoons 2 N_2O_4(g) + 6 H_2O(g)$, was carried out, A system was prepared with $[N_2O_4] = [H_2O] = 3.60$ M as the only components initially. At equilibrium, $[H_2O]$ is 0.60 M. Calculate the equilibrium concentration of O_2.

     a. 0.70 M
     b. 3.00 M
     c. 1.00 M
     d. 2.40 M
 ! e. 3.50 M

43. A system was charged with NOCl gas until the concentration was 0.398 moles per liter. The temperature of the system was increased to 245 °C and the system was allowed to undergo the reaction, $2 \text{ NOCl}(g) \rightleftharpoons 2 \text{ NO}(g) + Cl_2(g)$, until equilibrium was attained. The physical chemistry lab students did a calculation and found the the $[Cl_2]$ at that point was 0.0225 mol/liter. Calculate the value of K_c at that temperature.

    a. 2.87×10^{-3}
! b. 3.66×10^{-4}
    c. 7.19×10^{-5}
    d. 2.88×10^{-4}
    e. 9.14×10^{-5}

44. A study of the system, $XBr_2(g) \rightleftharpoons X(g) + Br_2(g)$, was carried out. A container was charged with an initial concentration of $[XBr_2] = 2.00 \text{ mol/L}$ as the only component initially. The system was allowed to react and come to equilibrium. If $K_c = 4.0 \times 10^{-8}$, what was the concentration of $X(g)$ at equilibrium?

    a. 0.000056 M
    b. 0.00020 M
! c. 0.00028 M
    d. 0.000000040 M
    e. 0.000000080 M

45. A study of the system, $H_2(g) + I_2(g) \rightleftharpoons 2 \text{ HI}(g)$, was carried out. $K_c = 54.9$ at 699.0 K for this reaction. A system was charged with 2.50 moles of HI in a 5.00 liter vessel as the only component initially. The system was brought up to 699.0 K and allowed to attain equilibrium. How many moles of H_2 should there be in the container at that time?

    a. 0.337 moles
    b. 1.25 moles
    c. 0.297 moles
    d. 0.500 moles
! e. 0.266 moles

46. A study of the system, $H_2(g) + I_2(g) \rightleftharpoons 2 \text{ HI}(g)$, was carried out. $K_c = 54.9$ at 699.0K for this reaction. A system was charged with 2.50 moles of H_2 and 2.50 moles I_2 in a 5.00 liter vessel as the only components initially. The system was brought up to 699.0 K and allowed to attain equilibrium. How many moles of H_2 should there be in the container at that time?

! a. 0.531 moles
    b. 0.674 moles
    c. 0.594 moles
    d. 1.00 moles
    e. 0.266 moles

47. A study of the system, $H_2(g) + I_2(g) \rightleftharpoons 2\, HI(g)$, was carried out. $K_c = 54.9$ at 699.0K for this reaction. A system was charged with 2.50 moles of H_2, and 2.50 moles I_2, and 5.00 moles of HI in a 5.00 liter vessel. The system was brought up to 699.0 K and allowed to attain equilibrium. How many moles of H_2 should there be in the container at that time?

     a. 1.35 moles
     b. 2.00 moles
     c. 5.00 moles
     d. 1.19 moles
!   e. 1.06 moles

48. For a system, $H_2(g) + I_2(g) \rightleftharpoons 2\, HI(g)$, $K_c = 62.9$ at 750 K. 2.80 moles of HI were placed in a 10.0 liter container, it was brought up to 750 K, and allowed to come to equilibrium. Which situation described below is true, at equilibrium?

     a. $[HI] = 2 \times [H_2]$
     b. $[HI] = [H_2]$
     c. $[HI] < [H_2]$
!   d. $[HI] > [H_2]$
     e. $[H_2] > [I_2]$

49. A student was assigned to carry out some calculation regarding the state of the system described by the equation, $I_2(g) + Br_2(g) \rightleftharpoons 2\, IBr(g)$. $K_c = 250$ for this system. The system was to be charged with 0.0500 moles of I_2 and of Br_2 and then allowed to attain equilibrium at the desired temperature. At that point, what value should the student doing the calculation obtain for the equilibrium concentration of $IBr(g)$?

     a. 0.0056 M
     b. 0.0444 M
!   c. 0.0888 M
     d. 0.0950 M
     e. 0.100 M

50. For the system, $H_2(g) + X_2(g) \rightleftharpoons 2\, HX(g)$, $K_c = 24.4$ at 300 K. A system was charged with 2.00 moles of HX in a 3.00 liter container. The catalyst was introduced using a remote unit, and the system was allowed to come to equilibrium. How many moles of H_2 will be present when the system reaches equilibrium?

!   a. 0.288 moles
     b. 0.337 moles
     c. 0.388 moles
     d. 0.404 moles
     e. 0.424 moles

51. For the system, $H_2(g) + X_2(g) \rightleftharpoons 2\,HX(g)$, $K_c = 24.4$ at 300 K. A system was charged with 1.00 moles of H_2 and 1.00 moles of I_2 in a 3.00 liter container. The catalyst was introduced using a remote unit, and the system was allowed to come to equilibrium. How many moles of H_2 will be present when the system reaches equilibrium?

! a. 0.288 moles
   b. 0.337 moles
   c. 0.388 moles
   d. 0.404 moles
   e. 0.442 moles

Fill in the Blanks

52. Write the correct expression for the equilibrium constant for the reaction below
$$CH_4(g) + 2\,NO_2(g) \rightleftharpoons CO_2(g) + 2\,H_2O(g) + N_2(g)$$

$$!(K_p = \frac{(p_{CO_2})(p_{H_2O})^2(p_{N_2})}{(p_{CH_4})(p_{NO_2})^2})$$

53. The expression for an equilibrium constant for a reaction in which all the components are gases is:
$$\frac{[N_2][O_2][Br_2]}{[NOBr]^2} = K_c$$
Write the balanced equation for the reaction described by this equilibrium constant

_____ (! $2\,NOBr(g) \rightleftharpoons N_2(g) + O_2(g) + Br_2(g)$)

54. Write the expression for the equilibrium constant, K_p, for the reaction,
$$N_2(g) + O_2(g) \rightleftharpoons 2\,NO(g)$$

$$!(K_p = \frac{(p_{NO})^2}{(p_{N_2})(p_{O_2})})$$

55. Write the expression for the equilibrium constant, K_p, for the reaction,
$$CO(g) + 2\,H_2(g) \rightleftharpoons CH_3OH(g)$$

$$!(K_p = \frac{(p_{CH_2OH})}{(p_{CO})(p_{H_2})^2})$$

56. Write the expression for the equilibrium constant, K_c, for the reaction,
$$2\,AsF_3(g) + 3\,CCl_4(g) \rightleftharpoons 2\,AsCl_3(g) + 3\,CCl_2F_2(g)$$

$$!(K_c = \frac{[AsCl_3]^2[CCl_2F_2]^3}{[AsF_3]^2[CCl_4]^3})$$

57. Write the expression for the equilibrium constant, K_p, for the reaction,

$$4\ HCl(g)\ +\ O_2(g)\ \rightleftharpoons\ 2\ H_2O(g)\ +\ 2\ Cl_2(g)$$

$$!(K_p = \frac{(p_{H_2O})^2(p_{Cl_2})^2}{(p_{HCl})^4(p_{O_2})})$$

58. Write the expression for the equilibrium constant, K_c, for the reaction,

$$N_2H_4(g)\ +\ 6\ H_2O_2(g)\ \rightleftharpoons\ 2\ NO_2(g)\ +\ 8\ H_2O(g)$$

$$!(K_c = \frac{[NO_2]^2[H_2O]^8}{[N_2H_4]\ [H_2O_2]^6})$$

59. Write the expression for the equilibrium constant, K_c, for the reaction,

$$SO_2Cl_2(g)\ +\ 2\ NO(g)\ \rightleftharpoons\ SO_2(g)\ +\ 2\ NOCl(g)$$

$$!(K_c = \frac{[SO_2]\ [NOCl]^2}{[SO_2Cl_2]\ [NO]^2})$$

60. Write the expression for the equilibrium constant, K_p, for the reaction,

$$NH_4Cl(s)\ \rightleftharpoons\ NH_3(g)\ +\ HCl(g)$$

$$!(K_p) = (p_{NH_3})(p_{HCl})^2$$

61. Write the expression for the equilibrium constant, K_p, for the reaction,

$$SnCl_2(s)\ +\ Cl_2(g)\ \rightleftharpoons\ SnCl_4(g)$$

$$!(K_p = \frac{(p_{SnCl_4})}{(p_{Cl_2})})$$

62. Write the expression for the equilibrium constant, K_c, for the reaction,

$$4\ Cr(s)\ +\ 3\ CCl_4(g)\ \rightleftharpoons\ 4\ CrCl_3(g)\ +\ 4\ C(s)$$

$$!(K_c = \frac{[CrCl_3]^4}{[CCl_4]^3})$$

63. Write the expression for the equilibrium constant, K_c, for the reaction,

$$C(s)\ +\ H_2O(g)\ \rightleftharpoons\ HCHO(g)$$

$$!(K_c = \frac{[HCHO]}{[H_2O]})$$

64. In a chemical reaction system which has reached equilibrium, the concentrations of the various species are constantly changing even though the total number of molecules is unchanging. (! F)

65. In a chemical reaction system which has reached equilibrium the net concentration of each species is unchanging even though particular molecules continue to react throughout the system. (! T)

Critical Thinking

66. A system was charged with NOCl gas until the concentration was 0.398 mol L^{-1}. The temperature of the system was increased to 245 °C and the system was allowed to undergo the reaction,

    $2 \, NOCl(g) \rightleftharpoons 2 \, NO(g) + Cl_2(g)$, until equilibrium was attained. The physical chemistry lab students did a calculation and found that the $[Cl_2]$ at that point was 0.0225 mol L^{-1}. Calculate the value of K_p at that temperature.

    a. 1.22×10^{-2}
    ! b. 1.55×10^{-2}
    c. 1.45×10^{-3}
    d. 4.46×10^{-3}
    e. 6.61×10^{-1}

67. A student was studying the reaction, $PCl_5(g) \rightleftharpoons PCl_3(g) + Cl_2(g)$. At some temperature, T, the value of K_p for the system is 0.550. A system was created by placing a certain quantity of PCl_5 into a closed reactor, then sealing it off and allowing the system to come to equilibrium. If the **total pressure** in the closed system was measured as 3.25 atm, what is the partial pressure of the $Cl_2(g)$ in the equilibrated system? _____ (! 0.895 atm)

68. A student was studying the reaction, $SO_2Cl_2(g) \rightleftharpoons SO_2(g) + Cl_2(g)$. The value of K_p for the system is 12.5 when the temperature is 565 K. A reactor vessel was charged with enough $SO_2Cl_2(g)$ to give it a pressure of 1.200 atm at 25.0 °C. The temperature of the sealed system was increased to 565 K and the system left undisturbed so it could come to equilibrium. This was determined by observing the **total pressure** of the system on the output device from the sensor. Calculate what the partial pressure of either the chlorine or the sulfur dioxide should be, in atmospheres, at equilibrium. _____ (! 1.965 atm)

69. A student was studying the reaction, $SO_2Cl_2(g) \rightleftharpoons SO_2(g) + Cl_2(g)$. The value of K_p for the system is 12.5 when the temperature is 565 K. A reactor vessel was charged with enough $SO_2Cl_2(g)$ to give it a pressure of 1.200 atm at 25.0 °C. The temperature of the sealed system was increased to 565 K and the system left undisturbed so it could come to equilibrium. This was determined by observing the **total pressure** of the system on the output device from the sensor. Calculate what the total pressure should be, in atmospheres, at equilibrium. _____ (! 4.239 atm)

Chapter 15 Acids and Bases: A Second Look

Multiple Choice

1. Which one of the following would not be acidic?

    a. grapefruit juice
    ! b. household ammonia
    c. carbonated water
    d. vinegar
    e. lemon juice

2. The conjugate acid of HPO_4^{2-} is

    a. H_2PO_4
    b. H_3PO_4
    c. PO_4^{3-}
    d. PO_4^{2-}
    ! e. $H_2PO_4^-$

3. The conjugate base of HPO_4^{2-} is

    a. H_2PO_4
    b. H_3PO_4
    ! c. PO_4^{3-}
    d. PO_4^{2-}
    e. $H_2PO_4^-$

4. The conjugate base of $H_2AsO_4^-$ is

    a. H_2AsO_4
    b. H_3AsO_4
    c. $HAsO_4^-$
    ! d. $HAsO_4^{2-}$
    e. AsO_4^{3-}

5. The conjugate acid of $H_2AsO_4^-$ is

    a. H_2AsO_4
    ! b. H_3AsO_4
    c. $HAsO_4^-$
    d. $HAsO_4^{2-}$
    e. AsO_4^{3-}

6. Which pair of reactants below will yield H_2SO_4 as one of its products?

      a. $SO_2 + OH^-$
      b. $SO_3 + OH^-$
      c. $SO_2 + H_2O$
      d. $SO_4^{2-} + OH^-$
 !   e. $SO_3 + H_2O$

7. Which pair of reactants below will yield H_2SO_3 as one of its products?

      a. $SO_2 + OH^-$
      b. $SO_3 + OH^-$
 !   c. $SO_2 + H_2O$
      d. $SO_4^{2-} + OH^-$
      e. $SO_3 + H_2O$

8. Which one of the five species shown below is the strongest oxyacid?

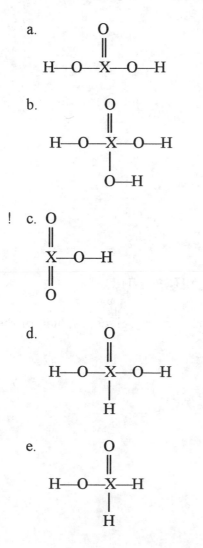

    a.

$$\overset{\displaystyle O}{\underset{\displaystyle}{\overset{\|}{H\!-\!O\!-\!X\!-\!O\!-\!H}}}$$

    b.

$$H\!-\!O\!-\!X\!-\!O\!-\!H$$ with O double-bonded above and $O\!-\!H$ below X

! c.

$$X\!-\!O\!-\!H$$ with O double-bonded above and below

    d.

$$H\!-\!O\!-\!X\!-\!O\!-\!H$$ with O double-bonded above and H below

    e.

$$H\!-\!O\!-\!X\!-\!H$$ with O double-bonded above and H below

9. Which one of the five species shown below is the strongest oxyacid?

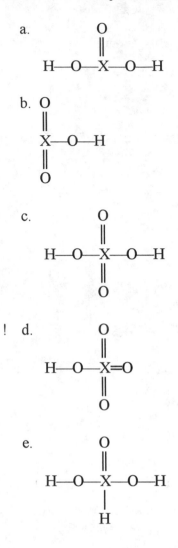

a.
$$\underset{\displaystyle H-O-X-O-H}{\overset{\displaystyle O}{\|}}$$

b.
$$\underset{\displaystyle O}{\overset{\displaystyle O}{\underset{\|}{\overset{\|}{X-O-H}}}}$$

c.
$$\overset{\displaystyle O}{\underset{\displaystyle O}{\overset{\|}{\underset{\|}{H-O-X-O-H}}}}$$

! d.
$$\overset{\displaystyle O}{\underset{\displaystyle O}{\overset{\|}{\underset{\|}{H-O-X=O}}}}$$

e.
$$\overset{\displaystyle O}{\underset{\displaystyle H}{\overset{\|}{\underset{|}{H-O-X-O-H}}}}$$

10. For the system

$$NH_2OH + CH_3NH_3^+ \rightleftharpoons CH_3NH_2 + NH_3OH^+$$
$$95\% \qquad 95\% \qquad 5\% \qquad 5\%$$

the state of equilibrium in the system is described by the numbers given. Which of the species is the strongest acid in the system?

    a. NH_2OH
    b. $CH_3NH_3^+$
    c. CH_3NH_2
! d. NH_3OH^+

11. Which one of the five species shown below is the weakest oxyacid?

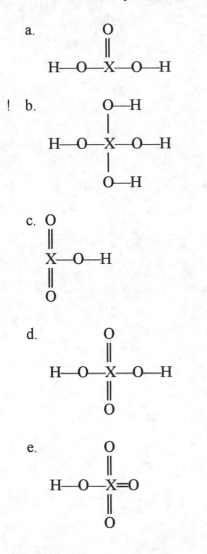

a.
$$O$$
$$\|$$
$$H-O-X-O-H$$

! b.
$$O-H$$
$$|$$
$$H-O-X-O-H$$
$$|$$
$$O-H$$

c.
$$O$$
$$\|$$
$$X-O-H$$
$$\|$$
$$O$$

d.
$$O$$
$$\|$$
$$H-O-X-O-H$$
$$\|$$
$$O$$

e.
$$O$$
$$\|$$
$$H-O-X=O$$
$$\|$$
$$O$$

12. For the system

$$NH_2OH + CH_3NH_3^+ \rightleftharpoons CH_3NH_2 + NH_3OH^+$$

95%   95 %   5 %   5 %

the state of equilibrium in the system is described by the numbers given. Which of the species is the weakest base in the system?

! a. NH_2OH
b. $CH_3NH_3^+$
c. CH_3NH_2
d. NH_3OH^+

13. Which one of the five species shown below is the strongest oxyacid?

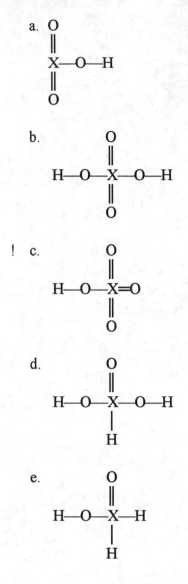

a.

$$O$$
$$\|$$
$$X—O—H$$
$$\|$$
$$O$$

b.

$$O$$
$$\|$$
$$H—O—X—O—H$$
$$\|$$
$$O$$

! c.

$$O$$
$$\|$$
$$H—O—X=O$$
$$\|$$
$$O$$

d.

$$O$$
$$\|$$
$$H—O—X—O—H$$
$$|$$
$$H$$

e.

$$O$$
$$\|$$
$$H—O—X—H$$
$$|$$
$$H$$

14. For the system

$$NH_2OH + CH_3NH_3^+ \rightleftharpoons CH_3NH_2 + NH_3OH^+$$

5%   5 %   95 %   95 %

the state of equilibrium in the system is described by the numbers given. Which of the species is the strongest acid in the system?

a. NH_2OH
! b. $CH_3NH_3^+$
c. CH_3NH_2
d. NH_3OH^+

15. For the system

$$NH_2OH + CH_3NH_3^+ \rightleftharpoons CH_3NH_2 + NH_3OH^+$$
     5%   5 %   95 %   95 %

the state of equilibrium in the system is described by the numbers given. Which of the species is the weakest base in the system?

    a. NH_2OH
    b. $CH_3NH_3^+$
! c. CH_3NH_2
    d. NH_3OH^+

16. Which one of the following solutions should have the **lowest** pH?

! a. $Al(NO_3)_3(aq)$
    b. $Ca(NO_3)_2(aq)$
    c. $KNO_3(aq)$
    d. $Mg(NO_3)_2(aq)$
    e. $Zn(NO_3)_2(aq)$

17. Which one of the following solutions should have the **highest** pH?

    a. $Al(NO_3)_3(aq)$
    b. $Ga(NO_3)_3(aq)$
! c. $AgNO_3(aq)$
    d. $Cu(NO_3)_2(aq)$
    e. $Zn(NO_3)_2(aq)$

18. Which one of the following solutions should have the **lowest** pH?

    a. $Zn(NO_3)_2(aq)$
    b. $Cd(NO_3)_2(aq)$
    c. $Ga(NO_3)_3 (aq)$
    d. $Hg(NO_3)_2(aq)$
! e. $Al(NO_3)_3(aq)$

19. Which one of the following solutions should have the **highest** pH?

    a. $Al(NO_3)_3(aq)$
    b. $Cd(NO_3)_2(aq)$
    c. $Ga(NO_3)_3 (aq)$
! d. $KNO_3(aq)$
    e. $Zn(NO_3)_2(aq)$

20. Five solutions were prepared by dissolving 0.00100 moles of each of the following in enough water to make 1.000 liters of solution. Which one of the solutions would you expect to have the lowest pH? The one made with

    a. CO_2
    b. P_4O_6
    c. P_4O_{10}
    d. SO_2
!   e. SO_3

21. Five solutions were prepared by dissolving 0.00100 moles of each of the following in enough water to make 1.000 liters of solution. Which one of the solutions would you expect to have the lowest pH? The one made with

    a. Na_2O
    b. BaO
    c. Ga_2O_3
    d. Al_2O_3
!   e. P_4O_6

22. CO_2 can react directly with OH^-, forming HCO_3^-. In this reaction,

    a. the CO_2 acts as a Brønsted acid, accepting a proton from the OH^- ion
    b. the CO_2 acts as a Lewis acid, accepting a proton from the OH^- ion
    c. the OH^- ion acts as a Brønsted base, donating a proton to the CO_2 molecule
    d. the OH^- ion acts as a Lewis acid, accepting an electron pair from the CO_2 molecule to form a coordinate covalent bond
!   e. the OH^- ion acts as a Lewis base, donating an electron pair to the CO_2 molecule to form a coordinate covalent bond

23. NH_3 can react directly with BF_3, forming NH_3—BF_3. In this reaction,

    a. the NH_3 acts as a Brønsted base, accepting a proton from the BF_3 molecule
    b. the NH_3 acts as a Lewis base, donating a proton to the BF_3 molecule
    c. the NH_3 acts as a Brønsted acid, donating a proton to the BF_3 molecule
!   d. the BF_3 molecule acts as a Lewis acid, accepting an electron pair from the NH_3 molecule to form a coordinate covalent bond
    e. the BF_3 molecule acts as a Lewis base, donating an electron pair to the NH_3 molecule to form a coordinate covalent bond

24. SO_2 can react directly with OH^-, forming HSO_3^-. In this reaction,

    a. the SO_2 acts as a Brønsted acid, accepting a proton from the OH^- ion
    b. the SO_2 acts as a Lewis acid, accepting a proton from the OH^- ion
    c. the OH^- ion acts as a Brønsted base, donating a proton to the SO_2 molecule
 ! d. the OH^- ion acts as a Lewis base, donating an electron pair to the SO_2 molecule to form a coordinate covalent bond
    e. the OH^- ion acts as a Lewis acid, accepting an electron pair from the SO_2 molecule to form a coordinate covalent bond

25. F^- ion can react directly with BF_3, forming the BF_4^- anion. In this reaction,

    a. the F^- ion acts as a Brønsted base, accepting a proton from the BF_3 molecule
    b. the F^- ion acts as a Lewis base, donating a proton to the BF_3 molecule
    c. the F^- ion acts as a Brønsted acid, donating a proton to the BF_3 molecule
 ! d. the BF_3 molecule acts as a Lewis acid, accepting an electron pair from the F^- ion to form a coordinate covalent bond
    e. the BF_3 molecule acts as a Lewis base, donating an electron pair to the F^- ion to form a coordinate covalent bond

26. An aqueous solution at 25.0 °C has a H^+ concentration of 4.0×10^{-2} molar. What is the OH^- concentration in the same solution, in moles per liter?

    a. 4.0×10^{-2}
    b. 4.0×10^{-9}
    c. 4.0×10^{-12}
 ! d. 2.5×10^{-13}
    e. 25.0

27. If the H^+ ion concentration in an aqueous solution at 25.0 °C has a value of 0.100 molar, then the OH^- concentration in moles per liter is

    a. 0.100
    b. 1.00×10^{-7}
    c. 100×10^{-12}
 ! d. 1.00×10^{-13}
    e. 4.00×10^{12}

28. If the OH^- ion concentration in an aqueous solution at 25.0 °C is 6.6×10^{-4} M, then the H^+ concentration in moles per liter in the same solution is

    a. 1.5×10^{-1}
    b. 1.5×10^{-4}
    c. 6.6×10^{-10}
 ! d. 1.5×10^{11}
    e. 6.6×10^{-11}

29. If the H^+ ion concentration in an aqueous solution at 25.0 °C is measured as 6.6×10^{-4} M, then the pH is

    a. 3.00
! b. 3.18
    c. 6.60
    d. 9.55
    e. 10.82

30. A mixture is made using 50.0 ml of 0.20 M NaOH(*aq*) and 50.0 ml of water. At 25.0 °C, what is its pH?

    a. 1.00
    b. 4.55
    c. 7.00
! d. 13.00
    e. 13.30

31. Calculate the pH of a mixture made by adding 50.0 ml of 0.20 M HCl(*aq*) to 150.0 ml of water if the temperature of the mixture is 25.0 °C.

    a. 0.70
    b. 1.00
    c. 1.18
! d. 1.30
    e. 13.00

32. Calculate the pH of a 0.020 M solution of $Ca(OH)_2$ whose temperature is 25.0 °C.

    a. 1.40
    b. 0.040
    c. 1.69
! d. 12.60
    e. 12.30

33. 40.0 ml of 0.10 M HCl(*aq*) was added to 50.0 ml of 0.10 M NaOH(*aq*) and the mixture was stirred, then tested with a pH meter. What pH should be obtained at 25.0 °C?

    a. 1.95
    b. 2.00
    c. 7.00
    d. 12.00
! e. 12.05

34. 50.0 ml of 0.10 M HCl(*aq*) was added to 40.0 ml of 0.10 M NaOH(*aq*) and the mixture was stirred, then tested with a pH meter. What reading should be obtained for the pH at 25.0 °C?

    ! a. 1.95
       b. 2.00
       c. 7.00
       d. 12.00
       e. 12.05

35. 20.0 ml of 0.10 M H_2SO_4(*aq*) was added to 50.0 ml of 0.10 M NaOH(*aq*) and the mixture was stirred, then tested with a pH meter. What reading should be obtained for the pH at 25.0 °C?

       a. 1.85
       b. 2.00
       c. 7.00
       d. 12.00
    ! e. 12.15

36. 40.0 ml of 0.20 M HCl(*aq*) was added to 50.0 ml of 0.20 M NaOH(*aq*) and the mixture was stirred, then tested with a pH meter. What reading should be obtained for the pH at 25.0 °C?

       a. 1.65
       b. 2.00
       c. 7.00
       d. 12.00
    ! e. 12.35

37. 40.0 ml of 0.20 M HCl(*aq*) was added to 50.0 ml of 0.10 M NaOH(*aq*) and the mixture was stirred, then tested with a pH meter. What pH should be obtained at 25.0 °C?

       a. 0.70
    ! b. 1.48
       c. 1.65
       d. 12.00
       e. 12.52

38. Given the following:
       0.20 M NaOH(*aq*)   0.20 M HCl(*aq*)
   A mixture is made using 50.0 ml of the HCl and 50.0 ml of the NaOH. What is its pH at 25.0 °C?

       a. 3.62
       b. 4.57
       c. 6.30
    ! d. 7.00
       e. 9.46

39. Given the following:

   0.20 M NaOH(aq)   0.20 M HCl(aq)

   A mixture is made using 50.0 ml of the NaOH and 25.0 ml of the HCl. What is its pH at 25.0 °C?

       a. 7.00
       b. 12.52
   ! c. 12.82
       d. 13.00
       e. 13.30

40. Given the following:

   0.20 M NaOH(aq)   0.20 M HCl(aq)

   A mixture is made using 50.0 ml of the HCl and 25.0 ml of the NaOH. What is its pH at 25.0 °C?

   ! a. 1.18
       b. 4.62
       c. 7.00
       d. 11.38
       e. 12.82

41. Given the following:

   NaOH(aq), pH = 13.301   HCl(aq), pH = 1.000

   A mixture is made using 50.0 ml of the HCl and 25.0 ml of the NaOH. What is its pH at 25.0 °C?

       a. 1.176
       b. 4.622
   ! c. 7.000
       d. 7.151
       e. 14.301

42. Given the following:

   NaOH(aq), pH = 13.301   HCl(aq), pH = 1.000

   A mixture is made using 50.0 ml of the HCl and 50.0 ml of the NaOH. What is its pH at 25.0 °C?

       a. 1.300
       b. 7.000
   ! c. 12.700
       d. 13.000
       e. 14.300

43. A solution is made by mixing 50.0 ml of a HCl(aq) solution which has a pH of 3.00 with 50.0 ml of a KOH solution which has a pH of 11.00. What is the pH of the mixture at 25.0 °C?

       a. 3.35
       b. 4.25
   ! c. 7.00
       d. 7.50
       e. 10.65

44. Given the following:

    NaOH(*aq*), pH = 13.00   HCl(*aq*), pH = 1.00

    A mixture is made using 50.0 ml of the HCl and 50.0 ml of the NaOH. What is its pH at 25.0 °C?

        a. 1.30
    ! b. 7.00
        c. 12.70
        d. 13.00
        e. 14.30

45. Given the following:

    NaOH(*aq*), pH = 13.00   HCl(*aq*), pH = 1.00

    A mixture is made using 50.0 ml of the HCl and 25.0 ml of the NaOH. What is its pH at 25.0 °C?

        a. 1.30
    ! b. 1.48
        c. 3.67
        d. 5.00
        e. 7.00

46. Given the following:

    NaOH(*aq*), pH = 13.00   HCl(*aq*), pH = 1.00

    A mixture is made using 25.0 ml of the HCl and 50.0 ml of the NaOH. What is its pH at 25.0 °C?

        a. 1.30
        b. 8.33
        c. 9.00
    ! d. 12.52
        e. 12.70

47. A 50.0 ml sample of an HCl(*aq*) solution was mixed with a 40.0 ml sample of a 0.200 molar NaOH(*aq*) solution. The pH of the mixture was measured and a value of 11.74 was obtained. What is the concentration of the HCl solution if the temperature is 25.0 °C?

        a. 0.025 molar
        b. 0.140 molar
    ! c. 0.150 molar
        d. 0.180 molar
        e. 0.200 molar

48. A solution is made by mixing 50.0 ml of a nitric acid solution which has a pH of 4.00 with 50.0 ml of a NaOH solution which has a pH of 11.00. What is the pH of the mixture at 25.0 °C?

        a. 7.00
        b. 7.50
        c. 10.35
    ! d. 10.65
        e. 10.95

49. A solution is made by mixing 100.0 ml of a HCl(*aq*) solution which has a pH of 3.00 with 50.0 ml of a KOH solution which has a pOH of 6.00. What is the pH of the mixture at 25.0 °C?

    a. 3.00
! b. 3.18
    c. 4.50
    d. 7.00
    e. 9.25

50. In the reaction, $HClO_3 + N_2H_4 \rightleftharpoons ClO_3^- + N_2H_5^+$, which one of the sets below constitutes a conjugate (acid-base) pair?

    a. $HClO_3$, N_2H_4
    b. N_2H_4, ClO_3^-
    c. $HClO_3$, $N_2H_5^+$
! d. N_2H_4, $N_2H_5^+$
    e. ClO_3^-, $N_2H_5^+$

51. In the reaction, $HClO_3 + N_2H_4 \rightleftharpoons ClO_3^- + N_2H_5^+$, which one of the sets below lists both of the acid species involved in the equilibrium?

    a. $HClO_3$, N_2H_4
    b. $HClO_3$, ClO_3^-
! c. $HClO_3$, $N_2H_5^+$
    d. N_2H_4, $N_2H_5^+$
    e. ClO_3^-, $N_2H_5^+$

52. In the reaction, $HClO_3 + N_2H_4 \rightleftharpoons ClO_3^- + N_2H_5^+$, which one of the sets below lists both of the base species involved in the equilibrium?

    a. $HClO_3$, N_2H_4
    b. $HClO_3$, ClO_3^-
    c. $HClO_3$, $N_2H_5^+$
    d. N_2H_4, $N_2H_5^+$
! e. ClO_3^-, N_2H_4

53. In the reaction, $H_2PO_4^- + HAsO_4^{2-} \rightleftharpoons HPO_4^{2-} + H_2AsO_4^-$, which one of the sets below constitutes a conjugate (acid-base) pair?

    a. $H_2PO_4^-$, $HAsO_4^{2-}$
    b. $H_2PO_4^-$, $H_2AsO_4^-$
! c. $H_2PO_4^-$, HPO_4^{2-}
    d. $HAsO_4^{2-}$, HPO_4^{2-}
    e. HPO_4^{2-}, $H_2AsO_4^-$

54. In the reaction, $H_2PO_4^- + HAsO_4^{2-} \rightleftharpoons HPO_4^{2-} + H_2AsO_4^-$, which one of the sets below lists both of the acid species involved in the equilibrium?

    a. $H_2PO_4^-$, $HAsO_4^{2-}$
! b. $H_2PO_4^-$, $H_2AsO_4^-$
    c. $H_2PO_4^-$, HPO_4^{2-}
    d. $HAsO_4^{2-}$, HPO_4^{2-}
    e. HPO_4^{2-}, $H_2AsO_4^-$

55. In the reaction, $H_2PO_4^- + HAsO_4^{2-} \rightleftharpoons HPO_4^{2-} + H_2AsO_4^-$, which one of the sets below lists both of the base species involved in the equilibrium?

    a. $H_2PO_4^-$, $HAsO_4^{2-}$
    b. $H_2PO_4^-$, $H_2AsO_4^-$
    c. $H_2PO_4^-$, HPO_4^{2-}
! d. $HAsO_4^{2-}$, HPO_4^{2-}
    e. HPO_4^{2-}, $H_2AsO_4^-$

56. In the reaction, $HSO_4^- + HS^- \rightleftharpoons H_2S + SO_4^{2-}$, which one of the sets below constitutes a conjugate (acid-base) pair?

    a. HSO_4^-, HS^-
    b. HSO_4^-, H_2S
! c. HS^-, H_2S
    d. HS^-, SO_4^{2-}
    e. H_2S, SO_4^{2-}

57. In the reaction, $HSO_4^- + HS^- \rightleftharpoons H_2S + SO_4^{2-}$, which one of the sets below lists both of the acid species involved in the equilibrium?

    a. HSO_4^-, HS^-
! b. HSO_4^-, H_2S
    c. HS^-, H_2S
    d. HS^-, SO_4^{2-}
    e. H_2S, SO_4^{2-}

58. In the reaction, $HSO_4^- + HS^- \rightleftharpoons H_2S + SO_4^{2-}$, which one of the sets below lists both of the base species involved in the equilibrium?

    a. HSO_4^-, HS^-
    b. HSO_4^-, H_2S
    c. HS^-, H_2S
! d. HS^-, SO_4^{2-}
    e. H_2S, SO_4^{2-}

59. In the reaction, $HSO_4^- + CN^- \rightleftharpoons HCN + SO_4^{2-}$, which one of the sets below constitutes a conjugate (acid-base) pair?

    a. HSO_4^-, CN^-
    ! b. CN^-, HCN
    c. CN^-, SO_4^{2-}
    d. HCN, SO_4^{2-}
    e. HCN, HSO_4^-

60. In the reaction, $HSO_4^- + CN^- \rightleftharpoons HCN + SO_4^{2-}$, which one of the sets below lists both of the acid species involved in the equilibrium?

    a. HSO_4^-, CN^-
    ! b. HSO_4^-, HCN
    c. CN^-, HCN
    d. CN^-, SO_4^{2-}
    e. SO_4^{2-}, HCN

61. In the reaction, $HSO_4^- + CN^- \rightleftharpoons HCN + SO_4^{2-}$, which one of the sets below lists both of the base species involved in the equilibrium?

    a. HSO_4^-, CN^-
    b. HSO_4^-, HCN
    c. SO_4^{2-}, HCN
    d. CN^-, HCN
    ! e. CN^-, SO_4^{2-}

62. Which one of the following four species is the most acidic substance?

    a. HClO
    b. $HClO_2$
    c. $HClO_3$
    ! d. $HClO_4$

63. Given the following substances in order of increasing acid strength,
       $HOCl(aq) < HC_2H_3O_2(aq) < HC_2O_4^-(aq) < HOCN(aq) < HNO_2(aq) < HCl(aq)$
    Which one of the species in the set listed **below** is the strongest base of that set?

    a. $Cl^-(aq)$
    ! b. $OCl^-(aq)$
    c. $H_2C_2O_4(aq)$
    d. $NO_2^-(aq)$
    e. $OCN^-(aq)$

64. Given the following substances in order of increasing acid strength,

$$HOCl(aq) < HC_2H_3O_2(aq) < HC_2O_4^-(aq) < HOCN(aq) < HNO_2(aq) < HCl(aq)$$

Which one of the species in the set listed **below** is the weakest base of that set?

    a. $C_2H_3O_2^-(aq)$
    b. $OCl^-(aq)$
    c. $H_2C_2O_4(aq)$
!   d. $NO_2^-(aq)$
    e. $OCN^-(aq)$

65. Given the following substances in order of increasing acid strength,

$$HOCl(aq) < HC_2H_3O_2(aq) < HC_2O_4^-(aq) < HOCN(aq) < HNO_2(aq) < HCl(aq)$$

Which one of the species in the set listed **below** is the strongest base of that set?

    a. $Cl^-(aq)$
    b. $HOCl(aq)$
!   c. $C_2O_4^{2-}(aq)$
    d. $NO_2^-(aq)$
    e. $OCN^-(aq)$

66. Given the following substances in order of increasing acid strength,

$$HOCl(aq) < HC_2H_3O_2(aq) < HC_2O_4^-(aq) < HOCN(aq) < HNO_2(aq) < HCl(aq)$$

Which one of the species in the set listed **below** is the weakest base of that set?

    a. $C_2H_3O_2^-(aq)$
    b. $OCl^-(aq)$
    c. $HC_2O_4^-(aq)$
    d. $HNO_2(aq)$
!   e. $OCN^-(aq)$

67. Which one of the following four species is the least acidic substance?

    a. HBr
    b. HCl
!   c. HF
    d. HI

68. Which one of the following four species is the most acidic substance?

    a. H_2O
    b. H_2S
    c. H_2Se
!   d. H_2Te

Fill in the Blanks

69. At a temperature of 50.0 °C, the value of the ion product constant for H_2O is 5.5×10^{-14}. What is the $[H^+]$ ion in pure water at this temperature? _____ ($! 2.3 \times 10^{-7}$)

70. Which one of the two species, H_2Se or H_3As, is the stronger Brønsted acid? _____ (! $_2Se$)

71. Which one of the two species, HF(*aq*) or HI(*aq*), is the weaker Brønsted acid? _____ (! HF)

72. Which one of the two species, H_2S or HBr, is the stronger Brønsted acid? _____ (! HBr)

73. Three oxyacids with the formulas shown are listed in order of *increasing* acid strength:
$$HZO_3 > HYO_3 > HXO_3$$
What is the formula for the strongest conjugate base of these acids? _____(! XO_3^-)

74. Three binary acids with the formulas shown are listed in order of *increasing* acid strength:
$$HZ > HY > HX$$
What is the formula for the strongest conjugate base of these acids? _____(! X^-)

True and False

75. The ion product constant for water, K_w, varies with the temperature of the water. (!T)

Critical Thinking

76. At 60 °C the value of K_w is 9.5×10^{-14}. Considering this, what is the calculated value for the pOH of a 2.00×10^{-3} M HCl(*aq*) solution at this temperature?

      a. 2.70
      b. 6.51
  ! c. 10.32
      d. 11.30
      e. 13.02

77. At 60 °C the value of K_w is 9.5×10^{-14}. Considering this, what is the calculated value for the pH of a 5.00×10^{-2} M $Ba(OH)_2$(*aq*) solution at this temperature?

      a. 1.00
      b. 1.30
  ! c. 12.02
      d. 12.70
      e. 13.00

78. At 60 °C the value of K_w is 9.5×10^{-14}. Considering this, what is the calculated value for the pOH of pure water this temperature?

       a. 9.50
  ! b. 6.51
       c. 7.00
       d. 7.49

79. At 60 °C the value of K_w is 9.5×10^{-14}. Considering this, what is the calculated value for the pH of a solution made by dissolving 1.00 g of sodium hydroxide in enough water to make 500 ml of solution at this temperature? _____ (! 11.72)

Chemicals in Our World 8 Ceramics and Superconductors

80. An immediate practical use of superconducting ceramic material is in

       a. development of dynamos generating electricity which will require less internal cooling to compensate for the effects of resistance heating in the coil elements
       b. development of resistance heating devices for living spaces which operate at comparable or lower cost than natural gas or heating oil
       c. fabrication of better magnetic resonance materials useful in development of MRI and other related technologies
  ! d. development of transmission cable that can carry significantly greater electrical loads for the same power losses or having significantly reduced mass and size
       e. fabrication of better fiber optics for signal transmission of information over long distances

81. Superconducting material research has enjoyed the greatest success in and is developing materials in the area of

  ! a. ceramic material made of mixed oxides of ions with 2+ and 3+ charges
       b. fluorocarbon polymers doped with copper oxide
       c. polychlorinated biphenyl polymers (PCBP) doped with lanthanide ions
       d. fluorocarbon polymers doped with mixed silver oxide-mercury oxide
       e. polychlorinated biphenyl polymers (PCBP) doped with mixed magnesium oxide–silver oxide

Chapter 16 Equilibria in Solutions of Weak Acids and Bases

Multiple Choice

1. The dissociation constant, K_a, for macnic acid is 5.0×10^{-5}. What is the pK_a of this acid?

    a. 2.00×10^4
    ! b. 4.30
    c. 5.70
    d. 1.75×10^{-1}
    e. 10.70

2. The dissociation constant, K_a, for lactic acid is 1.38×10^{-4}. What is the pK_a of this acid?

    a. 7.25×10^3
    b. 2.591
    ! c. 3.860
    d. 5.380
    e. 3.591

3. The dissociation constant, K_a, for benzoic acid is 6.28×10^{-5}. What is the pK_a of this acid?

    a. 1.592×10^4
    ! b. 4.202
    c. 4.452
    d. 5.640
    e. 9.800

4. A 0.100 M solution of an acid, HA, has a pH = 2.00. What is the value of the dissociation constant, K_a for this acid?

    a. 1.1×10^{-2}
    ! b. 1.1×10^{-3}
    c. 1.1×10^{-4}
    d. 1.0×10^{-3}
    e. 1.0×10^{-4}

5. A 0.200 M solution of an acid, H*Brun*, has a pH = 1.00. What is the value of the dissociation constant, K_a, for this acid?

    a. 0.200
    b. 0.0400
    c. 1.00×10^{-3}
    d. 1.00
    ! e. 1.00×10^{-1}

6. A 0.200 M solution of a weak base in water has a pH = 10.40. Calculate the value of K_b for this base.

    a. 1.0×10^{-5}
    ! b. 3.2×10^{-7}
    c. 2.2×10^{-5}
    d. 4.0×10^{-11}
    e. 5.0×10^{-5}

7. What is the pH of a 1.00×10^{-9} molar solution of HCl?

    a. 5.00
    b. 6.00
    c. 6.80
    ! d. 7.00
    e. 9.00

8. The dissociation constant, K_a, for benzoic acid, $HC_7H_5O_2$, is 6.28×10^{-5}. What is the pH of a 0.15 molar solution of this acid?

    a. 0.82
    ! b. 2.52
    c. 4.20
    d. 5.03
    e. 5.79

9. The dissociation constant, K_a, for acetic acid, $HC_2H_3O_2$, is 1.76×10^{-5}. What is the pH of a 0.0800 molar solution of this acid?

    a. 1.10
    b. 2.01
    ! c. 2.93
    d. 4.75
    e. 5.85

10. What is the pH of a 1.00 molar solution of nitrous acid? The K_a for nitrous acid is 7.1×10^{-4}.

    a. 1.57
    ! b. 1.58
    c. 1.60
    d. 2.67
    e. 3.15

11. The dissociation constant, K_a, for dichloroacetic acid, $HC_2HO_2Cl_2$, is 5.0×10^{-2}. What is the pH of a 0.15 molar solution of this acid?

      a. 1.06
 ! b. 1.16
      c. 1.30
      d. 1.56
      e. 1.82

12. The dissociation constant, K_b, for the weak base methylamine, CH_3NH_2, is 4.4×10^{-4}. What is the pH of a 0.080 molar solution of this base?

      a. 2.23
      b. 2.24
      c. 5.87
      d. 10.64
 ! e. 11.76

13. The dissociation constant, K_b, for the weak base trimethylamine, $(CH_3)_3N$, is 7.4×10^{-5}. What is the pH of a 0.040 molar solution of this base?

      a. 8.37
      b. 9.87
      c. 10.70
 ! d. 11.23
      e. 12.60

14. The dissociation constant, K_a, for HCN(aq) is 6.2×10^{-10}. What is the pH of a 0.10 molar solution of sodium cyanide?

      a. 5.10
      b. 8.90
      c. 9.21
 ! d. 11.10
      e. 11.30

15. The dissociation constant, K_a, for HOI(aq), hypoiodous acid, is 2.3×10^{-11}. What is the pH of a 0.050 molar solution of sodium hypoiodite?

      a. 5.97
      b. 8.03
      c. 10.64
 ! d. 11.65
      e. 12.70

16. Given the following:

$0.200M\ NH_3(aq)$ with $pK_b = 4.76$ $0.200M\ HC_2H_3O_2(aq)$ with $pK_a = 4.76$
$0.200M\ NaOH(aq)$ $0.200M\ HCl(aq)$

A mixture is made using 50.0 mL of the HCl and 50.0 mL of water. What is its pH?

    a. 0.70
! b. 1.00
    c. 1.30
    d. 1.61
    e. 2.00

17. What is the pH of a 1.00 molar solution of $NaCN(aq)$? The K_a for $HCN = 6.2 \times 10^{-10}$.

    a. 4.60
    b. 9.21
    c. 9.40
! d. 11.60
    e. 13.00

18. Given the following:

$0.200M\ NH_3(aq)$ with $pK_b = 4.76$ $0.200M\ HC_2H_3O_2(aq)$ with $pK_a = 4.76$
$0.200M\ NaOH(aq)$ $0.200M\ HCl(aq)$

A mixture is made using 50.0 mL of the HCl and 50.0 mL of the NH_3. What is its pH?

    a. 1.00
    b. 4.97
! c. 5.12
    d. 8.88
    e. 9.03

19. Given the following:

$0.200M\ NH_3(aq)$ with $pK_b = 4.76$ $0.200M\ HC_2H_3O_2(aq)$ with $pK_a = 4.76$
$0.200M\ NaOH(aq)$ $0.200M\ HCl(aq)$

A mixture is made using 50.0 mL of the $HC_2H_3O_2$ and 50.0 mL of the NaOH. What is its pH?

    a. 1.00
    b. 5.12
    c. 8.71
! d. 8.88
    e. 13.00

20. What is the pH of a 1.00 molar solution of $NaNO_2(aq)$? The K_a for nitrous acid is 7.0×10^{-4}.

    a. 1.57
    b. 3.15
    c. 5.42
! d. 8.58
    e. 10.85

21. What is the pH of a 1.00 molar solution of $NaNO_3(aq)$? The K_a for nitrous acid is 7.0×10^{-4}.

    a. 6.00
    b. 6.90
! c. 7.00
    d. 7.10
    e. 13.00

22. What is the pH of a 1.00 molar solution of KCl? The K_a for hypochlorous acid is 3.0×10^{-8}.

    a. 0.00
    b. 6.90
! c. 7.00
    d. 7.10
    e. 13.00

23. What is the pH of a 1.00 molar solution of $NH_4Cl(aq)$? The K_b for NH_3 is 1.8×10^{-5}.

    a. 2.37
! b. 4.63
    c. 9.26
    d. 9.37
    e. 11.63

24. What is the pH of a 1.00 molar solution of $NaC_2H_3O_2(aq)$? The K_a for acetic acid is 1.8×10^{-5}.

    a. 2.37
    b. 4.63
    c. 4.75
! d. 9.37
    e. 11.63

25. What is the pH of a 1.00 molar solution of $NaBr(aq)$? The K_a for hypobromous acid is 2.1×10^{-9}.

    a. 0.00
    b. 6.90
! c. 7.00
    d. 7.10
    e. 13.00

26. A buffer solution is prepared by taking 0.400 moles of acetic acid (pKa = 4.76) and 0.250 moles of sodium acetate in sufficient water to make 1.400 liters of solution. Calculate the pH of this solution.

      a. 4.46
!   b. 4.56
      c. 4.66
      d. 4.86
      e. 4.96

27. A buffer solution is prepared by taking 0.250 moles of acetic acid (pKa = 4.76) and 0.400 moles of sodium acetate in sufficient water to make 1.800 liters of solution. Calculate the solution pH.

      a. 4.56
      b. 4.66
      c. 4.86
!   d. 4.96
      e. 5.06

28. A buffer solution is prepared by taking 0.400 moles of acetic acid (pKa = 4.76) and 0.250 moles of calcium acetate in sufficient water to make 1.400 liters of solution. Calculate the pH of this solution.

      a. 4.46
      b. 4.56
      c. 4.66
!   d. 4.86
      e. 4.96

29. A buffer solution is prepared by taking 0.250 moles of acetic acid (pKa = 4.76) and 0.400 moles of barium acetate in sufficient water to make 1.400 liters of solution. Calculate the pH of this solution.

      a. 4.25
      b. 4.45
      c. 5.00
!   d. 5.27
      e. 5.35

30. The pK_a of acetic acid, $HC_2H_3O_2$, is 4.76. A buffer solution was made using an unspecified amount of acetic acid and 0.30 moles of $NaC_2H_3O_2$ in enough water to make 2.00 liters of solution. Its pH was measured as 4.40 on a meter. How many moles of $HC_2H_3O_2$ were used?

      a. 0.13 mol
      b. 0.18 mol
      c. 0.60 mol
!   d. 0.69 mol
      e. 1.37 mol

31. The pK_a of acetic acid, $HC_2H_3O_2$, is 4.76. A buffer solution was made using an unspecified amount of acetic acid and 0.30 moles of $NaC_2H_3O_2$ in enough water to make 1.50 liters of solution. Its pH was measured as 4.50 on a meter. How many moles of $HC_2H_3O_2$ were used?

     a. 0.31
!   b. 0.55
     c. 0.61
     d. 1.09
     e. 1.21

32. The pK_a of acetic acid, $HC_2H_3O_2$, is 4.76. A buffer solution was made using an unspecified amount of $NaC_2H_3O_2$ and 0.30 moles of acetic acid in enough water to make 2.00 liters of solution. Its pH was measured as 4.60 on a meter. How many moles of $NaC_2H_3O_2$ were used?

     a. 0.10
!   b. 0.21
     c. 0.30
     d. 0.42
     e. 0.44

33. The pK_a of acetic acid, $HC_2H_3O_2$, is 4.76. A buffer solution was made using an unspecified amount of $NaC_2H_3O_2$ and 0.30 moles of acetic acid in enough water to make 1.50 liters of solution. Its pH was measured as 4.55 on a meter. How many moles of $NaC_2H_3O_2$ were used?

     a. 0.10
!   b. 0.18
     c. 0.30
     d. 0.37
     e. 0.49

34. The pK_a of acetic acid, $HC_2H_3O_2$, is 4.76. A buffer solution contains $HC_2H_3O_2$ and $NaC_2H_3O_2$, has a pH of 4.60, and a *total* acetate concentration (*all forms*) of 0.400 molar. The $[C_2H_3O_2^-]$ is

     a. 0.12 M
!   b. 0.16 M
     c. 0.20 M
     d. 0.25 M
     e. 0.32 M

35. The pK_a of acetic acid, $HC_2H_3O_2$, is 4.76. A buffer solution contains $HC_2H_3O_2$ and $NaC_2H_3O_2$, has a pH of 4.76, and a *total* acetate concentration (*all forms*) of 0.400 molar. The $[C_2H_3O_2^-]$ is

     a. 0.100 M
     b. 0.150 M
!   c. 0.200 M
     d. 0.250 M
     e. 0.300 M

36. The pK_b of ammonia solution, $NH_3(aq)$, is 4.76. A buffer solution contains NH_4Cl and NH_3, has a pH of 9.45, and a *total* ammonia concentration (*all forms*) of 0.400 molar. The $[NH_4^+]$ is

    !   a.   0.153
        b.   0.186
        c.   0.210
        d.   0.247
        e.   0.300

37. The pK_b of ammonia solution, $NH_3(aq)$, is 4.76. A buffer solution contains NH_4Cl and NH_3, has a pH of 9.65, and a *total* ammonia concentration (*all forms*) of 0.350 molar. The $[NH_3]$ is

        a.   0.098
        b.   0.146
    !   c.   0.252
        d.   0.389
        e.   0.420

38. Here is a list of some weak acids and their pK's:
    H*Mac*, $pK_a = 4.46$ H*Tern*, $pK_a = 3.50$ H*Brun*, $pK_a = 5.33$ H*Tharn*, $pK_a = 7.33$
    H*Pen*, $pK_a = 8.24$ H*Fern*, $pK_a = 6.42$
    Which one of the sets below would be the best choice to prepare a buffer with pH = 7.00

        a.   brunic acid (H*Brun*), and either sodium or potassium brunate
        b.   macnic acid (H*Mac*), and either sodium or potassium macnate
        c.   pentic acid (H*Pen*), and either sodium or potassium pentate
    !   d.   tharnic acid (H*Tharn*), and either sodium or potassium tharnate
        e.   ternic acid (H*Tern*), and either sodium or potassium ternate

39. Here is a list of some weak acids and their pK's.
    H*Mac*, $pK_a = 4.46$ H*Tern*, $pK_a = 3.50$ H*Brun*, $pK_a = 5.33$ H*THarn*, $pK_a = 7.33$
    H*Pen*, $pK_a = 8.24$ H*Fern*, $pK_a = 6.42$
    Which one of the sets below would be the best choice to prepare a buffer with pH = 5.50

    !   a.   brunic acid (H*Brun*), and either sodium or potassium brunate
        b.   macnic acid (H*Mac*), and either sodium or potassium macnate
        c.   pentic acid (H*Pen*), and either sodium or potassium pentate
        d.   tharnic acid (H*THarn*), and either sodium or potassium tharnate
        e.   fernic acid (H*Fern*), and either sodium or potassium fernate

40. Which one of the following is the most appropriate chemical indicator to use in the titration of 0.100 molar $HCl(aq)$ by 0.100 molar $NaOH(aq)$? The $NaOH(aq)$ is the titrant.

        a.   thymol blue, for which $pK_{ind} = 8.8$ also, HInd is yellow and Ind⁻ is blue
        b.   bromothymol blue, for which $pK_{ind} = 6.8$, also HInd is yellow and Ind⁻ is blue
        c.   phenolphthalein, for which $pK_{ind} = 9.1$, also HInd is colorless and Ind⁻ is pink
        d.   cresol red, for which $pK_{ind} = 7.9$, also HInd is yellow and Ind⁻ is red
    !   e.   Any of these indicators will suffice for the titration of a strong acid by a strong base.

41. Here is a list of some weak acids and their pK's.

   HMac, pK$_a$ = 4.46   HTern, pK$_a$ = 3.50   HBrun, pK$_a$ = 5.33   HTHarn, pK$_a$ = 7.33
   HPen, pK$_a$ = 8.24   HFern, pK$_a$ = 6.42

   Which one of the sets below would be the best choice to prepare a buffer with pH = 3.75

   a. brunic acid (HBrun), and either sodium or potassium brunate
   b. fernic acid (HFern), and either sodium or potassium fernate
   c. pentic acid (HPen), and either sodium or potassium pentate
   d. tharnic acid (HTHarn), and either sodium or potassium tharnate
   ! e. ternic acid (HTern), and either sodium or potassium ternate

42. Given the following:

   0.200M NH$_3$(aq) with pK$_b$ = 4.76   0.200M HC$_2$H$_3$O$_2$(aq) with pK$_a$ = 4.76
   0.200M NaOH(aq)   0.200M HCl(aq)

   A mixture is made using 25.0 mL of the HCl and 50.0 mL of the NH$_3$. What is its pH?

   a. 1.18
   b. 8.87
   c. 8.94
   ! d. 9.24
   e. 9.54

43. Given the following:

   0.200M NH$_3$(aq) with pK$_b$ = 4.76   0.200M HC$_2$H$_3$O$_2$(aq) with pK$_a$ = 4.76
   0.200M NaOH(aq)   0.200M HCl(aq)

   A mixture is made using 50.0 mL of the HC$_2$H$_3$O$_2$ and 25.0 mL of the NaOH. What is its pH?

   a. 2.81
   b. 4.46
   ! c. 4.76
   d. 5.06
   e. 12.82

44. Which one of the following is the most appropriate chemical indicator to use in the titration of 0.100 molar acetic acid(aq) by 0.100 molar NaOH(aq)? This is the titration of a weak acid by a strong base. The NaOH(aq) is the titrant.

   a. phenol red, for which pK$_{ind}$ = 7.3, also HInd is yellow and Ind$^-$ is red
   b. bromothymol blue, for which pK$_{ind}$ = 6.8, also HInd is yellow and Ind$^-$ is blue
   ! c. phenolphthalein, for which pK$_{ind}$ = 9.1, also HInd is colorless and Ind$^-$ is pink
   d. cresol red, for which pK$_{ind}$ = 7.9, also HInd is yellow and Ind$^-$ is red
   e. These indicators will all work equally well for the titration of a weak acid by a strong base.

45. Which one of the following is the most appropriate chemical indicator to use in the titration of 0.100 molar ammonia solution by 0.100 molar HCl(aq)? The HCl(aq) is the titrant.

      a. thymol blue, for which pK_{ind} = 8.8, also HInd is yellow and Ind⁻ is blue
  ! b. methyl orange, for which pK_{ind} = 3.8, also HInd is red and Ind⁻ is yellow
      c. thymolphthalein, for which pK_{ind} = 9.9, also HInd is colorless and Ind⁻ is blue
      d. cresol red, pK_{ind} = for which 7.9, also HInd is yellow and Ind⁻ is red
      e. These indicators will all work equally well for the titration of a weak acid by a strong base.

46. A mixture contains 0.060 moles of NaH_2PO_4 and 0.080 moles of K_2HPO_4. It is titrated with 0.500 molar NaOH(aq) to neutralize it completely. How many mL of the NaOH solution are required?

      a. 280 mL
      b. 313.3 mL
      c. 372 mL
  ! d. 400 mL
      e. 440 mL

47. A solution is made by taking 100.0 mL of 4.0×10^{-3} molar NaOH(aq) and mixing in 10.0 mL of 4.0×10^{-2} molar HCl(aq). A small portion was tested using thymol blue indicator, for which the pK_{ind} = 8.8, and the colors are yellow for Hind, and blue for Ind⁻. What color would be observed?

      a. blue
      b. green
  ! c. yellow
      d. orange
      e. red

48. A solution is made by taking 100.0 mL of 2.0×10^{-2} molar NaOH(aq) and mixing in 50.0 mL of 3.0×10^{-2} molar HCl(aq). The acidity of a small portion was tested using tyrolian blue indicator, for which the pK_{ind} = 12.5, and the colors are blue for Hind, and yellow for Ind⁻. What color would be observed as a result of the testing?

  ! a. blue
      b. green
      c. yellow
      d. orange
      e. red

49. For H_3PO_3, which is actually a diprotic acid, $K_{a1} = 1.0 \times 10^{-2}$ and $K_{a2} = 2.6 \times 10^{-7}$. Calculate a value for the $[H^+]$ in a 0.500 molar solution of H_3PO_3.

      a. 1.0×10^{-2} mol L^{-1}
  ! b. 6.6×10^{-2} mol L^{-1}
      c. 7.1×10^{-2} mol L^{-1}
      d. 8.5×10^{-3} mol L^{-1}
      e. 3.3×10^{-3} mol L^{-1}

50. A solution is made by taking 2.42 grams of NaCl, 6.44 grams of NaClO$_4$, 3.81 grams of KNO$_3$, and 4.64 grams of KBr in enough water to make 500 mL of solution. A portion was treated with thymol blue indicator, for which the pK$_{ind}$ = 8.8, and the colors are yellow for Hind, and blue for Ind⁻. What color should be obtained with the test portion?

    a. blue
    b. green
!   c. yellow
    d. orange
    e. red

51. For H$_3$PO$_3$, which is actually a diprotic acid, K$_{a1}$ = 1.0 x 10^{-2} and K$_{a2}$ = 2.6 x 10^{-7}. Calculate a value for the [H$_2$PO$_3^-$] in a 0.500 molar solution of H$_3$PO$_3$.

    a. 1.0 x 10^{-2} mol L^{-1}
!   b. 6.6 x 10^{-2} mol L^{-1}
    c. 7.1 x 10^{-2} mol L^{-1}
    d. 8.5 x 10^{-3} mol L^{-1}
    e. 3.3 x 10^{-3} mol L^{-1}

52. For H$_3$PO$_3$, which is actually a diprotic acid, K$_{a1}$ = 1.0 x 10^{-2} and K$_{a2}$ = 2.6 x 10^{-7}. Calculate a value for the [HPO$_3^{2-}$] in a 0.500 molar solution of H$_3$PO$_3$.

!   a. 2.6 x 10^{-7} mol L^{-1}
    b. 6.6 x 10^{-2} mol L^{-1}
    c. 7.1 x 10^{-2} mol L^{-1}
    d. 8.5 x 10^{-5} mol L^{-1}
    e. 3.3 x 10^{-3} mol L^{-1}

53. Tenzic acid, H$_2$Tenz, is a diprotic acid with dissociation constants: K$_{a1}$ = 4.0 x 10^{-4}, K$_{a2}$ = 1.5 x 10^{-9}. Calculate a value for the [H$^+$] in a 0.500 molar solution of H$_2$Tenz.

!   a. 1.4 x 10^{-2} mol L^{-1}
    b. 1.6 x 10^{-2} mol L^{-1}
    c. 4.0 x 10^{-4} mol L^{-1}
    d. 2.0 x 10^{-2} mol L^{-1}
    e. 4.0 x 10^{-2} mol L^{-1}

54. Tenzic acid, H$_2$Tenz, is a diprotic acid with dissociation constants: K$_{a1}$ = 4.0 x 10^{-4}, K$_{a2}$ = 1.5 x 10^{-9}. Calculate a value for the [HTenz⁻] in a 0.500 molar solution of H$_2$Tenz.

!   a. 1.4 x 10^{-2} mol L^{-1}/L
    b. 1.6 x 10^{-2} mol L^{-1}/L
    c. 4.0 x 10^{-4} mol L^{-1}/L
    d. 2.0 x 10^{-2} mol L^{-1}/L
    e. 4.0 x 10^{-2} mol L^{-1}/L

55. Tenzic acid, H_2Tenz, is a diprotic acid with dissociation constants: $K_{a1} = 4.0 \times 10^{-4}$, $K_{a2} = 1.5 \times 10^{-9}$. Calculate a value for the $[Tenz^{2-}]$ in a 0.500 molar solution of H_2Tenz.

      a. 7.7×10^{-7} mol L^{-1}/L
      b. 2.7×10^{-5} mol L^{-1}/L
      c. 3.8×10^{-5} mol L^{-1}/L
      d. 4.0×10^{-4} mol L^{-1}/L
!   e. 1.5×10^{-9} mol L^{-1}/L

56. For H_3PO_4, a tripotic acid, $K_{a1} = 7.1 \times 10^{-3}$, $K_{a2} = 6.3 \times 10^{-8}$, and $K_{a3} = 4.5 \times 10^{-13}$. What is the pH of a solution which contains 0.200 moles of K_2HPO_4 and 0.300 moles of Na_3PO_4 per liter of solution?

      a. 7.20
      b. 7.34
      c. 12.17
      d. 12.35
!   e. 12.52

57. For H_3PO_4, a tripotic acid, $K_{a1} = 7.1 \times 10^{-3}$, $K_{a2} = 6.3 \times 10^{-8}$, and $K_{a3} = 4.5 \times 10^{-13}$ What is the pH of a solution which contains 0.300 moles of Na_2HPO_4 and 0.400 moles of KH_2PO_4 per liter of solution?

!   a. 7.08
      b. 7.20
      c. 7.33
      d. 10.20
      e. 12.22

58. Carbonic acid, H_2CO_3, is a diprotic acid with dissociation constants: $K_{a1} = 4.5 \times 10^{-7}$, $K_{a2} = 4.7 \times 10^{-11}$. What is the value of the ratio, $[H_2CO_3]/[HCO_3^-]$, in a solution containing both species which is maintained at pH = 7.00 by means of a buffer?

      a. 1.00
      b. 0.33
      c. 0.25
!   d. 0.22
      e. 1.33

59. The pH at the equivalence point of the titration of acetic acid solution by sodium hydroxide solution is

      a. < 2.00
      b. 3.50 < pH < 7.00
      c. 7.00
!   d. 7.00 < pH < 11.00
      e. > 11.0

60. The pH at the equivalence point of the titration of perchloric acid solution by sodium hydroxide solution is

    a. < 2.00
    b. $4.00 < pH < 7.00$
! c. 7.00
    d. $7.00 < pH < 11.00$
    e. > 11.0

61. The pH at the equivalence point of the titration of ammonia solution by hydrochloric acid solution is

    a. < 2.00
! b. $4.00 < pH < 7.00$
    c. 7.00
    d. $7.00 < pH < 11.00$
    e. > 11.0

Fill in the Blanks

62. The pK_a of a weak acid is 6.50. What is the value of K_a for this acid? _____ (! 3.2×10^{-7})

63. A 0.100 molar solution of a moderately strong monoprotic acid in water has a pH $= 1.88$. Calculate the value of K_a, the acid dissociation constant for this acid. _____ (! 2.00×10^{-3})

64. A solution of a weak monoprotic base B (0.50 M) and its salt BH^+Cl^- (0.80 M) has a pH $= 9.40$. What is the value of K_b for this base, B? _____ (! 4.0×10^{-5})

65. A solution of a weak monoprotic acid, Hac (0.50 molar) and its potassium salt Kac (0.75 molar) has a measured pH $= 4.88$. What is the value of K_a for this acid? _____ (! 2.0×10^{-5})

True and False

66. A relation involving acids and bases is, $K_a + K_b = K_w$. (! F)

67. A solution of sodium cyanide in water should be basic, not neutral or acidic. (! T)

68. The titration of a strong acid by a strong base gives sharper and more well defined end points than titration of a weak acid by a weak base. (! T)

69. A solution of ammonium nitrate in water should be basic, not neutral or acidic. (! F)

70. The pK_a is a reliable measure of the strength of an acid. Strong acids have larger pK_a values than weak acids. (! F)

71. A student does a titration of $NH_3(aq)$(pK_b = 4.76) with $HCl(aq)$, taking 500.0 mL of 0.300 M $NH_3(aq)$ and adding 100.0 mL of the HCl solution. He measured the pH of the mixture and found it was 8.94. What was the molarity of the HCl solution? _____ (! 1.00 molar)

72. A student does a titration of $NH_3(aq)$ (pK_b = 4.76) with $HCl(aq)$, taking 500.0 mL of 0.300 M $NH_3(aq)$ and adding 100.0 mL of the HCl solution. He measured the pH of the mixture and found it was 9.54. What was the molarity of the HCl solution? _____ (! 0.500 molar)

73. The pK_b for $NH_3(aq)$ is 4.76. What should be the pH of a mixture containing 100.0 mL of 0.300 M $NH_4Cl(aq)$, 100 mL of 0.300 M $NH_3(aq)$, and 100 mL of 0.100 M NaOH? _____ (! 9.54)

74. The pK_a for $HC_2H_3O_2(aq)$ is 4.76. What should be the pH of a mixture containing 100.0 mL of 0.300 M $NaC_2H_3O_2(aq)$, 100 mL of 0.300 M $HC_2H_3O_2(aq)$, and 100 mL of 0.100 M NaOH? _____ (! 5.06)

75. The pK_b for $NH_3(aq)$ is 4.76. What should be the pH of a mixture containing 100.0 mL of 0.300 M $NH_4Cl(aq)$, 100 mL of 0.300 M $NH_3(aq)$, and 100 mL of 0.100 M $HCl(aq)$? _____ (! 8.94)

76. The pK_a for $HC_2H_3O_2(aq)$ is 4.76. What should be the pH of a mixture containing 100.0 mL of 0.300 M $NaC_2H_3O_2(aq)$, 100 mL of 0.300 M $HC_2H_3O_2(aq)$, and 100 mL of 0.100 M $HCl(aq)$? _____ (! 4.46)

77. A mixture contains 400.0 mL of 1.00 M $NH_3(aq)$, whose pK_b is 4.76, and 400.0 mL of 1.00 M $NH_4Cl(aq)$. 200.0 mL of 0.500 M $NaOH(aq)$ was added to the mixture. What was the pH of the mixture before addition of the base and after addition of the base? _____ , _____ (! 9.24, 9.46)

78. A mixture contains 400.0 mL of 1.00 M $NH_3(aq)$, whose pK_b is = 4.76, and 400.0 mL of 1.00 M $NH_4Cl(aq)$. 200.0 mL of 0.500 M $HCl(aq)$ was added to the mixture. What is the pH of the buffer before addition of the acid and after addition of the acid? _____ , _____ (! 9.24, 9.02)

79. A mixture contains benzoic acid, a monoprotic acid (K_a = 6.28 x 10^{-5}, 0.250 M), and sodium benzoate (0.400 M). 500 mL of this buffer was treated with 250 mL of a NaOH solution whose pH was 13.574. What should the pH be after addition of the base? _____ (! 4.52)

80. A student was instructed to prepare 2.00 liters of a buffer solution using 0.600 moles of sodium dihydrogen phosphate and 0.400 moles of sodium monohydrogen phosphate as the only solutes. He got the instructions reversed somehow and made the solution using 0.400 moles of sodium dihydrogen phosphate and 0.600 moles of sodium monohydrogen phosphate. He asked the postdoc student what to do. "No problem", was the reply, "just add enough solid sodium hydroxide or 6.00 molar $HCl(aq)$ to get the pH to where it should have been". How many pH units off the target value was the pH of the solution the student prepared at first? What should he add to the 2.00 liters of solution he now has, and in what quantity?

_____

(! he was off by 0.602 pH units, he needs to add 8.00 grams of solid NaOH)

81. A mixture contains benzoic acid, a monoprotic acid (K_a = 6.28 x 10^{-5}, 0.250 M), and sodium benzoate (0.400 moles/liter). How many mL of a HCl(*aq*) solution whose pH is 0.523 should be added to 500 mL of this buffer to change its pH from what it is to pH = 4.20? _____ (! 125 mL)

Critical Thinking, Level 2

82. Tyrone Ogunmakinwa and Kevin Vitellan are only ones left in the AP Chemistry competition. They were presented with this problem: For H_3PO_4, a triprotic acid, K_{a1} = 7.1 x 10^{-3}, K_{a2} = 6.3 x 10^{-8} and K_{a3} = 4.5 x 10^{-13}. A student prepared 2.500 liters of an aqueous solution which contained the following substances as its only solutes:

0.300 moles of nitric acid
0.200 moles of hydrochloric acid
0.500 moles of sodium dihydrogen orthophosphate
0.400 moles of sodium orthophosphate

Calculate the value that should be obtained for the pH of this solution. _____ (! 6.90)

83. Tyrone Ogunmakinwa and Kevin Vitellan are still tied in the AP Chemistry competition. They were presented with this next problem: For H_3PO_4, a triprotic acid, K_{a1} = 7.1 x 10^{-3}, K_{a2} = 6.3 x 10^{-8} and K_{a3} = 4.5 x 10^{-13}. A student prepared the following mixture: Take :

150 mL of 3.00 molar nitric acid
150 mL of 0.200 molar hydrochloric acid
96.0 grams of sodium dihydrogen orthophosphate
98.4 grams of sodium orthophosphate
add them to enough water to make 2.00 liters of solution.

Calculate the value that should be obtained for the pH of this solution. _____ (! 6.87 -- 6.88)

84. For H_3PO_4, a tripotic acid, K_{a1} = 7.1 x 10^{-3}, K_{a2} = 6.3 x 10^{-8} and K_{a3} = 4.5 x 10^{-13}. What is the pH of an aqueous solution which was prepared using 0.200 moles of KH_2PO_4 and 0.300 moles of Na_3PO_4 per liter of solution as the only solutes? _____ (! 11.74)

85. For H_3PO_4, a tripotic acid, K_{a1} = 7.1 x 10^{-3}, K_{a2} = 6.3 x 10^{-8} and K_{a3} = 4.5 x 10^{-13}. What is the pH of an aqueous solution which was prepared using 0.500 moles of KH_2PO_4 , 0.200 moles of Na_2HPO_4, and 0.200 moles of Na_3PO_4 per liter of solution as the only solutes? _____ (! 7.50)

Chapter 17 Solubility and Simultaneous Equilibria

Multiple Choice

1. The expression for the solubility product of $Ba_3(AsO_4)_2$ is

! a. $[Ba^{2+}]^3[AsO_4^{3-}]^2$
b. $[3Ba^{2+}]^3[2AsO_4^{3-}]^2$
c. $3[Ba^{2+}] \times 2[AsO_4^{3-}]$
d. $3[Ba^{2+}]^3 + 2[AsO_4^{3-}]^2$
e. $[Ba^{2+}]_3[AsO_4^{3-}]_2$

2. The expression for the solubility product of copper(II) hydroxide is

a. $[Cu^{2+}][2\ OH^-]$
b. $[Cu^{2+}] \times 2[OH^-]^2$
c. $[Cu^{2+}]^2[OH^-]$
! d. $[Cu^{2+}][OH^-]^2$
e. $[Cu^{2+}] \times ½[OH^-]^2$

3. The expression for the solubility product of silver oxalate ($Ag_2C_2O_4$) is

a. $[Ag_2^{2+}][C_2O_4^{2-}]$
b. $[Ag^+][C_2O_4^{2-}]^2$
c. $2[Ag^+][C_2O_4^{2-}]$
! d. $[Ag^+]^2[C_2O_4^{2-}]$
e. $2[Ag^+]^2[C_2O_4^{2-}]$

4. The solubility of Ag_2NtO_4, silver nortonate, in pure water is 4.0×10^{-5} moles per liter. Calculate the value of K_{sp} for silver nortonate.

a. 1.6×10^{-9}
b. 6.4×10^{-14}
! c. 2.6×10^{-13}
d. 4.0×10^{-5}
e. 4.0×10^{-15}

5. Which one of the following salts has the highest solubility in water, expressed in moles per liter?

a. PbF_2, $K_{sp} = 3.6 \times 10^{-8}$
b. Ag_2CrO_4, $K_{sp} = 1.2 \times 10^{-12}$
c. CaF_2, $K_{sp} = 3.9 \times 10^{-11}$
! d. BaF_2, $K_{sp} = 1.7 \times 10^{-6}$
e. PbI_2, $K_{sp} = 7.9 \times 10^{-9}$

6. The solubility of silver sulfate (Ag_2SO_4), in moles per liter, can be expressed in terms of the resulting ion concentrations. Which one of the following relationships is correct?

      a. solubility = $2[Ag^+]$
      b. solubility = $[Ag^+]$
      c. solubility = $[2Ag^+]$
      d. solubility = $2[SO_4^{2-}]$
!   e. solubility = $[SO_4^{2-}]$

7. The solubility product for Ag_3PO_4 is: $K_{sp} = 2.8 \times 10^{-18}$. What is the solubility of Ag_3PO_4 in water, in moles per liter?

!   a. 1.8×10^{-5} M
      b. 2.5×10^{-5} M
      c. 1.9×10^{-86} M
      d. 3.1×10^{-5} M
      e. 4.1×10^{-5} M

8. The solubility product for $BaSO_4$ is 1.1×10^{-10}. Calculate the solubility of $BaSO_4$ in pure water, in moles per liter.

      a. 5.5×10^{-11} mol L^{-1}
!   b. 1.0×10^{-5} mol L^{-1}
      c. 2.1×10^{-5} mol L^{-1}
      d. 1.1×10^{-10} mol L^{-1}
      e. 2.2×10^{-10} mol L^{-1}

9. The solubility product for $PbCl_2$ is 1.7×10^{-5}. What is the solubility of $PbCl_2$ in pure water, in moles per liter?

      a. 2.4×10^{-4} mol L^{-1}
      b. 6.2×10^{-2} mol L^{-1}
      c. 7.7×10^{-3} mol L^{-1}
!   d. 1.6×10^{-2} mol L^{-1}
      e. 6.0×10^{-5} mol L^{-1}

10. Calculate the concentration of chloride ions in a saturated solution of lead(II) chloride. The $K_{sp} = 1.7 \times 10^{-5}$.

      a. 2.4×10^{-4} M
      b. 4.8×10^{-4} M
      c. 3.9×10^{-2} M
      d. 1.2×10^{-1} M
!   e. 3.2×10^{-2} M

11. The solubility product of barium fluoride (BaF_2) is 1.7×10^{-6}. Calculate the concentration of fluoride ions in a saturated solution of barium fluoride.

      a. 7.6×10^{-3} M
!   b. 1.5×10^{-2} M
      c. 3.4×10^{-5} M
      d. 1.7×10^{-6} M
      e. 3.4×10^{-6} M

12. The solubility product for $Mg_3(PO_4)_2$ is 6.3×10^{-26}. What is the solubility of $Mg_3(PO_4)_2$ in pure water, in grams per liter?

      a. 1.7×10^{-23} g L^{-1}
      b. 3.4×10^{-7} g L^{-1}
!   c. 9.4×10^{-4} g L^{-1}
      d. 1.2×10^{-3} g L^{-1}
      e. 2.4×10^{-3} g L^{-1}

13. The solubility of lead iodide is 578 m g L^{-1} at 25 °C. What is the solubility product for PbI_2?

!   a. 8.0×10^{-9}
      b. 1.6×10^{-6}
      c. 1.1×10^{-11}
      d. 2.7×10^{-12}
      e. 6.3×10^{-6}

14. The solubility of barium carbonate is 14.8 m g L^{-1} at 30 °C. Calculate the K_{sp} value for $BaCO_3$.

      a. 7.5×10^{-5}
      b. 1.5×10^{-4}
!   c. 5.6×10^{-9}
      d. 7.5×10^{-6}
      e. 1.5×10^{-3}

15. What is the solubility, in moles per liter, of AgCl ($K_{sp} = 1.8 \times 10^{-10}$) in 0.0100 molar aqueous potassium chloride solution?

      a. 7.5×10^{-5} mol L^{-1}
!   b. 1.8×10^{-8} mol L^{-1}
      c. 1.3×10^{-6} mol L^{-1}
      d. 3.6×10^{-8} mol L^{-1}
      e. 1.5×10^{-7} mol L^{-1}

16. The K_{sp} value for MgF_2 is 6.9×10^{-9}. A 0.10 M NaF solution is saturated with magnesium fluoride. How many parts per million (ppm) of magnesium are there in this saturated solution?
    a. 0.0013
    b. 40
    c. 0.040
!   d. 0.017
    e. 2.65

17. The solubility product of Ag_2CrO_4 is 1.2×10^{-12}. How many parts per million (ppm) of silver are there in a saturated solution of silver chromate in pure water?

    a. 0.012
    b. 0.24
    c. 7.2
!   d. 14
    e. 1.6

18. The solubility of barium sulfate varies with the composition of the solvent. In which one of the solvent mixtures below would $BaSO_4$ have the lowest solubility?

    a. pure water
    b. 0.10 M $Na_2SO_4(aq)$
!   c. 1.0 M $(NH_4)_2SO_4(aq)$
    d. 0.5 M $Ba(NO_3)_2(aq)$
    e. 1.0 M $HCl(aq)$

19. Which one of the following solids would be more soluble in a solution of one of the common strong acids than in pure water?

    a. KCl
    b. $MgCl_2$
    c. $NaNO_3$
    d. LiBr
!   e. $ZnCO_3$

20. Which one of the following solids would be more soluble in a 1.00 molar solution of one of the common strong acids than in pure water?

    a. LiCl
!   b. ZnS
    c. $NaNO_3$
    d. K_2SO_4
    e. $MgCl_2$

21. $ZnCO_3$, a slightly soluble substance, is least soluble in which one of the following solvents?

    a. pure water
  ! b. 0.20 M $ZnCl_2$
    c. 0.10 M Na_2CO_3
    d. 0.10 M HCl
    e. 0.20 M NaCl

22. What is the maximum concentration of Mg^{2+} ion that can co-exist with F^- ion present in a 0.10 M NaF(aq) solution without causing any precipitate of magnesium fluoride to form? The K_{sp} of MgF_2 is 6.6×10^{-9}.

    a. 1.3×10^{-7} M
    b. 6.6×10^{-9} M
    c. 6.6×10^{-8} M
    d. 1.6×10^{-7} M
  ! e. 6.6×10^{-7} M

23. Calculate the minimum concentration of Ag^+ ion that must be added to (or built up in) a 0.140 M Na_2CrO_4 solution in order to initiate a precipitate of silver chromate. The K_{sp} of Ag_2CrO_4 is 1.2×10^{-12}.

    a. 4.8×10^{-9} mol L^{-1}
  ! b. 2.9×10^{-6} mol L^{-1}
    c. 2.0×10^{-6} mol L^{-1}
    d. 9.5×10^{-7} mol L^{-1}
    e. 1.4×10^{-6} mol L^{-1}

24. The solubility product for Ag_3PO_4 is 2.8×10^{-18}. What is the solubility of silver phosphate in solution which also contains 0.10 moles of silver nitrate per liter?

    a. 4.4×10^{-4} mol L^{-1}
    b. 4.4×10^{-15} mol L^{-1}
  ! c. 2.8×10^{-15} mol L^{-1}
    d. 3.6×10^{-16} mol L^{-1}
    e. 2.8×10^{-13} mol L^{-1}

25. The solubility product of lead fluoride, (PbF_2) is 3.6×10^{-8}. What is its solubility in 0.10 M NaF solution, in grams per liter?

  ! a. 8.8×10^{-4} g L^{-1}
    b. 3.9×10^{-4} g L^{-1}
    c. 13 g L^{-1}
    d. 3.9×10^{-3} g L^{-1}
    e. 8.8×10^{-5} g L^{-1}

26. How many parts per million of calcium are there in a saturated solution of CaF_2 ($K_{sp} = 3.9 \times 10^{-11}$) in pure water.

        a. 1.4
        b. 3.2
 ! c. 8.6
        d. 17
        e. 21

27. NaOH is added to sea water containing 0.050 moles per liter of Mg^{2+} ion until the pH reaches 12.0. A certain quantity of $Mg(OH)_2$ precipitates. What is the concentration of the magnesium ions remaining in the solution, in moles per liter? The K_{sp} of $Mg(OH)_2$ is 7.1×10^{-12}.

        a. 1.5×10^{-7} M
        b. 5.0×10^{-8} M
        c. 7.1×10^{-9} M
 ! d. 7.1×10^{-8} M
        e. 7.1×10^{-6} M

28. Sea water contains magnesium ions, Mg^{2+}. A solution of sea water was treated with sodium hydroxide until its pH was 11.0. If the K_{sp} of $Mg(OH)_2$ is 7.1×10^{-12}, what is the maximum concentration of magnesium ions remaining in the water?

        a. 7.1×10^{-9} mol L^{-1}
        b. 7.1×10^{-19} mol L^{-1}
        c. 5.0×10^{-8} mol L^{-1}
        d. 4.4×10^{-4} mol L^{-1}
 ! e. 7.1×10^{-6} mol L^{-1}

29. Will a precipitate form (yes or no) when 20.0 mL of 1.8×10^{-3} M $Pb(NO_3)_2$ is added to 30.0 mL of 5.0×10^{-4} M Na_2SO_4? The K_{sp} of $(PbSO_4)$ is 6.3×10^{-7}.

 ! a. no, because the ion product < K_{sp}
        b. no, because the ion product > K_{sp}
        c. yes, because the ion product < K_{sp}
        d. yes, because the ion product > K_{sp}
        e. no, because the ion product > K_{sp}

30. Will a precipitate of MgF_2 form when 300 mL of 1.1×10^{-3} M $MgCl_2$ solution is added to 500 mL of 1.2×10^{-3} M NaF? The K_{sp} of MgF_2 is 6.9×10^{-9}.

        a. yes, because the ion product, $Q > K_{sp}$
 ! b. no, because the ion product, $Q < K_{sp}$
        c. no, because the ion product, $Q = K_{sp}$
        d. yes, because the ion product, $Q < K_{sp}$
        e. no, because the ion product, $Q > K_{sp}$

31. In an experiment, it is planned to add 300 mL of 2.0×10^{-5} M $AgNO_3$ to 200 mL of 2.5×10^{-9} M NaI. Will a precipitate form? What is the precipitate? K_{sp} (AgI) $= 8.3 \times 10^{-17}$.

      a. yes, the ppt is $AgNO_3(s)$
      b. yes, the ppt is $NaNO_3(s)$
      c. yes, the ppt is $NaI(s)$
!   d. yes, the ppt is $AgI(s)$
      e. no

32. For $PbCl_2$, $K_{sp} = 1.7 \times 10^{-5}$. Will a precipitate of $PbCl_2$ form when 200 mL of 3.0×10^{-2} M $Pb(NO_3)_2$ solution is added to 300 mL of 5.0×10^{-2} M KCl? Choose one of the following.

      a. yes, the ion product, $Q_{sp} > K_{sp}$
!   b. no, the ion product, $Q_{sp} < K_{sp}$
      c. no, the ion product, $Q_{sp} = K_{sp}$
      d. yes, the ion product, $Q_{sp} < K_{sp}$
      e. no, because the ion product, $Q_{sp} > K_{sp}$

33. Will a precipitate form when 250 mL of 0.20 M Na_2CrO_4 is added to 250 mL of 0.20 M $AgNO_3$? What will be the concentration of the Ag^+ ion remaining in solution when equilibrium is reached? The K_{sp} for Ag_2CrO_4 is 1.2×10^{-12}.

!   a. yes, $[Ag^+] = 4.9 \times 10^{-6}$ M
      b. yes, $[Ag^+] = 2.0 \times 10^{-5}$
      c. yes, $[Ag^+] = 2.4 \times 10^{-11}$ M
      d. no, $[Ag^+] = 1.0 \times 10^{-3}$ M
      e. no, $[Ag^+] = 2.0 \times 10^{3}$ M

34. $PbCO_3$, $PbCl_2$, PbI_2, and PbS are all only very slightly soluble in pure water. Which one (ones) should be significantly more soluble in acidic solution than in pure water?

      a. PbI_2, PbS and $PbCO_3$
!   b. only $PbCO_3$ and PbS
      c. only $PbCl_2$ and PbI_2
      d. only $PbCO_3$
      e. All four are significantly more soluble in acidic solution.

35. The group, $Zn(NO_3)_2$, $Zn(CO_3)_2$, $ZnCl_2$, and ZnS contains some salts which are only very slightly soluble in pure water. Of these salts, which one(s) should be significantly more soluble in acidic solution than in pure water?

      a. $Zn(NO_3)_2$, $Zn(CO_3)_2$, and $ZnCl_2$
      b. $Zn(NO_3)_2$, and $Zn(CO_3)_2$
      c. $ZnCl_2$, and ZnS
      d. $Zn(CO_3)_2$, and $ZnCl_2$
!   e. $Zn(CO_3)_2$, and ZnS

36. Zinc carbonate, a slightly soluble substance, is most soluble in which of the following solvents?

    a. water
    b. 0.1 M $ZnCl_2(aq)$
    c. 0.1 M $NaOH(aq)$
 ! d. 0.1 M $HCl(aq)$
    e. 0.2 M $Na_2CO_3(aq)$

37. Given the following information:
$$Ni(OH)_2(s) \rightleftharpoons Ni^{2+}(aq) + 2\ OH^-(aq) \quad K_{sp} = 6.0 \times 10^{-16}$$
$$H_2O(l) \rightleftharpoons H^+(aq) + OH^-(aq) \quad K_w = 1.0 \times 10^{-14}$$
Which choice gives the equilibrium constant for the reaction,
$$Ni(OH)_2(s) + 2\ H^+(aq) \rightleftharpoons Ni^{2+}(aq) + 2\ H_2O(l)$$

    a. K_{sp}/K_w
    b. K_{sp}/K_w
 ! c. K_{sp}/K_w^2
    d. K_w^2/K_{sp}
    e. $2 \times K_w/K_{sp}$

38. A saturated solution of mercurous chromate (mercury(I) chromate) in water contains a lot of mercury by environmental standards, about 17.9 parts per million. From this information, calculate a value for the solubility product constant of mercury(I) chromate.

    a. 1.42×10^{-12}
 ! b. 1.99×10^{-9}
    c. 2.84×10^{-12}
    d. 3.98×10^{-19}
    e. 7.96×10^{-9}

39. The pH of a saturated solution of cerium(III) hydroxide in water is 9.20. How many parts per million of cerium are there in the solution, if the atomic weights are:
        cerium—140.115   hydrogen—1.00794   oxygen—15.9994

 ! a. 0.74
    b. 0.88
    c. 1.01
    d. 2.2
    e. 3.0

40. The pH of a saturated solution of cerium(III) hydroxide in water is 9.20. Calculate a value for the solubility product constant of cerium(III) hydroxide from this data.

    a. 2.5×10^{-10}
    b. 8.4×10^{-11}
    c. 4.0×10^{-19}
!   d. 2.1×10^{-20}
    e. 6.3×10^{-20}

41. The value of the solubility product constant for barium carbonate is 5.0×10^{-9}, while that of barium chromate is 2.1×10^{-10}. From this data, what is the value of K_c for the reaction,

$$BaCO_3(s) + CrO_4^{2-}(aq) \rightleftharpoons BaCrO_4(s) + CO_3^{2-}(aq)$$

    a. 1.1×10^{-18}
    b. 4.2×10^{-2}
    c. 4.8×10^{-9}
    d. 4.9
!   e. 24

42. Hydrazine, N_2H_4, is a weak molecular base with a value of 9.6×10^{-7} for K_b. An aqueous solution contains 0.200 M N_2H_4 **and** 0.376 M $N_2H_5^+Cl^-$ per liter as the only solutes. If the K_{sp} of $Fe(OH)_2$ is 7.9×10^{-16}, what is the maximum $[Fe^{2+}]$ that can coexist with these solutes in the solution?

    a. 1.5×10^{-9} M
    b. 4.1×10^{-9} M
    c. 0.00024 M
    d. 0.00086 M
!   e. 0.0030 M

43. Methylamine, CH_3NH_2, is a weak molecular base with a value of 4.4×10^{-4} for K_b. An aqueous solution contains 0.200 M CH_3NH_2 **and** 0.400 M $CH_3NH_3^+Cl^-$ per liter as the only solutes. If the K_{sp} of $Mg(OH)_2$ is 7.1×10^{-12}, what is the maximum $[Mg^{2+}]$ that can coexist with these solutes in the solution?

    a. 8.1×10^{-9}
    b. 3.2×10^{-8}
    c. 9.2×10^{-6}
!   d. 1.5×10^{-4}
    e. 3.7×10^{-1}

44. Methylamine, CH_3NH_2, is a weak molecular base with a value of 4.4×10^{-4} for K_b. An aqueous solution contains 0.200 M CH_3NH_2 **and** 0.300 M $CH_3NH_3^+Cl^-$ per liter as the only solutes. If the K_{sp} of $Fe(OH)_2$ is 7.9×10^{-16}, what is the maximum $[Fe^{2+}]$ that can coexist with these solutes in the solution?

      a. 1.8×10^{-12}
      b. 9.0×10^{-12}
      c. 1.8×10^{-9}
!   d. 9.2×10^{-9}
      e. 9.2×10^{-6}

45. Dimethylamine, $(CH_3)_2NH$, is a weak molecular base with a value of 9.6×10^{-4} for K_b. An aqueous solution contains 0.350 M $(CH_3)_2NH$ **and** 0.250 M $(CH_3)_2NH_2^+Cl^-$ per liter as the only solutes. If the K_{sp} of $Mg(OH)_2$ is 7.1×10^{-12}, what is the maximum $[Mg^{2+}]$ that can coexist with these solutes in the solution?

      a. 1.7×10^{-7}
!   b. 3.9×10^{-6}
      c. 7.7×10^{-6}
      d. 1.5×10^{-5}
      e. 4.9×10^{-3}

46. A sample of ground water has a calcium ion concentration of 308 parts per million. If fluoride ion is to be added to this water solution, how many mg of NaF can be added, per liter, without causing any calcium fluoride to precipitate? The K_{sp} of CaF_2 is 3.9×10^{-11}.

      a. 1.5 mg
!   b. 3.0 mg
      c. 6.0 mg
      d. 6.8 mg
      e. 9.2 mg

47. A sample of ground water has a calcium ion concentration of 308 parts per million. What is the maximum quantity of NaOH that can be added, per liter, without causing any calcium hydroxide to precipitate? The K_{sp} of calcium hydroxide is 6.5×10^{-6}.

      a. 0.10 g
      b. 0.34 g
      c. 0.58 g
!   d. 1.16 g
      e. 1.69×10^{-2} g

48. The K_{sp} of calcium fluoride is 3.9×10^{-11}. A 0.420 g sample of NaF and a 1.110 g sample of calcium chloride was added to a 1.000 liter volumetric flask, and distilled water was added to the mark. After placing the stopper and shaking the flask to dissolve as much chemicals as would dissolve, what would be the calcium ion concentration remaining in solution afterwards? Be mindful that a precipitate may be formed.

    a. 0.0036 mole per liter
! b. 0.0051 mole per liter
    c. 0.0054 mole per liter
    d. 0.0058 mole per liter
    e. 0.0100 mole per liter

49. The K_{sp} of calcium fluoride is 3.9×10^{-11}. A 0.420 g sample of NaF and a 1.110 g sample of calcium chloride was added to a 1.000 liter volumetric flask, and distilled water was added to the mark. After placing the stopper and shaking the flask to dissolve as much chemicals as would dissolve, how many grams of precipitate, if any, would be formed?

    a. 0.00 g
    b. 0.039 g
! c. 0.39 g
    d. 0.41 g
    e. 0.77 g

50. The K_{sp} value for barium chromate is 2.1×10^{-10}. A 4.16 g sample of $BaCl_2$ and a 5.83 g sample of potassium chromate were added to a 1.000 liter volumetric flask, and distilled water was added to the mark. After placing the stopper and shaking the flask to dissolve as much chemicals as would dissolve, what would be the barium ion concentration remaining in solution afterwards? Be mindful that a precipitate may be formed.

    a. 2.5×10^{-8} mole per liter
! b. 2.1×10^{-8} mole per liter
    c. 2.5×10^{-7} mole per liter
    d. 1.5×10^{-6} mole per liter
    e. 1.5×10^{-5} mole per liter

51. The K_{sp} value for barium chromate is 2.1×10^{-10}. A 4.16 g sample of $BaCl_2$ and a 5.83 g sample of potassium chromate were added to a 1.000 liter volumetric flask, and distilled water was added to the mark. After placing the stopper and shaking the flask to dissolve as much chemicals as would dissolve, how many grams of precipitate, if any, would be formed?

    a. 0.00 g
    b. 0.0315 g
    c. 3.15 g
! d. 3.51 g
    e. 3.68 g

52. The pH of the blood carrying carbon dioxide to and from the lungs is of critical importance. The values of K_{a1} and K_{a2} for the CO_2—HCO_3^-—CO_3^{2-} system at body temperature are 7.9×10^{-7} and 4.7×10^{-11}. What is the ratio of $[CO_2]/[HCO_3^-]$ in blood if the pH of the CO_2 carrying blood is 7.30?

    ! a. 0.063 to 1
    b. 0.067 to 1
    c. 0.077 to 1
    d. 0.25 to 1
    e. 0.83 to 1

53. The pH of the blood carrying carbon dioxide to and from the lungs is of critical importance. The values of K_{a1} and K_{a2} for the CO_2—HCO_3^-—CO_3^{2-} system at body temperature are 7.9×10^{-7} and 4.7×10^{-11}. What per cent of the carbon dioxide being carried by the blood is actually in the form of CO_2 as opposed to HCO_3^- if the pH of the blood carrying the respiration product to the lungs is 7.30?

    ! a. 6.0 per cent
    b. 6.3 per cent
    c. 7.1 per cent
    d. 45.5 per cent
    e. 94 per cent

Fill in the Blanks

54. A precipitate will form when an anion solution and a cation solution are mixed if the _____ exceeds the value of the _____ (! ion product, solubility product constant)

55. Addition of a common ion to a solution of a slightly soluble salt will _____ the solubility of the slightly soluble salt. (! decrease)

56. Carbonic acid, H_2CO_3, is a diprotic acid with dissociation constants: $K_{a1} = 4.5 \times 10^{-7}$, $K_{a2} = 4.7 \times 10^{-11}$. Calculate the pH of a 0.100 molar solution of Na_2CO_3, which is the sodium salt of the one of the conjugate bases of this acid. _____ (! 11.65)

57. For H_3PO_3, which is actually a diprotic acid, $K_{a1} = 1.0 \times 10^{-2}$ and $K_{a2} = 2.6 \times 10^{-7}$. Calculate the pH of a 0.100 molar solution of Na_2HPO_3, which is a salt of one of the conjugate bases of this acid. _____ (! 9.79)

58. The pH of a saturated solution of $Mg(OH)_2$, whose K_{sp} is 7.1×10^{-12}, is _____ (! 10.38)

59. The pH of a saturated solution of $Ca(OH)_2$ is 12.37. What is the K_{sp} of $Ca(OH)_2$? _____ (! 6.4×10^{-6})

60. The formation constant for the diammine silver(I) ion is 1.6×10^7, while the solubility product constant for silver chloride is 1.8×10^{-10}. What is the equilibrium constant for the reaction,

    $AgCl(s) + 2\,NH_3(aq) \rightleftharpoons Ag(NH_3)_2^+(aq) + Cl^-(aq)$? _____ (! 2.9×10^{-3})

61. The formation constant for the bis(thiosulfato)argentate(I) ion is 2.0×10^{13}, while the solubility product constant for silver bromide is 5.0×10^{-13}. What is the equilibrium constant for the reaction,

$$AgBr(s) + 2 S_2O_3^{2-}(aq) \rightleftharpoons Ag(S_2O_3)_2^{3-}(aq) + Br^-(aq)? \underline{\hspace{1cm}} (1.0 \times 10^1)$$

62. The formation constant for the diammine silver(I) ion is 1.6×10^7, while the solubility product constant for silver chloride is 1.8×10^{-10}. Given the reaction,

$$AgCl(s) + 2 NH_3(aq) \rightleftharpoons Ag(NH_3)_2^+(aq) + Cl^-(aq)$$

What is the solubility, in moles per liter, of silver chloride in 1.00 molar ammonia solution? \underline{\hspace{1cm}} $(! 4.8 \times 10^{-2} \text{ mol L}^{-1})$

63. The formation constant for the bis(thiosulfato)argentate(I) ion is 2.0×10^{13}, while the solubility product constant for silver bromide is 5.0×10^{-13}. Considering the reaction,

$$AgBr(s) + 2 S_2O_3^{2-}(aq) \rightleftharpoons Ag(S_2O_3)_2^{3-}(aq) + Br^-(aq)$$

What is the solubility, in moles per liter, of silver bromide in 0.200 molar sodium thiosulfate solution? \underline{\hspace{1cm}} $(! 8.6 \times 10^{-2} \text{ mol L}^{-1})$

64. The formation constant for the bis(thiosulfato)argentate(I) ion, $[Ag(S_2O_3)_2]^{3-}$, is 2.0×10^{13}, while the solubility product constant for silver iodide is 8.3×10^{-17}. A 0.200 molar solution of $Na_2S_2O_3$ is saturated with AgI. What is the concentration of free iodide ion in the saturated solution? \underline{\hspace{1cm}} $(! 7.5 \times 10^{-3} \text{ molar})$

65. The formation constant for the tris(ethylenediammine)nickel(II) complex ion, $[Ni(en)_3]^{2+}$, is 4.1×10^{17}. What is the concentration of the free nickel(II) ion in a solution in which the equilibrium concentration of free ethylenediamine is 0.400 molar, and that of the nickel complex above is 0.0100 molar? \underline{\hspace{1cm}} $(! 3.8 \times 10^{-19} \text{ molar})$

66. The value K_{a2} for the CO_2—HCO_3^-—CO_3^{2-} system at room temperature is 4.7×10^{-11}, while the K_{sp} for $BaCO_3$ is 5.0×10^{-9}. Calculate the equilibrium constant for the reaction,

$$BaCO_3(s) + H^+(aq) \rightleftharpoons Ba^{2+}(aq) + HCO_3^-(aq)$$

\underline{\hspace{1cm}} $(! 106)$

True and False

67. The oxide ion can exist in aqueous solutions provided the pH is higher than 11.00. $(! F)$

68. The sulfide ion is too basic to exist as such in aqueous solutions. $(! T)$

Critical Thinking

69. A saturated solution of silver nortonate, Ag_2NtO_4, in water contains 72 ppm of silver. How many parts per million of silver would there be in a 1.00 molar aqueous solution of Na_2NtO_4 which has been saturated with silver nortonate? \underline{\hspace{1cm}} $(! 1.3 \text{ ppm})$

70. NaOH is added to sea water containing 0.050 moles per liter of Mg^{2+} ion until the pH reaches 12.0. A certain quantity of $Mg(OH)_2$ precipitates. How many parts per billion of magnesium are left behind in the solution? The K_{sp} of $Mg(OH)_2$ is 7.1×10^{-12}.

      a. 1.2 ppb
      b. 12 ppb
      c. 0.17 ppb
!   d. 1.7 ppb
      e. 173 ppb

71. Consider the equilibrium,

$$AgCl(s) + Br^-(aq) \rightleftharpoons AgBr(s) + Cl^-(aq)$$

whose equilibrium constant is related to $K_{sp}(AgCl) = 1.8 \times 10^{-10}$ and $K_{sp}(AgBr) = 5.0 \times 10^{-13}$. Calculate the equilibrium constant for the reaction, and tell whether AgCl will react with 1.00 molar $KBr(aq)$ to a significant extent. _____ , _____ (! 3.6×10^2, yes)

72. The solubility product of silver chromate, Ag_2CrO_4, is 1.20×10^{-12}. Silver chromate will dissolve in aqueous ammonia to a slight extent due to complex ion formation. If the formation constant for the $[Ag(NH_3)_2]^+$ ion is $1.60 \times 10^{+7}$, calculate the solubility of Ag_2CrO_4 in 0.500 molar ammonia solution, in moles per liter. _____ (! 1.09×10^{-1} mol L^{-1})

73. A saturated solution of silver nortonate, Ag_2NtO_4, in water contains 72 ppm of silver. What is the K_{sp} of Ag_2NtO_4? _____ (! 1.5×10^{-10})

74. The solubility product constant for silver chromate, Ag_2CrO_4, is 1.2×10^{-12}, while the formation constant for the diammine silver ion, $Ag(NH_3)_2^+$, is $1.6 \times 10^{+7}$. Silver chromate is considerably more soluble in ammonia solutions that in pure water. Calculate the solubility, in moles per liter, of silver chromate in 1.00 M $NH_3(aq)$.

      a. 0.108 mol L^{-1}
      b. 0.158 mol L^{-1}
      c. 0.203 mol L^{-1}
!   d. 0.223 mol L^{-1}
      e. 0.248 mol L^{-1}

75. The solubility product constant for zinc carbonate, $ZnCO_3$, is 1.00×10^{-10}, while the formation constant for the tetrammine zinc ion, $Zn(NH_3)_4^{2+}$, is $7.80 \times 10^{+8}$. Zinc carbonate is considerably more soluble in ammonia solutions that in pure water. If some solid zinc carbonate is shaken with a 1.00 M aqueous solution of NH_3, how many moles of zinc carbonate would dissolve per liter of the ammonia solution?

      a. 2.00×10^{-3} mol L^{-1}
      b. 1.00×10^{-2} mol L^{-1}
      c. 1.03×10^{-1} mol L^{-1}
!   d. 1.13×10^{-1} mol L^{-1}
      e. 2.05×10^{-1} mol L^{-1}

76. The value of K_b for methylamine, CH_3NH_2, is 4.4 x 10^{-4}. Methylamine is a weak molecular base. An aqueous solution contains 6.21 g of methylamine **and** 23.63 g of $CH_3NH_3^+Cl^-$ per liter as the only solutes. If the K_{sp} value for magnesium hydroxide is 7.1 x 10^{-12}, what is the maximum amount of Mg^{2+} in parts per million that this solution can hold without causing precipitation of any magnesium as magnesium hydroxide? _____ (! 2.7 ppm Mg^{2+})

77. The value of K_b for dimethylamine, $(CH_3)_2NH$, is 9.6 x 10^{-4}. Dimethylamine is a weak molecular base. An aqueous solution contains 15.78 g of dimethylamine **and** 20.39 g of $(CH_3)_2NH_2^+Cl^-$ per liter as the only solutes. If the K_{sp} value for magnesium hydroxide is 7.1 x 10^{-12}, what is the maximum amount of Mg^{2+} in parts per million that this solution can hold without causing precipitation of any magnesium as magnesium hydroxide? _____ (! 0.096 ppm Mg^{2+})

78. The value of K_b for trimethylamine, $(CH_3)_3N$, is 7.4 x 10^{-5}. Trimethylamine is a weak molecular base. An aqueous solution contains 8.867 g of trimethylamine **and** 33.45 g of $(CH_3)_3NH^+Cl^-$ per liter as the only solutes. If the K_{sp} for cadmium hydroxide is 5.0 x 10^{-15}, what is the maximum amount of Cd^{2+} in parts per million that this solution can hold without causing precipitation of any cadmium as cadmium hydroxide? Ignore any possibility of forming cadmium complexes with trimethylamine. _____ (! 0.56 ppm Cd^{2+})

79. The value K_{a2} for the CO_2—HCO_3^-—CO_3^{2-} system at room temperature is 4.7 x 10^{-11}, while the K_{sp} for $BaCO_3$ is 5.0 x 10^{-9}. Based on the reaction, $BaCO_3(s) + H^+(aq) \rightleftharpoons Ba^{2+}(aq) + HCO_3^-(aq)$, calculate the solubility of $BaCO_3(s)$ in a non-interacting buffer whose pH is 9.00. _____ (! 3.3 x 10^{-4} mol L^{-1})

Chemicals in Our World 9 The Carbonate Buffer and Mountaineering

80. Respiration in the body starts with uptake of $O_2(g)$ in the lungs by _____ to form _____ (! hemoglobin, oxyhemoglobin)

81. Respiration in the lungs also involves the reaction of HCO_3^- ions in the blood to perform a very important function. Write the equation for the chemical reaction involved.
_____ (! $H^+(aq) + HCO_3^-(aq) \rightleftharpoons CO_2(g) + H_2O$)

82. The equilibria involved in the respiration processes are influenced markedly by the pH level in the blood. How is the pH level in the blood maintained at the proper level?
_____ (! by chemical buffers of a biological nature)

83. When carbon dioxide is removed too rapidly from the blood by respiration in the lungs due to prolonged rapid breathing, low external air pressure, or other reason, the pH of the blood tends to decrease or increase? _____ (! increase)

Chapter 18 Thermodynamics

Multiple Choice

1. The standard enthalpy of reaction, ΔH°_{rxn} for
$$C_2H_2(g) + 2\ H_2(g) \rightarrow C_2H_6(g)$$
   is -311.5 kJ mol^{-1}. Determine the value of ΔE°_{rxn} for this reaction.

   ! a. -306.5 kJ mol^{-1}
      b. -309.0 kJ mol^{-1}
      c. -314.0 kJ mol^{-1}
      d. -316.46 kJ mol^{-1}
      e. +4646 kJ mol^{-1}

2. The standard enthalpy of reaction, ΔH°_{rxn}, for
$$NH_3(g) + HCl(g) \rightarrow NH_4Cl(s)$$
   is -175.9 kJ mol^{-1}. Determine the value of ΔE°_{rxn} for this reaction.

      a. -164.8 kJ mol^{-1}
   ! b. -170.9 kJ mol^{-1}
      c. -173.4 kJ mol^{-1}
      d. -180.9 kJ mol^{-1}
      e. +5134 kJ mol^{-1}

3. The standard enthalpy of reaction, ΔH°_{rxn}, for the reaction,
$$C_4H_{10}(g) + 13/2\ O_2(g) \rightarrow 4\ CO_2(g) + 5\ H_2O(l)$$
   is -2877 kJ mol^{-1}. Determine the value of ΔE°_{rxn} for this reaction.

   ! a. -2868 kJ mol^{-1}
      b. -2871 kJ mol^{-1}
      c. -2880 kJ mol^{-1}
      d. -2886 kJ mol^{-1}
      e. +2886 kJ mol^{-1}

4. The standard enthalpy of reaction, ΔH°_{rxn}, for the reaction,
$$CaO(s) + SO_3(g) \rightarrow CaSO_4(s)$$
   is -401.5 kJ mol^{-1}. Determine the value of ΔE°_{rxn} for this reaction.

      a. -362.2 kJ mol^{-1}
   ! b. -399.0 kJ mol^{-1}
      c. -404.0 kJ mol^{-1}
      d. -2880 kJ mol^{-1}
      e. +2077 kJ mol^{-1}

5. Which one of the processes below is the one which is accompanied by an increase in entropy?

    a. setting up a stack of dominos
    b. setting up decorations on a Christmas tree
    c. filing correspondence in file folders and placing them in hanging file folders
! d. dropping a glass pane on the front walk of your residence
    e. restocking a canned goods shelf display in a supermarket

6. Which one of the following reactions is accompanied by an *increase* in entropy?

    a. $ZnS(s) + 3/2\ O_2(g) \rightarrow ZnO(s) + SO_2(g)$
! b. $CH_4(g) + H_2O(g) \rightarrow CO(g) + 3H_2(g)$
    c. $BaO(s) + CO_2(g) \rightarrow BaCO_3(s)$
    d. $Na_2CO_3(s) + CO_2(g) + H_2O(g) \rightarrow 2\ NaHCO_3(s)$
    e. $N_2(g) + 3\ H_2(g) \rightarrow 2\ NH_3(g)$

7. Which one of the following reactions is accompanied by an *increase* in entropy?

    a. $2\ H(g) \rightarrow H_2(g)$
    b. $NiCl_2(s) + 6\ NH_3(g) \rightarrow NiCl_2 \cdot 6NH_3(s)$
! c. $I_2(g) \rightarrow 2\ I(g)$
    d. $ZnO(s) + CO_2(g) \rightarrow ZnCO_3(s)$
    e. $C_2H_4(g) + Cl_2(g) \rightarrow C_2H_4Cl_2(l)$

8. Which one of the following reactions is accompanied by an *increase* in entropy?

    a. $C_{12}H_{20}(l) + 17\ O_2(g) \rightarrow 12\ CO_2(g) + 10\ H_2O(l)$
! b. $NH_4Cl(s) \rightarrow NH_3(g) + HCl(g)$
    c. $2\ C_2H_2(g) + 5\ O_2(g) \rightarrow 4\ CO_2(g) + 2\ H_2O(s)$
    d. $Ba(OH)_2(s) + 2\ HCl(g) \rightarrow BaCl_2 \cdot 2H_2O(s)$
    e. $(CH_3)_2CO(l) + 4\ O_2(g) \rightarrow 3\ CO_2(g) + 3\ H_2O(l)$

9. Which one of the following reactions is accompanied by an *increase* in entropy?

    a. $C_8H_{16}(l) + 12\ O_2(g) \rightarrow 8\ CO_2(g) + 8\ H_2O(l)$
    b. $N_2(g) + 3\ H_2(g) \rightarrow 2\ NH_3(g)$
    c. $2\ C_2H_2(g) + 5\ O_2(g) \rightarrow 4\ CO_2(g) + `2\ H_2O(s)$
    d. $Ba(OH)_2(s) + CO_2(g) \rightarrow BaCO_3(s) + H_2O(l)$
! e. $NH_4NO_2(s) \rightarrow N_2(g) + 2\ H_2O(l)$

10. Which statement below is always true for a spontaneous chemical reaction

    a. $\Delta S_{sys} + \Delta S_{surr} = 0$
    b. $\Delta S_{sys} + \Delta S_{surr} < 0$
! c. $\Delta S_{sys} + \Delta S_{surr} > 0$
    d. $\Delta S_{sys} - \Delta S_{surr} = 0$
    e. $\Delta S_{sys} - \Delta S_{surr} < 0$

11. Which one of the following statements is true?

    a. Spontaneous changes are *always* accompanied by an increase in the entropy of the system.
    b. Spontaneous changes are *always* accompanied by a decrease in the entropy of the system.
    c. Spontaneous changes are *always* accompanied by an increase in the enthalpy of the system.
    d. Spontaneous changes are *always* accompanied by a decrease in the enthalpy of the system.
 ! e. Most highly exothermic chemical reactions are also spontaneous chemical reactions.

12. Which one of the following processes is accompanied by a decrease in the entropy of the system?

    a. the mixing of one liter of water with one liter of ethylene glycol to produce one liter of an antifreeze solution
    b. the breaking of a large rock into very many smaller pieces of crushed gravel
    c. the thawing of the frozen orange juice concentrate which was left in the car
    d. the spontaneous chemical reaction of TNT (a solid chemical compound) wherein it decomposes into several simple compounds, some of which are gaseous
 ! e. the absorption of odorous gaseous compounds by the charcoal filter in your home central air cleaning unit

13. For a chemical reaction, ΔH is < 0 and ΔS is < 0 also. This means that

    a. we conclude the reaction must be spontaneous regardless of temperature and becomes even more so at higher temperatures
    b. we conclude the reaction must be spontaneous regardless of temperature and becomes even more so at lower temperatures
 ! c. we conclude the reaction may or may not be spontaneous, but spontaneity is favored, or at least enhanced, by low temperatures rather than by high temperatures
    d. we conclude the reaction may or may not be spontaneous, but spontaneity is favored, or at least enhanced, by high temperatures rather than by low temperatures
    e. we cannot make any conclusion about spontaneity or even tendencies from the limited information presented

14. For a chemical reaction, ΔH is > 0 while ΔS is < 0. This means that

 ! a. we conclude the reaction must be non-spontaneous regardless of temperature and becomes even more so at higher temperatures
    b. we conclude the reaction must be spontaneous regardless of temperature and becomes even more so at lower temperatures
    c. we conclude the reaction may or may not be spontaneous, but spontaneity is favored, or at least enhanced, by low temperatures rather than by high temperatures
    d. we conclude the reaction may or may not be spontaneous, but spontaneity is favored, or at least enhanced, by high temperatures rather than by low temperatures
    e. we cannot make any conclusion about spontaneity or even tendencies from the limited information presented

15. Of the species listed below, which one should possess the highest standard entropy ($S°$)?

        a. $(CH_3)_2CO(l)$
!   b. $C_4H_{10}(g)$
        c. $K_2SO_4(s)$
        d. $H_2O(l)$
        e. $Ar(g)$

16. Of the species listed below, which one should possess the lowest standard entropy ($S°$)?

        a. $CH_4(g)$
        b. $COCl_2(g)$
        c. $NH_3(g)$
        d. $H_2O(g)$
!   e. $Ar(g)$

17. Of the species listed below, which one should possess the highest standard entropy ($S°$)?

        a. CH_3—CH_2—O—$H(l)$
        b. $SnCl_4(l)$
        c. $TiCl_4(l)$
        d. $H_2O(l)$
!   e. CH_3—CH_2—CH_2—CH_2—CH_2—$Cl(l)$

18. Which one of the sets below has the species listed in order of increasing standard entropy, $S°$?

        a. $Au(s) < C_6H_5NO_2(l) < CaCO_3(s) < H_2O(l)$
!   b. $Au(s) < CaCO_3(s) < H_2O(l) < C_6H_5NO_2(l)$
        c. $CaCO_3(s) < H_2O(l) < Au(s) < C_6H_5NO_2(l)$
        d. $Au(s) < H_2O(l) < CaCO_3(s) < C_6H_5NO_2(l)$
        e. $C_6H_5NO_2(l) < CaCO_3(s) < Au(s) < H_2O(l)$

19. Which one of the sets below has the species listed in order of increasing standard entropy, $S°$?

        a. $NaHCO_3(s) < C_2H_5OH(l) < Cr(s) < N_2(g)$
        b. $Cr(s) < N_2(g) < NaHCO_3(s) < C_2H_5OH(l)$
        c. $Cr(s) < C_2H_5OH(l) < NaHCO_3(s) < N_2(g)$
!   d. $Cr(s) < NaHCO_3(s) < C_2H_5OH(l) < N_2(g)$
        e. $N_2(g) < NaHCO_3(s) < Cr(s) < C_2H_5OH(l)$

20. Which one of the sets below has the species listed in order of increasing standard entropy, $S°$?

!   a. $CaSO_4(s) < CH_3CH_2$—O—$H(l) < Ar(g) < CH_3$—CH_2—$Cl(g)$
        b. CH_3CH_2—O—$H(l) < Ar(g) < CaSO_4(s) < CH_3$—$CH_2$—$Cl(g)$
        c. $CaSO_4(s) < CH_3$—CH_2—$Cl(g) < CH_3CH_2$—O—$H(l) < Ar(g)$
        d. $CaSO_4(s) < Ar(g) < CH_3$—CH_2—O—$H(l) < CH_3$—CH_2—$Cl(g)$
        e. CH_3—CH_2—$Cl(g) < CH_3CH_2$—O—$H(l) < CaSO_4(s) < Ar(g)$

21. Using the standard entropy values:
$$H_2(g), S° = +130.6 \text{ J mol}^{-1} \text{ K}^{-1}$$
$$I_2(s), S° = +116.12 \text{ J mol}^{-1} \text{ K}^{-1}$$
$$HI(g), S° = +206.0 \text{ J mol}^{-1} \text{ K}^{-1}$$
calculate the standard entropy change, $\Delta S°$, for the reaction:
$$H_2(g) + I_2(s) \rightarrow 2 HI(g)$$

    a. -40.8 kJ
    b. +40.8 kJ
    c. -165.3 kJ
 ! d. +165.3 kJ
    e. +206.0 kJ

22. Using the standard entropy values:
$$NO(g), S° = +210.6 \text{ J mol}^{-1} \text{ K}^{-1}$$
$$O_2(g), S° = +205.0 \text{ J mol}^{-1} \text{ K}^{-1}$$
$$NO_2(g), S° = +240.5 \text{ J mol}^{-1} \text{ K}^{-1}$$
calculate the standard entropy change, $\Delta S°$, for the reaction:
$$NO(g) + ½ O_2(g) \rightarrow NO_2(g)$$

 ! a. -72.6 kJ
    b. -175.1 kJ
    c. -246.1 kJ
    d. +246.1 kJ
    e. -656.1 kJ

23. Using the standard entropy values:
$$C_2H_4(g), S° = +219.8 \text{ J mol}^{-1} \text{ K}^{-1}$$
$$H_2(g), S° = +130.6 \text{ J mol}^{-1} \text{ K}^{-1}$$
$$C_2H_6(g), S° = +229.5 \text{ J mol}^{-1} \text{ K}^{-1}$$
calculate the standard entropy change, $\Delta S°$, for the reaction:
$$C_2H_4(g) + H_2(g) \rightarrow C_2H_6(g)$$

    a. +89.2 kJ
    b. -98.9 kJ
 ! c. -120.9 kJ
    d. +140.3 kJ
    e. +579.9 kJ

24. The criterion for a spontaneous chemical reaction is

    a. $\Delta G = 0$
    b. $\Delta H > 0$
    c. $\Delta S = 0$
    d. $\Delta E > 0$
 ! e. $\Delta G < 0$

25. Using the standard entropy values:
$$SO_2(g), S° = +248.0 \text{ J mol}^{-1} \text{ K}^{-1}$$
$$SO_3(g), S° = +256.0 \text{ J mol}^{-1} \text{ K}^{-1}$$
$$NO(g), S° = +210.6 \text{ J mol}^{-1} \text{ K}^{-1}$$
$$NO_2(g), S° = +240.5 \text{ J mol}^{-1} \text{ K}^{-1}$$
calculate the standard entropy change, $\Delta S°$, for the reaction:
$$NO_2(g) + SO_2(g) \rightarrow NO(g) + SO_3(g)$$

    a. -6.2 kJ
    b. -18.8 kJ
! c. -21.9 kJ
    d. -37.9 kJ
    e. +52.9 kJ

26. As electrical energy is withdrawn from an automobile storage battery, which one of the following occurs?

    a. ΔG decreases
! b. ΔG increases
    c. ΔG does not change
    d. ΔE increases
    e. ΔH increases

27. Using the standard free energies of formation:
$$NO_2(g), \Delta G°_f = +51.84 \text{ kJ mol}^{-1}$$
$$NO(g), \Delta G°_f = +86.69 \text{ kJ mol}^{-1}$$
$$SO_2(g), \Delta G°_f = -300.0 \text{ kJ mol}^{-1}$$
$$SO_3(g), \Delta G°_f = -370.0 \text{ kJ mol}^{-1}$$
calculate the standard free energy change, $\Delta G°$, for the reaction:
$$NO_2(g) + SO_2(g) \rightarrow NO(g) + SO_3(g)$$

! a. -35.15 kJ
    b. -104.9 kJ
    c. -429.2 kJ
    d. -619.6 kJ
    e. -808.5 kJ

28. Which one of observables associated with the following symbols is the one which is dependent on how a chemical reaction is carried out, not on just the initial and final states?

    a. ΔS
    b. ΔH
    c. ΔE
! d. w
    e. ΔG

29. Using the standard free energies of formation:

$$BaCO_3(s), \Delta G°_f = -1139.0 \text{ kJ mol}^{-1}$$
$$BaSO_4(s), \Delta G°_f = -1353.0 \text{ kJ mol}^{-1}$$
$$CO_2(g), \Delta G°_f = -394.4 \text{ kJ mol}^{-1}$$
$$SO_3(g), \Delta G°_f = -370.0 \text{ kJ mol}^{-1}$$

calculate the standard free energy change, $\Delta G°$, for the reaction:

$$BaCO_3(s) + SO_3(g) \rightarrow BaSO_4(s) + CO_2(g)$$

   a. +189.6 kJ
! b. -238.4 kJ
   c. +472.4 kJ
   d. +1727.6 kJ
   e. -2516.4 kJ

30. Given the data:

$$H_2(g), \Delta H°_f = 0.00 \text{ kJ mol}^{-1}, S° = +130.6 \text{ J mol}^{-1} \text{ K}^{-1}$$
$$I_2(s), \Delta H°_f = 0.00 \text{ kJ mol}^{-1}, S° = +116.12 \text{ J mol}^{-1} \text{ K}^{-1}$$
$$HI(g), \Delta H°_f = +26 \text{ kJ mol}^{-1}, S° = +206 \text{ J mol}^{-1} \text{ K}^{-1}$$

calculate the standard free energy change, $\Delta G°$, for the reaction:

$$H_2(g) + I_2(s) \rightarrow 2 HI(g)$$

! a. +2.7 kJ
   b. -46.5 kJ
   c. +64.1 kJ
   d. +128.2 kJ
   e. -165.3 kJ

31. Given the data:

$$Ag_2O(s), \Delta H°_f = -31.1 \text{ kJ mol}^{-1}, S° = +121.3 \text{ J mol}^{-1} \text{ K}^{-1}$$
$$O_2(g), \Delta H°_f = 0.00 \text{ kJ mol}^{-1}, S° = +205 \text{ J mol}^{-1} \text{ K}^{-1}$$
$$Ag(s), \Delta H°_f = 0.00 \text{ kJ mol}^{-1}, S° = +42.55 \text{ J mol}^{-1} \text{ K}^{-1}$$

calculate the standard free energy change $\Delta G°$, for the reaction:

$$Ag_2O(s) \rightarrow 2 Ag(s) + \tfrac{1}{2} O_2(g)$$

! a. +11.3 kJ
   b. -24.0 kJ
   c. -38.2 kJ
   d. -50.4 kJ
   e. -50.9 kJ

32. Given the data:

$$N_2(g), \Delta H°_f = 0.00 \text{ kJ mol}^{-1}, S° = +191.5 \text{ J mol}^{-1} \text{ K}^{-1}$$
$$H_2(g), \Delta H°_f = 0.00 \text{ kJ mol}^{-1}, S° = +130.6 \text{ J mol}^{-1} \text{ K}^{-1}$$
$$NH_3(g), \Delta H°_f = -46.0 \text{ kJ mol}^{-1}, S° = +192.5 \text{ J mol}^{-1} \text{ K}^{-1}$$

calculate the standard free energy change, $\Delta G°$ for the reaction:

$$N_2(g) + 3 H_2(g) \rightarrow 2 NH_3(g)$$

   a. -7.4 kJ
! b. -32.9 kJ
   c. -84.6 kJ
   d. +112.3 kJ
   e. -151.1 kJ

33. Given the data:

$$NH_3(g), \Delta H°_f = -46.0 \text{ kJ mol}^{-1}, S° = +192.5 \text{ J mol}^{-1} \text{ K}^{-1}$$
$$NO(g), \Delta H°_f = +90.4 \text{ kJ mol}^{-1}, S° = +210.6 \text{ J mol}^{-1} \text{ K}^{-1}$$
$$H_2O(l), \Delta H°_f = -286 \text{ kJ mol}^{-1}, S° = +69.96 \text{ J mol}^{-1} \text{ K}^{-1}$$
$$O_2(g), \Delta H°_f = 0.00 \text{ kJ mol}^{-1}, S° = +205 \text{ J mol}^{-1} \text{ K}^{-1}$$

calculate the standard free energy change, $\Delta G°$, for the reaction:

$$2 NH_3(g) + 5/2 O_2(g) \rightarrow 2 NO(g) + 3 H_2O(l)$$

   a. -100.8 kJ
   b. -206.7 kJ
   c. -276.5 kJ
! d. -505.8 kJ
   e. -664.3 kJ

34. Assuming that, since the physical states do not change, the values of ΔH and ΔS do not change as we shift temperature, and using,

$$CdO(s), \Delta H°_f = -258.2 \text{ kJ mol}^{-1}, S° = +54.8 \text{ J mol}^{-1} \text{ K}^{-1}$$
$$CdSO_4(s), \Delta H°_f = -933.5 \text{ kJ mol}^{-1}, S° = +123 \text{ J mol}^{-1} \text{ K}^{-1}$$
$$SO_3(g), \Delta H°_f = -396 \text{ kJ mol}^{-1}, S° = +256 \text{ J mol}^{-1} \text{ K}^{-1}$$

calculate a value for the free energy change, $\Delta G^{1\ atm}$ for the reaction,

$$CdSO_4(s) \rightarrow CdO(s) + SO_3(g) \text{ at 750 K}$$

   a. +223.3 kJ
! b. +138.5 kJ
   c. +296.0 kJ
   d. +420.5 kJ
   e. +335.3 kJ

35. Assuming that, since the physical states do not change, the values of ΔH and ΔS do not change as we shift temperature, and using,

$$CaO(s), \Delta H^\circ_f = -635.5 \text{ kJ mol}^{-1}, S^\circ = +40.0 \text{ J mol}^{-1} \text{ K}^{-1}$$
$$CaCO_3(s), \Delta H^\circ_f = -1207 \text{ kJ mol}^{-1}, S^\circ = +92.9 \text{ J mol}^{-1} \text{ K}^{-1}$$
$$CO_2(g), \Delta H^\circ_f = -394 \text{ kJ mol}^{-1}, S^\circ = +213.6 \text{ J mol}^{-1} \text{ K}^{-1}$$

calculate a value for the free energy change, $\Delta G^{1 \text{ atm}}$ for the reaction,

$$CaCO_3(s) \rightarrow CaO(s) + CO_2(g) \text{ at } 815 \text{ }^\circ C$$

! a. +2.6 kJ
  b. +46.5 kJ
  c. +177.3 kJ
  d. +308.5 kJ
  e. +352.4 kJ

36. Given the data:

$$PbO(s), \Delta H^\circ_f = -217.3 \text{ kJ mol}^{-1}, S^\circ = +68.7 \text{ J mol}^{-1} \text{ K}^{-1}$$
$$PbO_2(s), \Delta H^\circ_f = -277.0 \text{ kJ mol}^{-1}, S^\circ = +68.6 \text{ J mol}^{-1} \text{ K}^{-1}$$
$$O_2(g), \Delta H^\circ_f = 0.00 \text{ kJ mol}^{-1}, S^\circ = +205 \text{ J mol}^{-1} \text{ K}^{-1}$$

calculate the standard free energy change, ΔG°, for the reaction:

$$PbO(s) + \tfrac{1}{2} O_2(g) \rightarrow PbO_2(s)$$

  a. +1.45 kJ
! b. -29.1 kJ
  c. -68.3 kJ
  d. -90.3 kJ
  e. -120.9 kJ

37. Assuming that, since the physical states do not change, the values of ΔH and ΔS do not change as we shift temperature, and using,

$$N_2(g), \Delta H^\circ_f = 0.00 \text{ kJ mol}^{-1}, S^\circ = +191.5 \text{ J mol}^{-1} \text{ K}^{-1}$$
$$H_2(g), \Delta H^\circ_f = 0.00 \text{ kJ mol}^{-1}, S^\circ = +130.6 \text{ J mol}^{-1} \text{ K}^{-1}$$
$$NH_3(g), \Delta H^\circ_f = -46.0 \text{ kJ mol}^{-1}, S^\circ = +192.5 \text{ J mol}^{-1} \text{ K}^{-1}$$

calculate a value for the free energy change, $\Delta G^{1 \text{ atm}}$ for the reaction,

$$N_2(g) + 3 H_2(g) \rightarrow 2 NH_3(g) \text{ at } 500 \text{ }^\circ C$$

  a. +7.2 kJ
  b. +18.8 kJ
  c. +54.2 kJ
! d. +61.3 kJ
  e. +83.3 kJ

38. Assuming that, since the physical states do not change, the values of ΔH and ΔS do not change as we shift temperature, and using,

$$NH_3(g), \Delta H°_f = -46.0 \text{ kJ mol}^{-1}, S° = +192.5 \text{ J mol}^{-1} \text{ K}^{-1}$$
$$NO(g), \Delta H°_f = +90.4 \text{ kJ mol}^{-1}, S° = +210.6 \text{ J mol}^{-1} \text{ K}^{-1}$$
$$H_2O(l), \Delta H°_f = -286 \text{ kJ mol}^{-1}, S° = +69.96 \text{ J mol}^{-1} \text{ K}^{-1}$$
$$O_2(g), \Delta H°_f = 0.00 \text{ kJ mol}^{-1}, S° = +205.0 \text{ J mol}^{-1} \text{ K}^{-1}$$

calculate a value for the free energy change, $\Delta G^{1 \text{ atm}}$ for the reaction,

$$2 \text{ NH}_3(g) + 5/2 \text{ O}_2(g) \rightarrow 2 \text{ NO}(g) + 3 \text{ H}_2\text{O}(l) \text{ at } 350 \text{ °C}$$

    a. -76.73 kJ
    b. -108.7 kJ
    c. -492.0 kJ
! d. -419.2 kJ
    e. -678.8 kJ

39. Using the data:

$$C_2H_4(g), \Delta H°_f = +51.9 \text{ kJ mol}^{-1}, S° = 219.8 \text{ J mol}^{-1} \text{ K}^{-1}$$
$$CO_2(g), \Delta H°_f = -394.0 \text{ kJ mol}^{-1}, S° = 213.6 \text{ J mol}^{-1} \text{ K}^{-1}$$
$$H_2O(l), \Delta H°_f = -286.0 \text{ kJ mol}^{-1}, S° = 69.96 \text{ J mol}^{-1} \text{ K}^{-1}$$
$$O_2(g), \Delta H°_f = 0.00 \text{ kJ mol}^{-1}, S° = 205 \text{ J mol}^{-1} \text{ K}^{-1}$$

calculate the maximum amount of useful work that can be obtained, at 25.0 °C, from the process:

$$C_2H_4(g) + 3 \text{ O}_2(g) \rightarrow 2 \text{ CO}_2(g) + 2 \text{ H}_2\text{O}(l)$$

! a. 1332 kJ
    b. 1380 kJ
    c. 1451 kJ
    d. 1492 kJ
    e. 2422 kJ

40. Given the data:

$$Ni(CO)_4(g), \Delta H°_f = -220.0 \text{ kJ mol}^{-1}, S° = +399 \text{ J mol}^{-1} \text{ K}^{-1}$$
$$Ni(s), \Delta H°_f = 0.00 \text{ kJ mol}^{-1}, S° = +30 \text{ J mol}^{-1} \text{ K}^{-1}$$
$$CO(g), \Delta H°_f = -110.0 \text{ kJ mol}^{-1}, S° = +197.9 \text{ J mol}^{-1} \text{ K}^{-1}$$

calculate the standard free energy change, $\Delta G°$, for the reaction,

$$Ni(CO)_4(g) \rightarrow Ni(s) + 4 \text{ CO}(g)$$

    a. -94 kJ
    b. -169 kJ
    c. -271 kJ
! d. -346 kJ
    e. -412 kJ

41. Assuming that, since the physical states do not change, the values of ΔH and ΔS do not change as we shift temperature, and using,

$$Ni(CO)_4(g), \Delta H°_f = -220.0 \text{ kJ mol}^{-1}, S° = +399 \text{ J mol}^{-1} \text{ K}^{-1}$$
$$Ni(s), \Delta H°_f = 0.00 \text{ kJ mol}^{-1}, S° = +30 \text{ J mol}^{-1} \text{ K}^{-1}$$
$$CO(g), \Delta H°_f = -110.0 \text{ kJ mol}^{-1}, S° = +197.9 \text{ J mol}^{-1} \text{ K}^{-1}$$

calculate a value for the free energy change, $\Delta G^{1 \text{ atm}}$ for the reaction,

$$Ni(CO)_4(g) \rightarrow Ni(s) + 4 CO(g)$$

      a. -36 kJ
      b. -404 kJ
!   c. -680 kJ
      d. +234 kJ
      e. +404 kJ

42. Using the data:

$$C_2H_6(g), \Delta H°_f = -84.5 \text{ kJ mol}^{-1}, S° = +229.5 \text{ J mol}^{-1} \text{ K}^{-1}$$
$$CO_2(g), \Delta H°_f = -394.0 \text{ kJ mol}^{-1}, S° = +213.6 \text{ J mol}^{-1} \text{ K}^{-1}$$
$$H_2O(l), \Delta H°_f = -286.0 \text{ kJ mol}^{-1}, S° = +69.96 \text{ J mol}^{-1} \text{ K}^{-1}$$
$$O_2(g), \Delta H°_f = 0.00 \text{ kJ mol}^{-1}, S° = +205 \text{ J mol}^{-1} \text{ K}^{-1}$$

calculate the maximum amount of useful work that can be obtained, at 25.0 °C, from the process:

$$2 C_2H_6(g) + 7 O_2(g) \rightarrow 4 CO_2(g) + 6 H_2O(l), \text{ per mole of } C_2H_6$$

      a. -1426 kJ
!   b. -1469 kJ
      c. -1654 kJ
      d. -2166 kJ
      e. -3029 kJ

43. Using the data:

$$Ag_2O(s), \Delta H°_f = -31.1 \text{ kJ mol}^{-1}, S° = +121.3 \text{ J mol}^{-1} \text{ K}^{-1}$$
$$Ag(s), \Delta H°_f = 0.00 \text{ kJ mol}^{-1}, S° = +42.55 \text{ J mol}^{-1} \text{ K}^{-1}$$
$$O_2(g), \Delta H°_f = 0.00 \text{ kJ mol}^{-1}, S° = +205.0 \text{ J mol}^{-1} \text{ K}^{-1}$$

if we assume that, since the physical states do not change, $\Delta H^{1 \text{ atm}}$ and $\Delta S^{1 \text{ atm}}$ are independent of temperature between -50.0 °C and 950.0 °C, calculate the value of $\Delta G^{1 \text{ atm}}$ for the reaction at 650 °C:

$$Ag_2O(s) \rightarrow 2 Ag(s) + \tfrac{1}{2} O_2(g)$$

      a. -12.0 kJ
!   b. -30.1 kJ
      c. -41.5 kJ
      d. -51.0 kJ
      e. -85.5 kJ

44. The reaction, $M_2O_3(s) + C(s) \rightarrow M(s) + CO_2(g)$, is spontaneous at low temperatures but non-spontaneous at high temperatures. If we assume that, since the physical states do not change, the values of $\Delta H^{1\ atm}$ and $\Delta S^{1\ atm}$ are constant over a wide temperature range, including 25.0°C, we can deduce that, over this range

    a. $\Delta H < 0$ and $\Delta S > 0$
! b. $\Delta H < 0$ and $\Delta S < 0$
    c. $\Delta H > 0$ and $\Delta S < 0$
    d. $\Delta H > 0$ and $\Delta S > 0$
    e. the information is insufficient to make any judgment as to the signs of ΔH and ΔS

45. Given the data:
    $Ag_2O(s)$, $\Delta H^{\circ}_f = -31.1$ kJ mol^{-1}, $S^{\circ} = +121.3$ J mol^{-1} K^{-1}
    $Ag(s)$, $\Delta H^{\circ}_f = 0.00$ kJ mol^{-1}, $S^{\circ} = +42.55$ J mol^{-1} K^{-1}
    $O_2(g)$, $\Delta H^{\circ}_f = 0.00$ kJ mol^{-1}, $S^{\circ} = +205.0$ J mol^{-1} K^{-1}
Calculate the temperature at which $\Delta G^{1\ atm} = 0$ for the reaction, $Ag_2O(s) \rightarrow 2\ Ag(s) + \frac{1}{2}\ O_2(g)$. Assume that, since the physical states do not change, $\Delta H^{1\ atm}$ and $\Delta S^{1\ atm}$ are independent of temperature between -50.0 °C and 950.0 °C.

! a. +196 °C
    b. +246 °C
    c. +423 °C
    d. +610 °C
    e. +818 °C

46. The thermochemical equation representing one process used for the synthesis of ammonia involves the equilibrium shown,
$$N_2(g) + 3\ H_2(g) \rightleftharpoons 2\ NH_3(g)$$
For this reaction, $\Delta H^{\circ} = -92.2$ kJ, $\Delta G^{\circ} = -33.4$ kJ. This leads one to conclude that

    a. the coefficients give us the mole ratios but not the volume ratios of the reacting species
! b. an increase in pressure favors an increase in the yield of ammonia
    c. carrying out the reaction at a higher temperature shifts the position of equilibrium to the right, thus favoring an increase in the yield of ammonia
    d. cooling the mixture to remove ammonia from the reaction mixture unfortunately also decreases the overall yield of ammonia
    e. the mixture does not need heating, in fact, cooling the mixture assists the rapid establishment of equilibrium

47. The reaction, $2 MO(s) + CO_2(g) \rightarrow M_2O_3(s) + CO(s)$ is spontaneous at high temperatures but non-spontaneous at low temperatures. If we assume that, since the physical states do not change, the values of $\Delta H^{1\ atm}$ and $\Delta S^{1\ atm}$ are constant over a wide temperature range, including 25.0°C, we can deduce that, over this range

      a. $\Delta H < 0$ and $\Delta S > 0$
      b. $\Delta H < 0$ and $\Delta S < 0$
      c. $\Delta H > 0$ and $\Delta S < 0$
!   d. $\Delta H > 0$ and $\Delta S > 0$
      e. the information is insufficient to make any judgment as to the signs of ΔH and ΔS

Fill in the Blanks

48. Using the data,

$$I_2(g), \Delta H°_f = +62.4 \text{ kJ mol}^{-1}, S° = +260.7 \text{ J mol}^{-1} \text{ K}^{-1}$$
$$I_2(s), \Delta H°_f = 0.00 \text{ kJ mol}^{-1}, S° = +116.12 \text{ J mol}^{-1} \text{ K}^{-1}$$

calculate the temperature at which solid iodine should have a vapor pressure of 1.00 atm, based on the reaction, $I_2(g) \rightleftharpoons I_2(s)$. This is the temperature at which $\Delta G^{1\ atm} = 0$. _____
(! 158-159 °C)

49. For a chemical reaction, $\Delta H° = +21.16 \text{ kJ mol}^{-1}$. The value of $\Delta S°$ for the same reaction was +74.50 J mol^{-1} K^{-1}. If, since the physical states do not change, the value of ΔH and ΔS do not change with temperature over the range of interest, what should be the value of $\Delta G^{1\ atm}$ at +550.0 °C? _____
(!-40.16 k J mol^{-1} K^{-1})

50. For a chemical reaction, $\Delta H° = +31.16 \text{ kJ mol}^{-1}$. The value of $\Delta S°$ for the same reaction was +74.50 J mol^{-1} K^{-1}. If, since the physical states do not change, the value of ΔH and ΔS do not change with temperature over the range of interest, at what temperature should $\Delta G^{1atm} = 0.0$, in °C? _____
(! +145.1 °C)

51. For the system, $2 NO_2(g) \rightleftharpoons N_2O_4(g)$, $\Delta G° = -5.40$ kJ. Calculate the value of the equilibrium constant, K_p, for this system. _____ (! 8.83 atm^{-1})

52. Given the following values for components of a system, at 410 K.
     $PCl_5, \Delta H_f = -370.0 \text{ kJ mol}^{-1}, S = 375.0 \text{ J mol}^{-1} \text{ K}^{-1}$.
     $PCl_3, \Delta H_f = -293.0 \text{ kJ mol}^{-1}, S = 320.5 \text{ J mol}^{-1} \text{ K}^{-1}$.
     $Cl_2, \Delta H_f = 000.0 \text{ kJ mol}^{-1}, S = 230.0 \text{ J mol}^{-1} \text{ K}^{-1}$.
Calculate a value of K_c at 410 K for

     $PCl_5(g) \rightleftharpoons PCl_3(g) + Cl_2(g)$ _____ (! $K_c = 6.77 \times 10^{-3}$)

53. For the system, $2 NO_2(g) \rightleftharpoons N_2O_4(g)$, $\Delta G° = -5.40$ kJ. If the system was initialized using enough NO_2 to create a partial pressure of 0.50 atm and enough N_2O_4 to create a partial pressure of 0.35 atm, calculate the value of ΔG_{298} for the other than standard conditions prevailing at the start. _____ (! -4.57 kJ)

54. Given the following values for components of a system, at 410 K and 1 atm:

For PCl_5, $\Delta H_f = -370.0$ kJ mol^{-1}, S = 375.0 J mol^{-1}K^{-1}.
For PCl_3, $\Delta H_f = -293.0$ kJ mol^{-1}, S = 320.5 J mol^{-1}K^{-1}.
For Cl_2, $\Delta H_f = 000.0$ kJ mol^{-1}, S = 230.0 J mol^{-1}K^{-1}.

Calculate a value for K_p at 410 K for

$$PCl_5(g) \rightleftharpoons PCl_3(g) + Cl_2(g) \qquad \underline{\hspace{2cm}} \qquad (!\,K_p = 0.228 \text{ atm})$$

55. Given the following values for components of a system, at 298.15 K and 1 atm:

For PCl_5, $\Delta H_f = -374.9$ kJ mol^{-1}, S = 364.6 J mol^{-1}K^{-1}.
For PCl_3, $\Delta H_f = -287.0$ kJ mol^{-1}, S = 311.8 J mol^{-1}K^{-1}.
For Cl_2, $\Delta H_f = 000.0$ kJ mol^{-1}, S = 223.0 J mol^{-1}K^{-1}.

Calculate values for K_c and K_p at 298.15 K for

$$PCl_5(g) \rightleftharpoons PCl_3(g) + Cl_2(g) \qquad \underline{\hspace{3cm}} \qquad (!\,K_c = 1.27 \times 10^{-8}, K_p = 3.10 \times 10^{-7} \text{ atm})$$

56. For the system,

$$PCl_5(g) + 2\,NO(g) \rightleftharpoons PCl_3(g) + 2\,NOCl(g)$$

$\Delta G° = -9.720$ kJ. If a system is charged with 0.200 atm of PCl_5, 0.800 atm of PCl_3, 0.800 atm of NOCl, and 0.100 atm of NO, what is the initial value of ΔG_{298} for the other than standard conditions given above? $\underline{\hspace{2cm}}$ (!\,+4.02 kJ)

57. Using these bond enthalpies, $\Delta H°$:

C—C: 348 kJ	C=C: 612 kJ	C≡C: 960 kJ
C—H: 412 kJ	C—N: 305 kJ	C—O: 360 kJ
C=O: 743 kJ	H—H: 436 kJ	H—O: 463 kJ
H—N: 388 kJ	O=O: 498 kJ	

Calculate the value of $\Delta H°$ of reaction for

$$H_2C=CH_2(g) + H_2(g) \rightarrow CH_3—CH_3(g)$$

$\underline{\hspace{3cm}}$ (!\, 124 kJ)

True and False

58. The standard entropy, S° for an element in its standard state is always zero. (!\,F)

59. A negative value for the standard molar entropy, S°, of a chemical substance indicates that the substance is **unstable** and may decompose or detonate if mishandled. (!\,F)

60. The entropy of a solid amorphous substance at absolute zero is 0 according to the third law of thermodynamics. (!\,F)

61. Three factors which, acting together determine whether a reaction is spontaneous or not, are entropy, internal energy, and enthalpy. (!\,F, temperature is also needed)

62. The equation, $\Delta H°_{reaction} = \Delta H°_{f\,(products)} - \Delta H°_{f\,(reactants)}$ is a statement of the second law of thermo-dynamics. (! F)

Critical Thinking

63. The reaction, $Al_2O_3(s) + 3/2\ C(s) \rightarrow 3/2\ CO_2(g) + 2\ Al(s)$ is endothermic. At 25.0°C, $\Delta G° = +990.4\ kJ\ mol^{-1}$, while at 1000 °C, the value of the corresponding parameter is $\Delta G^{1\ atm} = +680.8\ kJ\ mol^{-1}$. If we make the assumption that, since the physical states do not change, the values of $\Delta H^{1\ atm} = \Delta H°$ and $\Delta S^{1\ atm} = \Delta S°$ throughout this temperature range and slightly beyond, calculate values for $\Delta H°$ and $\Delta S°$ for the reaction. _____ (! $\Delta H° = +1085\ kJ\ mol^{-1}$, $\Delta S° = +318\ J\ mol^{-1}\ K^{-1}$)

64. The reaction, $Fe_2O_3(s) + 3/2\ C(s) \rightarrow 3/2\ CO_2(g) + 2\ Fe(s)$ is endothermic. At 25.0°C, $\Delta G° = +148.9\ kJ\ mol^{-1}$, while at 750 °C, the value of the corresponding parameter is $\Delta G^{1\ atm} = -51.2\ kJ\ mol^{-1}$. If we make the assumption that, since the physical states do not change, the values of $\Delta H^{1\ atm} = \Delta H°$ and $\Delta S^{1\ atm} = \Delta S°$ throughout this temperature range and beyond, calculate values for $\Delta H°$ and $\Delta S°$ for the reaction. _____ (! $\Delta H° = +231.2\ kJ\ mol^{-1}$, $\Delta S° = +276\ J\ mol^{-1}\ K^{-1}$)

65. The species in the reaction, $2\ KNO_3(s) + 2\ C(s) \rightarrow K_2CO_3(s) + N_2(g) + 3/2\ CO_2(g)$ have the values for standard enthalpies of formation,

$$KNO_3(s),\ \Delta H°_f = -492.7\ kJ\ mol^{-1}$$
$$CO_2(g),\ \Delta H°_f = -394.0\ kJ\ mol^{-1}$$
$$K_2CO_3(s),\ \Delta H°_f = -1146\ kJ\ mol^{-1}$$

Make the assumption that, since the physical states do not change, the values of $\Delta H^{1\ atm} = \Delta H°$ and $\Delta S^{1\ atm} = \Delta S°$ throughout a broad temperature range, and use this information to determine which of the following conditions may apply.

   ! a. The reaction is spontaneous at all temperatures.
      b. The reaction is non-spontaneous at all temperatures.
      c. The reaction is spontaneous at low temperatures but non-spontaneous at high temperatures.
      d. The reaction is non-spontaneous at low temperatures but spontaneous at high temperatures.
      e. It is impossible to make any judgment about spontaneity because insufficient information can be gleaned from the data and equations presented.

Use these bond enthalpies, $\Delta H°$, to work out problems 66 through 72:

C—C: 348 kJ	C=C: 612 kJ	C≡C: 960 kJ
C—H: 412 kJ	C—N: 305 kJ	C—O: 360 kJ
C=O: 743 kJ	H—H: 436 kJ	H—O: 463 kJ
H—N: 388 kJ	O=O: 498 kJ	

66. Calculate the value of $\Delta H°$ for the reaction,
$$H_2C=CH_2(g) + H_2O(g) \rightarrow CH_3-CH_2-O-H(g)$$

_____ (! –45 kJ mol^{-1})

67. Calculate the value of $\Delta H°$ for the reaction,

$$CH_3—CH_2—CH_2—O—H(g) + O=O(g) \rightarrow CH_3—CH_2—\overset{\displaystyle \|}{\underset{\displaystyle O}{C}}—O—H(g) + H_2O(g)$$

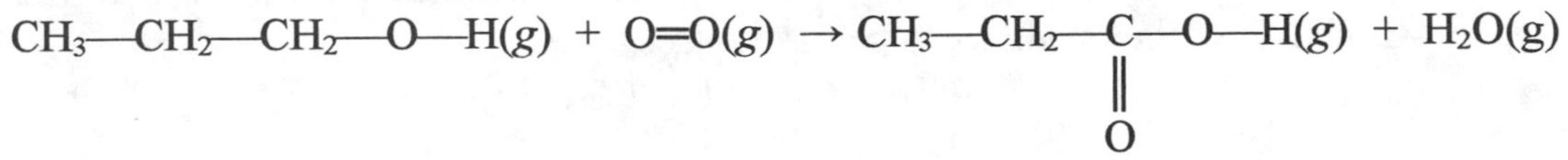

_____ (! –347 kJ mol^{-1})

68. Calculate the value of $\Delta H°$ for the reaction, per mole of the carbon containing compound

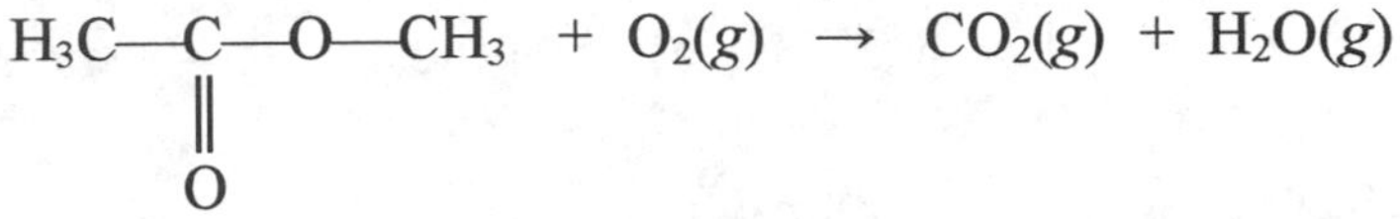

$$H_3C—\overset{\displaystyle \|}{\underset{\displaystyle O}{C}}—O—CH_3 + O_2(g) \rightarrow CO_2(g) + H_2O(g)$$

_____ (! –1210 kJ mol^{-1})

69. You'll notice that the two compounds shown below have the same molecular formula, but different structural formulas. Calculate the difference in molar bond enthalpy between the two.

$$CH_3—CH_2—O—H(g) \text{ and } CH_3—O—CH_3(g)$$

_____ (! 39 kJ mol^{-1})

70. Calculate the value of $\Delta H°$ for the reaction, per mole, for the conversion of isopropyl alcohol into acetone by the reaction shown below.

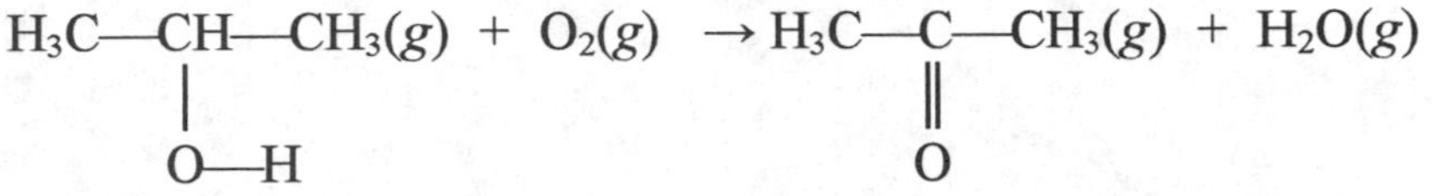

$$H_3C—\underset{\displaystyle \underset{\displaystyle O—H}{|}}{CH}—CH_3(g) + O_2(g) \rightarrow H_3C—\overset{\displaystyle \|}{\underset{\displaystyle O}{C}}—CH_3(g) + H_2O(g)$$

_____ (! –185 kJ mol^{-1})

71. The polymerization of ethylene to form polyethylene is an interesting reaction. For starters, calculate the value of ΔH for the formation of a gaseous tetramer with the structure shown below from ethylene, $C_2H_4(g)$. This is not to say that it is the preferred structure for the C_8H_{16} compound that would be formed. With this value in hand, and considering entropy changes, would you expect this reaction to be spontaneous at high temperatures?

$$H_3C—CH_2—\underset{\displaystyle \underset{\displaystyle H_3C}{|}}{C}=\underset{\displaystyle \underset{\displaystyle CH_3}{|}}{C}—CH_2—CH_3(g)$$

_____

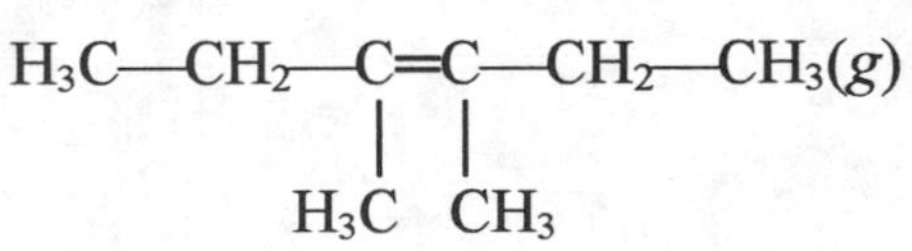

(! -252 kJ mol^{-1}, since ΔS is negative, it is non-spontaneous at high temperatures)

72. Methyl ethyl ketone, whose structural formula is shown below, is a volatile, highly combustible substance which has been used in commercial nail polish remover formulations. Using the bond energies from the table provided above, calculate the value of ΔH for the reaction of gaseous MEK with excess oxygen. Consider all the products to be gases also.

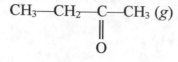

_____ ($! -1826$ kJ mol^{-1})

73. The species in the reaction, $KClO_3(s) \rightarrow KCl(s) + 3/2\ O_2(g)$ have the values for standard enthalpies of formation:

$$KClO_3(s),\ \Delta H^\circ_f = -391.2\ \text{kJ mol}^{-1}$$
$$KCl(s),\ \Delta H^\circ_f = -436.8\ \text{kJ mol}^{-1}$$

Make the assumption that, since the physical states do not change, the values of $\Delta H^{1\ atm} = \Delta H^\circ$ and $\Delta S^{1\ atm} = \Delta S^\circ$ throughout a broad temperature range, and use this information to determine which of the following conditions may apply.

! a. The reaction is spontaneous at all temperatures.
  b. The reaction is non-spontaneous at all temperatures.
  c. The reaction is spontaneous at low temperatures but non-spontaneous at high temperatures.
  d. The reaction is non-spontaneous at low temperatures but spontaneous at high temperatures.
  e. It is impossible to make any judgment about spontaneity because insufficient information can be gleaned from the data and equations presented.

Chapter 19 Electrochemistry

Multiple Choice

1. Electrolysis is

    a. the splitting atomic nuclei by electrical energy
    b. the splitting of atoms by electrical energy
    c. the passage of electrical energy through a split-field armature
    ! d. the chemical reaction which accompanies passage of electrical energy through a liquid electrolyte
    e. the chemical reaction which accompanies passage of electrical energy through a metallic liquid

2. An electrolyte is (the best answer, please)

    a. a solute which conducts electrical energy
    b. an inert electrode which conducts electrical energy
    c. a metal which conducts electrical energy through a solution
    ! d. a pure liquid or solution, containing ions, which conducts electrical energy
    e. a solution which conducts electricity

3. Anions

    ! a. are charged ions which move toward the anode of an electrolysis cell
    b. are charged ions which move toward the negative electrode of an electrolysis cell
    c. are charged ions which move toward the north pole of a magnetic field
    d. are positively charged ions which result from electrical discharge in a liquid solution
    e. are ions which attach themselves to any electrode to react chemically during electrolysis

4. Which statement below about electroplating is an incorrect statement?

    a. Nickel sulfate solution is the electrolyte used in nickel electroplating.
    b. Chromic acid (H_2CrO_4) solution is the electrolyte used in chromium electroplating.
    ! c. Silver nitrate solution is the electrolyte used in silver electroplating.
    d. Cyanide baths with gold complexes are the electrolyte used in gold electroplating.
    e. Cyanide baths with cadmium complexes are the electrolyte used in cadmium electroplating.

5. Which one among the following metals is the only one which can be prepared by electrolysis of an aqueous solution of one of its salts?

    a. aluminum
    ! b. copper
    c. magnesium
    d. potassium
    e. sodium

6. The products of the electrolysis of molten magnesium chloride using platinum electrodes (an inert electrode) are

      a. hydrogen gas and chlorine gas
  ! b. magnesium metal and chlorine gas
      c. magnesium metal and oxygen gas
      d. magnesium metal and hydroxide ions
      e. chlorine gas and platinum-magnesium alloy

7. The products of the electrolysis of aqueous magnesium chloride using platinum electrodes (an inert electrode) are

      a. magnesium metal and chlorine gas
      b. magnesium metal and oxygen gas
      c. magnesium metal and hydroxide ions
  ! d. hydrogen gas and chlorine gas
      e. chlorine gas and platinum-magnesium alloy

8. When an aqueous solution of sodium chloride is electrolyzed, a gas is observed to form at the anode. The gas is

  ! a. chlorine
      b. hydrogen
      c. hydrogen peroxide
      d. oxygen
      e. sodium

9. When an aqueous solution of copper sulfate is electrolyzed, a gas is observed to form at the anode. The gas is

      a. hydrogen
      b. hydrogen sulfide
      c. hydrogen peroxide
  ! d. oxygen
      e. sulfur dioxide

10. When an aqueous solution of sodium sulfate is electrolyzed, a gas is observed to form at the anode. The gas is

      a. hydrogen
      b. hydrogen sulfide
      c. hydrogen peroxide
  ! d. oxygen
      e. sulfur dioxide

11. When an aqueous solution of sodium sulfate is electrolyzed, a gas is observed to form at the cathode. The gas is

   !　a. hydrogen
   　　b. hydrogen sulfide
   　　c. hydrogen peroxide
   　　d. oxygen
   　　e. sulfur dioxide

12. When an aqueous solution of magnesium sulfate is electrolyzed, what product is formed at the cathode?

   !　a. hydrogen
   　　b. hydrogen sulfide
   　　c. magnesium
   　　d. oxygen
   　　e. sulfur dioxide

13. When an aqueous solution of nickel sulfate is electrolyzed, what product is formed at the anode?

   　　a. hydrogen
   　　b. hydrogen sulfide
   　　c. nickel
   !　d. oxygen
   　　e. sulfur dioxide

14. When fused sodium chloride is electrolyzed, which statement below correctly describes what occurs?

   　　a. gaseous chlorine is formed at the cathode
   　　b. hydrogen gas is formed at the cathode
   !　c. liquid sodium is formed at the cathode
   　　d. liquid chlorine is formed at the anode
   　　e. solid sodium is formed at the anode

15. Which statement below is true?

   　　a. Electrolysis cells generate electrical energy when the terminals are reversed
   　　b. Electrolysis was discovered by Lewis Latimer
   !　c. Galvanic cells generate electrical energy rather than consuming it
   　　d. Galvanic cells were invented by Thomas Edison
   　　e. The Laws of Electrolysis were discovered by Granville Woods

16. When an aqueous solution of $AgNO_3$ is electrolyzed, a gas is observed to form at the anode. The gas is:

      a. dinitrogen tetroxide
      b. hydrogen
      c. mononitrogen monoxide
      d. nitrogen dioxide
!   e. oxygen

17. When an aqueous solution of sodium chloride is electrolyzed, hydrogen gas is evolved at the cathode. The solution near the cathode becomes:

      a. acidic
!   b. basic
      c. bubbly
      d. colored
      e. viscous

18. When an aqueous solution of sodium sulfate is electrolyzed, a gas is evolved at the anode. The solution near the anode becomes:

!   a. acidic
      b. basic
      c. bubbly
      d. colored
      e. viscous

19. When copper is refined using the electrolysis technique, which statement below is true?

!   a. Impure copper goes into solution at the anode, and pure copper plates out on the cathode.
      b. Impure copper goes into solution at the cathode, and pure copper plates out on the anode.
      c. Pure copper goes into solution from the anode and falls to the bottom of the tank .
      d. Pure copper goes into solution from the cathode and falls to the bottom of the tank.
      e. Pure copper on the bottom of the tank goes into solution and plates out on the cathode.

20. The half-reaction that occurs at the cathode during electrolysis of aqueous sodium iodide solution is:

!   a. $2\,H_2O + 2\,e^- \rightarrow H_2(g) + 2\,OH^-(aq)$
      b. $I_2(aq) + 2\,e^- \rightarrow 2\,I^-(aq)$
      c. $2\,I^-(aq) \rightarrow I_2(aq) + 2\,e^-$
      d. $Na^+(aq) + e^- \rightarrow Na(s)$
      e. $Na(s) \rightarrow Na^+(aq) + e^-$

21. The half-reaction that occurs at the cathode during electrolysis of aqueous $CuCl_2$ solution is,

    a. $Cl_2(g) + 2\,e^- \rightarrow 2\,Cl^-(aq)$
    b. $2\,Cl^-(aq) \rightarrow Cl_2(g) + 2\,e^-$
! c. $Cu^{2+}(aq) + 2\,e^- \rightarrow Cu(s)$
    d. $Cu^+(aq) + e^- \rightarrow Cu(s)$
    e. $2\,H_2O + 2\,e^- \rightarrow H_2(g) + 2\,OH^-(aq)$

22. The half-reaction that should occur at the anode during electrolysis of aqueous potassium bromide solution is:

    a. $Br_2(g) + 2\,e^- \rightarrow 2\,Br^-(aq)$
! b. $2\,Br^-(aq) \rightarrow Br_2(l) + 2\,e^-$
    c. $2\,H_2O \rightarrow O_2(g) + 4\,H^+(aq) + 4\,e^-$
    d. $2\,H^+(aq) + e^- \rightarrow H_2(g)$
    e. $Na^+(aq) + e^- \rightarrow Na(s)$

23. The unit of electrical energy used in our work is the

    a. ampere
    b. coulomb
! c. joule
    d. volt
    e. watt

24. A unit of electrical charge used in our work is the

    a. ampere
! b. coulomb
    d. joule
    c. volt
    e. watt

25. The unit of electrical current used in our work is the

! a. ampere
    b. coulomb
    d. joule
    c. volt
    e. watt

26. The Faraday is a unit of

    a. capacitance
    b. current
    c. power
    d. pressure
! e. quantity of electrical charge

27. The quantity of electrical charge can be calculated as

    ! a. the product of current in amperes by time in seconds
      b. the product of potential, in volts, by time in seconds
      c. the product of power, in watts, by time in seconds
      d. the product of energy, in joules, by time in seconds
      e. the product of volts times coulombs

28. One equivalent of electrical charge contains

      a. 4.184 joules
      b. 3,600 coulombs
      c. 23,060 joules
    ! d. 96,485 coulombs
      e. 3.47×10^8 coulombs

29. How many Faradays of charge are required to cause reduction of 0.200 mole of Cr^{2+} ion to metallic chromium?

      a. 0.0670 Faradays
      b. 0.200 Faradays
    ! c. 0.400 Faradays
      d. $0.200 \times 96,485$ Faradays
      e. $0.400 \times 96,485$ Faradays

30. How many coulombs of charge are required for the reduction of 0.20 mol of Cr^{3+} ions to Cr metal?

      a. 0.60 coulombs
      b. 3.0 coulombs
      c. 2.9×10^4 coulombs
    ! d. 5.8×10^4 coulombs
      e. 9.65×10^4 coulombs

31. How many Faradays of electrical charge are transferred in an electrolysis cell when a current of 2.0 amperes flows for 12 hours?

      a. 6.2×10^{-3} Faraday
    ! b. 0.90 Faraday
      c. 1.1 Faradays
      d. 24 Faradays
      e. 8.6×10^4 Faradays

32. How many Faradays of electrical charge are transferred in an electrolysis cell when a current of 3.0 amperes flows for exactly 4 hours and 30 minutes?

    ! a. 5.0×10^{-1}
        b. 8.4×10^{-3}
        c. 1.4×10^{-4}
        d. 13.5
        e. 17.9

33. What electrical current, in amperes, is required to produce 2.00 Faradays of electrical charge over the course of an 8.000 hour period in an electrolysis cell?

        a. 1.57 amperes
    ! b. 6.70 amperes
        c. 107 amperes
        d. 6.03×10^{3} amperes
        e. 2.41×10^{4} amperes

34. What electrical current, in amperes, is required to produce 2.00 Faradays of electrical charge over the course of a 4 hour and 30 minutes and 30 seconds period in an electrolysis cell?

        a. 0.0224 amperes
        b. 0.0841 amperes
        c. 0.336 amperes
        d. 11.6 amperes
    ! e. 11.9 amperes

35. A metal object is to be gold-plated by an electrolytic procedure using aqueous $Au(CN)_4^-$, a gold(III) complex ion, as the electrolyte. Calculate the number of grams of gold deposited in 3.00 minutes by a constant current of 10.0 amperes?

        a. 0.00689 gram
    ! b. 1.22 gram
        c. 1.32 gram
        d. 1.77 gram
        e. 3.55 gram

36. How long will it take to produce 78.0 g of Al metal by the reduction of Al^{3+} ions in an electrolysis cell with a current of 2.00 amperes?

        a. 419 seconds
        b. 4.34 hours
        c. 13.0 hours
    ! d. 116 hours
        e. 6.98×10^{3} hours

37. How many grams of nickel would be electroplated by passing a constant current of 7.20 amperes through a solution of $NiSO_4$ for 90.0 minutes?

      a. 0.200 g
      b. 0.400 g
!   c. 11.8 g
      d. 23.7 g
      e. 47.3 g

38. How many coulombs (q) of electrical charge must pass through an electrolysis cell to reduce 0.44 mol of Ca^{2+} ion to calcium metal?

      a. 0.88 coulomb
      b. 2.1×10^4 coulomb
      c. 4.25×10^4 coulomb
!   d. 8.5×10^4 coulomb
      e. 1.93×10^4 coulomb

39. How many grams of chromium would be electroplated by passing a constant current of 5.2 amperes through a solution containing chromium(III) sulfate for 45.0 minutes?

      a. 9.3×10^{-4} g
      b. 0.042 g
      c. 24 g
!   d. 2.5 g
      e. 2.3×10^{10} g

40. How many coulombs would be required to electroplate 35.0 grams of chromium by passing an electrical current through a solution containing aqueous $CrCl_3$?

      a. 0.16×10^4 coulomb
      b. 6.40×10^4 coulomb
      c. 6.50×10^4 coulomb
!   d. 1.95×10^5 coulomb
      e. 1.01×10^7 coulomb

41. How many minutes would be required to electroplate 25.0 grams of chromium by passing a constant current of 4.8 amperes through a solution containing $CrCl_3$?

      a. 161 minutes
      b. 322 minutes
!   c. 483 minutes
      d. 1.11×10^4 minutes
      e. 2.01×10^4 minutes

42. The reaction, $Au(CN)_4^-(aq) + 3e^- \rightarrow Au(s) + 4\ CN^-$, is being used in electrolysis to plate 45.00 grams of gold on a medallion. How many amperes should the current be, if the time is to run from 9:30:00 A.M. to 3:30:00 P.M. the same day?

    a. 1.003
    b. 1.021
    c. 3.010
! d. 3.062
    e. 6.020

43. The reaction, $Au(CN)_4^-(aq) + 3\ e^- \rightarrow Au(s) + 4\ CN^-(aq)$ is being used in electrolysis to plate 18.25 grams of gold on a medallion. If 2.525 amperes will be used starting at 11:30:00 A.M., at what time should it be shut off?

    a. 1:10:00 P.M.
! b. 2:27:02 P.M.
    c. 3:15:03 P.M.
    d. 3:45:06 P.M.
    e. 4:35:32 P.M.

44. An electroplating bath containing K_2CrO_4 solution is used for chromium plating. If a current of 6.250 amperes was passed through the system for a 6 hr 35 min 20 sec time period, how many grams of Cr would be plated out on the object at the cathode?

! a. 13.32 g
    b. 26.63 g
    c. 36.16 g
    e. 39.95 g
    e. 79.89 g

45. Aluminum does not corrode as does iron, because:

! a. a protective layer of Al_2O_3 forms on the metal surface
    b. Al does not react with $O_2(g)$
    c. Al is harder to oxidize than is Fe
    d. Fe gives cathodic protection to Al
    e. the electrical circuit cannot be completed on an Al surface

46. Iron objects such as storage tanks and underground pipelines can be protected from corrosion by connecting them via a wire to a piece of:

    a. copper
    b. lead
! c. magnesium
    d. silver
    e. tin

47. Why is cryolite, Na_3AlF_6, mixed with alumina prior to electrolysis to produce Al?

    a. because sodium is produced which in turn displaces the aluminum
    b. the aluminum in cryolite is easier to reduce than that in alumina
    c. to provide more fluoride ions
!   d. to reduce the temperature required to bring the alumina into solution
    e. to shift the equilibrium to the right

48. How long would it take to deposit 500 g of silver metal from a solution containing Ag^+ ions using a current of 3.00 amperes?

    a. 41.4 minutes
    b. 1242 minutes
!   c. 2485 minutes
    d. 4969 minutes
    e. 149000 minutes

49. How many liters of chlorine gas, measured at STP, would be produced by the electrolysis of molten sodium chloride using a current of 3.50 amperes for exactly 46 minutes?

!   a. 1.12 liters
    b. 2.24 liters
    c. 11.2 liters
    d. 22.4 liters
    e. 44.8 liters

50. When aqueous brine is electrolyzed, the products are:

!   a. chlorine gas and sodium hydroxide solution
    b. chlorine gas and sodium metal
    c. Na_2O and HCl
    d. NaCl and sodium metal
    e. $NaClO_3$ and $NaClO_2$

51. The Downs cell is used in the electrolytic manufacture of

    a. chlorine gas and sodium hydroxide
    b. hydrogen gas and chlorine gas
    c. hydrogen gas and sodium hydroxide
!   d. sodium metal and chlorine gas
    e. sodium metal and sodium hydroxide

52. A galvanic cell has two electrodes. Which statement below is correct?

      a. Oxidation takes place at the anode, which is positively charged.
!   b. Oxidation takes place at the anode, which is negatively charged.
      c. Oxidation takes place at the cathode, which is positively charged.
      d. Oxidation takes place at the cathode, which is negatively charged.
      e. Oxidation take place at the dynode, which is uncharged.

53. A galvanic cell has two electrodes. Which statement below is correct?

      a. Reduction takes place at the anode, which is positively charged.
      b. Reduction takes place at the anode, which is negatively charged.
!   c. Reduction takes place at the cathode, which is positively charged.
      d. Reduction takes place at the cathode, which is negatively charged.
      e. Reduction takes place at the dynode, which is uncharged.

54. Using these metal ion/metal reaction potentials

Cu^{2+}/Cu	Ag^+/Ag	Co^{2+}/Co	Nt^{2+}/Nt	Zn^{2+}/Zn
0.34	+0.80	-0.28	-1.10	-0.76

Based on the data above, which one of the species below is the best reducing agent?

      a. $Co(s)$
!   b. $Zn(s)$
      c. $Nt^{2+}(aq)$
      d. $Cu(s)$
      e. $Ag^+(aq)$

55. Using these metal ion/metal reaction potentials

Cu^{2+}/Cu	Ag^+/Ag	Co^{2+}/Co	Nt^{2+}/Nt	Zn^{2+}/Zn
0.34	+0.80	-0.28	-1.10	-0.76

Based on the data above, which one of the species below is the best oxidizing agent?

      a. $Co(s)$
      b. $Zn(s)$
      c. $Nt^{2+}(aq)$
      d. $Cu(s)$
!   e. $Ag^+(aq)$

56. Using these metal/metal ion reduction potentials

Cd^{2+}/Cd	Zn^{2+}/Zn	Ni^{2+}/Ni	Xp^+/Xp	Cu^{2+}/Cu
-0.40 v	-0.76 v	-0.25 v	+0.62 v	+0.34 v

Based on the data above, which one of the species below is the best reducing agent?

!   a. $Cd(s)$
      b. $Zn^{2+}(aq)$
      c. $Ni(s)$
      d. $Xp^+(aq)$
      e. $Cu(s)$

57. Using these metal/metal ion reduction potentials

Cd^{2+}/Cd	Zn^{2+}/Zn	Ni^{2+}/Ni	Xp^+/Xp	Cu^{2+}/Cu
-0.40 v	-0.76 v	-0.25 v	+0.62 v	+0.34 v

Based on the data above, which one of the species below is the best oxidizing agent?

    a. $Cd(s)$
    b. $Zn^{2+}(aq)$
    c. $Ni(s)$
!   d. $Xp^+(aq)$
    e. $Cu(s)$

58. Using these metal ion/metal standard reduction potentials

Cd^{2+}/Cd	Zn^{2+}/Zn	Ni^{2+}/Ni	Xp^+/Xp	Cu^{2+}/Cu
-0.40 v	-0.76 v	-0.25 v	+0.62 v	+0.34 v

Based on the data above, which one of the species below is the best oxidizing agent?

    a. $Xp(s)$
    b. $Cu(s)$
    c. $Cd^{2+}(aq)$
    d. $Zn^{2+}(aq)$
!   e. $Ni^{2+}(aq)$

59. Using these metal ion/metal standard reduction potentials

Co^{2+}/Co	Cu^{2+}/Cu	Ag^+/Ag	Zn^{2+}/Zn	Ni^{2+}/Ni	Cd^{2+}/Cd
-0.28 v	+0.34 v	+0.80 v	-0.76 v	-0.25 v	-0.40 v

Calculate the standard cell potential for the cell whose net reaction is

$$Cu^{2+}(aq) + Cd(s) \rightleftharpoons Cd^{2+}(aq) + Cu(s)$$

    a. +0.76 volt
    b. +0.06 volt
    c. -0.06 volt
!   d. +0.74 volt
    e. +0.20 volt

60. Using these metal ion/metal reaction potentials

Cu^{2+}/Cu	Ag^+/Ag	Co^{2+}/Co	Nt^{2+}/Nt	Zn^{2+}/Zn
+0.34	+0.80	-0.28	-1.10	-0.76

Calculate the standard cell potential for the cell whose net reaction is

$$Nt(s) + Ag^+(aq) \rightleftharpoons Nt^{2+}(aq) + Ag(s)$$

    a. -0.300 volt
    b. +0.300 volt
    c. -1.90 volt
!   d. +1.90 volt
    e. +2.70 volt

61. Which choice correctly presents the anode reaction in the galvanic cell with the cell reaction,

$$Nt(s) + Ag^+(aq) \rightleftharpoons Nt^{2+}(aq) + Ag(s)$$

a. $Nt^{2+}(aq) + 2\,e^- \rightleftharpoons Nt(s)$
b. $Ag^+(aq) + e^- \rightleftharpoons Ag(s)$
! c. $Nt(s) \rightleftharpoons Nt^{2+}(aq) + 2\,e^-$
d. $Ag(s) \rightleftharpoons Ag^+(aq) + e^-$
e. $2H^+(aq) + 2\,e^- \rightleftharpoons H_2(g)$

62. Using the standard reduction potentials

$Au^{3+}(aq) + 3\,e^- \rightleftharpoons Au(s)$	+1.42 volt
$Ca^{2+}(aq) + 2\,e^- \rightleftharpoons Ca(s)$	-2.76 volt

Calculate the value of $E^\circ_{(cell)}$ for the cell reaction:

$$2\,Au(s) + 3\,Ca^{2+}(aq) \rightleftharpoons 2\,Au^{3+}(aq) + 3\,Ca(s)$$

a. -1.34 volt
b. +1.34 volt
! c. -4.18 volt
d. +4.18 volt
e. -1.34 volt

63. Using the standard reduction potentials

$Mg^{2+}(aq) + 2\,e^- \rightleftharpoons Mg(s)$	-2.37 volt
$NO_3^-(aq) + 4\,H^+(aq) + 3\,e^- \rightleftharpoons NO(g) + 2\,H_2O$	+0.96 volt

Calculate the value of $E^\circ_{(cell)}$ for the cell with the reaction:

$$3\,Mg(s) + NO_3^-(aq) + 8\,H^+(aq) \rightleftharpoons 3\,Mg^{2+}(aq) + 2\,NO(g) + 4\,H_2O$$

a. +1.41 volt
b. -1.41 volt
! c. +3.33 volt
d. +8.46 volt
e. -8.46 volt

64. Using the standard reduction potentials

$$Cr^{3+}(aq) + 3\ e^- \rightleftharpoons Cr(s) \qquad\qquad -0.40\ \text{volt}$$

$$Cl_2(g) + 2\ e^- \rightleftharpoons 2\ Cl^-(aq) \qquad\qquad +1.36\ \text{volt}$$

Calculate the value of $E°_{(cell)}$ for the cell with the reaction:

$$2\ Cr(s) + 3\ Cl_2(g) \rightleftharpoons 2\ Cr^{3+}(aq) + 6\ Cl^-(aq)$$

    a. -0.96 volt
    b. +0.96 volt
!   c. +1.76 volt
    d. -1.76 volt
    e. +0.98 volt

65. For the reaction, $2\ Cr^{2+}(aq) + Cl_2(g) \rightleftharpoons 2\ Cr^{3+}(aq) + 2\ Cl^-(aq)$, the value of $E°_{(cell)}$ is 1.78 volt. What is the value of $E°_{(cell)}$ for

$$Cr^{3+}(aq) + Cl^-(aq) \rightleftharpoons Cr^{2+}(aq) + ½\ Cl_2(g)$$

!   a. -1.78 volt
    b. +0.89 volt
    c. +1.78 volt
    d. -0.89 volt
    e. -3.56 volt

66. Using the standard reduction potentials

$$Ni^{2+}(aq) + 2\ e^- \rightleftharpoons Ni(s) \quad -0.25\ \text{volt}$$

$$Fe^{3+}(aq) + e^- \rightleftharpoons Fe^{2+}(aq)\ +0.77\ \text{volt}$$

Calculate the value of $E°_{(cell)}$ for the cell with the reaction:

$$Ni^{2+}(aq) + 2\ Fe^{2+}(aq) \rightleftharpoons Ni(s) + 2\ Fe^{3+}(aq)$$

    a. +0.52 volt
!   b. -1.02 volt
    c. +2.81 volt
    d. +1.02 volt
    e. -2.81 volt

67. The cell described by the net reaction

$$Zb^{4+}(aq) + Cl_2(g) + 2\ H_2O \rightleftharpoons ZbO_2^{2+}(aq) + 2\ Cl^-(aq) + 4\ H^+(aq)$$

has a standard potential value of 0.32 volt. Using the half cell value for

$$Cl_2(g) + 2\ e^- \rightleftharpoons 2\ Cl^-(aq) \qquad\qquad +1.36\ \text{volt}$$

determine a value for the standard reduction potential of the half cell,
    $(Pt)/ZbO_2^{2+}(aq),H^+(aq),Zb^{4+}(aq)$

    a. -1.04 volt
!   b. +1.04 volt
    c. -1.68 volt
    d. +1.68 volt
    e. +2.40 volt

68. The cell described by the net reaction
$$2\,U(s)\ +\ 3\,Cl_2(g)\ \rightleftharpoons\ 6\,Cl^-(aq)\ +\ 2\,U^{3+}(aq)$$
has a standard cell potential of 3.16 volts. Using the standard potential value shown for
$$Cl_2(g)\ +\ 2\,e^-\ \rightleftharpoons\ 2\,Cl^-(aq)\ E^\circ = +1.36\ volt$$
determine a value for the standard reduction potential of the $(Pt)/U^{3+}(aq)/U(s)$ half cell

   ! a. -1.80 volt
       b. +1.80 volt
       c. -1.96 volt
       d. -4.52 volt
       e. +4.52 volt

69. The cell described by the net reaction,
$$2\,Co^{3+}(aq)\ +\ 2\,Cl^-(aq)\ \rightleftharpoons\ 2\,Co^{2+}(aq)\ +\ Cl_2(g)$$
has a standard potential of 0.46 volt. Using the standard potential value shown for
$$Cl_2(g)\ +\ 2\,e^-\ \rightleftharpoons\ 2\,Cl^-(aq)\qquad\qquad E^\circ = +1.36\ volt$$
determine a value for the standard reduction potential of the $(Pt)/Co^{3+}(aq),Co^{2+}(aq)$ half cell.

       a. -0.90 volt
       b. +0.90 volt
       c. +0.91 volt
       d. -1.82 volt
   ! e. +1.82 volt

70. Which one of chemical species in the galvanic cell represented as
$$Sn(s)/Sn^{2+}(aq)//NO_3^-(aq)/NO(g)/(Pt)$$
is the species undergoing reduction?

   ! a. $NO_3^-(aq)$
       b. $NO(g)$
       c. $Pt(s)$
       d. $Sn(s)$
       e. $Sn^{2+}(aq)$

71. A galvanic cell is composed of these two half cells, with the standard reduction potentials shown
$$Co^{2+}(aq)\ +\ 2\,e^-\ \rightleftharpoons\ Co(s)\qquad\qquad -0.28\ volt$$
$$Cd^{2+}(aq)\ +\ 2\,e^-\ \rightleftharpoons\ Cd(s)\qquad\qquad -0.40\ volt$$
What is the standard free energy for the cell reaction of this galvanic cell?

       a. -12 kJ
       b. +12 kJ
   ! c. -23 kJ
       d. +23 kJ
       e. -46 kJ

72. A galvanic cell is composed of these two half cells, with the standard reduction potentials shown

$$Co^{2+}(aq) + 2\,e^- \rightleftharpoons Co(s) \qquad\qquad -0.28\ \text{volt}$$
$$Cd^{2+}(aq) + 2\,e^- \rightleftharpoons Cd(s) \qquad\qquad -0.40\ \text{volt}$$

The actual concentrations are: $Co^{2+}(aq) = 0.00100$ M, $Cd^{2+} = 0.100$ M. What is the actual potential of this galvanic cell?

  ! a. +0.06 volt
     b. +0.12 volt
     c. +0.24 volt
     d. +0.33 volt
     e. +0.68 volt

73. A galvanic cell is composed of these two half cells, with the standard reduction potentials shown

$$Co^{2+}(aq) + 2\,e^- \rightleftharpoons Co(s) \qquad\qquad -0.28\ \text{volt}$$
$$Cd^{2+}(aq) + 2\,e^- \rightleftharpoons Cd(s) \qquad\qquad -0.40\ \text{volt}$$

The actual concentrations are: $Co^{2+}(aq) = 0.100$ M, $Cd^{2+} = 0.0100$ M. What is the actual potential of this galvanic cell?

     a. +0.06 volt
     b. +0.09 volt
  ! c. +0.15 volt
     d. +0.18 volt
     e. +0.24 volt

74. A galvanic cell is composed of these two half cells, with the standard reduction potentials shown

$$Co^{2+}(aq) + 2\,e^- \rightleftharpoons Co(s) \qquad\qquad -0.28\ \text{volt}$$
$$Cd^{2+}(aq) + 2\,e^- \rightleftharpoons Cd(s) \qquad\qquad -0.40\ \text{volt}$$

The actual $Co^{2+}(aq)$ concentration is 0.100 M, the $Cd^{2+}(aq)$ concentration is unknown. The actual cell potential was measured as 0.16 volts. Calculate the actual concentration of the $Cd^{2+}(aq)$ ion.

     a. 0.0011 M
  ! b. 0.0044 M
     c. 0.011 M
     d. 0.022 M
     e. 0.044 M

75. A galvanic cell is composed of these two half cells, with the standard reduction potentials shown

$Co^{2+}(aq) + 2\,e^- \rightleftharpoons Co(s)$ -0.28 volt

$Cd^{2+}(aq) + 2\,e^- \rightleftharpoons Cd(s)$ -0.40 volt

The actual concentrations are: $Co^{2+}(aq) = 0.00100$ M, $Cd^{2+} = 0.100$ M. What is the free energy change associated with this particular design?

     a. - 5.87 kJ/mol
!   b. -11.7 kJ/mol
     c. -23.5 kJ/mol
     d. -35.2 kJ/mol
     e. -47.0 kJ/mol

76. A galvanic cell is composed of these two half cells, with the standard reduction potentials shown

$Co^{2+}(aq) + 2\,e^- \rightleftharpoons Co(s)$ -0.28 volt

$Cd^{2+}(aq) + 2\,e^- \rightleftharpoons Cd(s)$ -0.40 volt

The actual concentrations are: $Co^{2+}(aq) = 0.100$ M, $Cd^{2+} = 0.0100$ M. What is the free energy change associated with this particular design?

     a. - 5.87 kJ/mol
     b. -11.7 kJ/mol
!   c. -28.9 kJ/mol
     d. -35.2 kJ/mol
     e. -47.0 kJ/mol

77. A galvanic cell is composed of these two half cells, with the standard reduction potentials shown

$Co^{2+}(aq) + 2\,e^- \rightleftharpoons Co(s)$ -0.28 volt

$Cr^{3+}(aq) + 3\,e^- \rightleftharpoons Cr(s)$ -0.74 volt

What is the standard free energy for the cell reaction of this galvanic cell?

     a. -88.8 kJ
     b. -178 kJ
!   c. -266 kJ
     d. -295 kJ
     e. -590 kJ

78. A galvanic cell is composed of these two half cells, with the standard reduction potentials shown

$Co^{2+}(aq) + 2\,e^- \rightleftharpoons Co(s)$ -0.28 volt

$Cr^{3+}(aq) + 3\,e^- \rightleftharpoons Cr(s)$ -0.74 volt

The actual concentrations are: $Co^{2+}(aq) = 0.0100$ M, $Cr^{3+} = 0.00100$ M. What is the actual potential of this galvanic cell?

     a. +0.40 volt
!   b. +0.46 volt
     c. +0.52 volt
     d. +0.54 volt
     e. +1.02 volt

79. A galvanic cell is composed of these two half cells, with the standard reduction potentials shown

$$Co^{2+}(aq) + 2 e^- \rightleftharpoons Co(s) \qquad -0.28 \text{ volt}$$

$$Cr^{3+}(aq) + 3 e^- \rightleftharpoons Cr(s) \qquad -0.74 \text{ volt}$$

The actual concentrations are: $Co^{2+}(aq) = 0.00100$ M, $Cr^{3+} = 0.100$ M. What is the actual potential of this galvanic cell?

    a. +0.33 volt
! b. +0.39 volt
    c. +0.45 volt
    d. +0.94 volt
    e. +1.61 volt

80. A galvanic cell is composed of these two half cells, with the standard reduction potentials shown

$$Co^{2+}(aq) + 2 e^- \rightleftharpoons Co(s) \qquad -0.28 \text{ volt}$$

$$Cr^{3+}(aq) + 3 e^- \rightleftharpoons Cr(s) \qquad -0.74 \text{ volt}$$

The actual $Co^{2+}(aq)$ concentration is 0.00100 M, while the $Cr^{3+}(aq)$ concentration is unknown. The actual cell potential measured 0.38 volts. What is the actual concentration of the Cr^{3+} ion in the cell?

    a. 0.00180 M
    b. 0.00500 M
    c. 0.0090 M
    d. 0.0360 M
! e. 0.360 M

81. A galvanic cell is composed of these two half cells, with the standard reduction potentials shown

$$Co^{2+}(aq) + 2 e^- \rightleftharpoons Co(s) \qquad -0.28 \text{ volt}$$

$$Cr^{3+}(aq) + 3 e^- \rightleftharpoons Cr(s) \qquad -0.74 \text{ volt}$$

The actual concentrations are: $Co^{2+}(aq) = 0.0100$ M, $Cr^{3+} = 0.00100$ M. What is the free energy change associated with this particular design?

    a. - 38.6 kJ
    b. - 44.4 kJ
    c. -232 kJ
! d. -266 kJ
    e. -301 kJ

82. A galvanic cell is composed of these two half cells, with the standard reduction potentials shown

$$Co^{2+}(aq) + 2 e^- \rightleftharpoons Co(s) \qquad -0.28 \text{ volt}$$

$$Cr^{3+}(aq) + 3 e^- \rightleftharpoons Cr(s) \qquad -0.74 \text{ volt}$$

The actual concentrations are: $Co^{2+}(aq) = 0.00100$ M, $Cr^{3+} = 0.100$ M. What is the free energy change associated with this particular design?

    a. -159 kJ
    b. -188 kJ
    c. -191 kJ
! d. -226 kJ
    e. -261 kJ

83. Which statement is true in regard to a galvanic cell?

> ! a. $E^°$ for the cell is always positive
> b. $E^°$ for the cell is always negative
> c. The standard reduction potential for the anode reaction is always positive
> d. The standard reduction potential for the anode reaction is always negative
> e. The standard reduction potential for the cathode reaction is always positive

84. The standard reduction potentials of $Cu^{2+}(aq)/Cu(s)$ and $Ag^+(aq)/Ag(s)$ are +0.34 and +0.80 volts, respectively. Determine the value of the actual cell potential, E, (in volts) for the following cell at 25.0 °C.

$$Cu(s)|Cu^{2+}(0.250 \text{ M})||Ag^+(0.0010 \text{ M})|Ag(s)$$

> ! a. +0.30 volt
> b. +0.14 volt
> c +0.62 volt
> d. +0.78 volt
> e. +0.39 volt

85. The standard reduction potentials for the reduction of $Ag^+(aq)$ to $Ag(s)$ and $Fe^{3+}(aq)$ to $Fe^{2+}(aq)$ are +0.800 and +0.770 volts, respectively. Calculate the equilibrium constant, K, for the reaction,

$$Ag^+(aq) + Fe^{2+}(aq) \rightleftharpoons Ag(s) + Fe^{3+}(aq)$$

> a. 1.66
> ! b. 3.21
> c. 6.4
> d. $1.6 \times 10^{+4}$
> e. 6.1×10^{-4}

Use the standard potentials below to answer questions 86 and 87

$$Nt^{2+}(aq) + 2e \rightleftharpoons Nt(s) \qquad -1.10 \text{ volt}$$
$$Xp^+(aq) + e \rightleftharpoons Xp(s) \qquad +1.13 \text{ volt}$$
$$M^{2+}(aq) + 2e \rightleftharpoons M(s) \qquad -1.38 \text{ volt}$$
$$Q_2(g) + 2e \rightleftharpoons 2Q^-(aq) \qquad +0.48 \text{ volt}$$
$$Ro^{2+}(aq) + 2e \rightleftharpoons Ro(s) \qquad -0.78 \text{ volt}$$

86. Which one of the following listed species is the best oxidizing agent?

> a. Nt(s)
> b. $Q^-(aq)$
> c. $M^{2+}(aq)$
> ! d. $Xp^+(aq)$
> e. $Nt^{2+}(aq)$

87. Which one of the following listed species is the best reducing agent?

    ! a. Nt(s)
       b. Q⁻(aq)
       c. M²⁺(aq)
       d. Xp⁺(aq)
       e. Nt²⁺(aq)

Fill in the Blanks

88. In the lead storage battery, the electrolyte is _____ (! sulfuric acid solution)

89. In the zinc-carbon dry cell, the electrode at which oxidation takes place has a _____ charge. (! negative)

90. In the nickel-cadmium storage cell (the "nicad" battery) the electrolyte is _____ (! sodium hydroxide solution)

91. In the Hall process for manufacture of aluminum, the anodes are constructed of _____ (! carbon)

True and False

92. When an electrical current is passed through fused (molten) magnesium chloride, chlorine gas is produced at the negatively charged electrode. (! F)

93. During the electrolysis of water, oxygen gas is formed at the anode. (! T)

94. Lithium metal can be produced readily by the electrolysis of aqueous solutions of lithium nitrate, or lithium chloride. (! F)

95. If the brine bath is stirred during electrolysis, a different set of products are obtained than would be obtained by electrolysis of an unstirred bath. (! T)

96. The SI unit of charge is the Faraday. (! F)

Critical Thinking

97. An old classmate who works for Eagle metals on the night shift was supposed to do this gold plating job wherein he put 4.5000 troy ounces of gold (1 troy ounce = 31.103486 gram) on a medallion using the reaction,

$$Au(CN)_4^-(aq) + 3\,e^- \;\rightleftharpoons\; Au(s) + 4\,CN^-$$

He somehow got 4.8527 troy ounces of gold on the medallion instead of the correct amount. Please tell him how many hours, minutes, and seconds he should run the cells with the leads reversed, using a current of 1.350 amperes, to rectify the error and bring the medallions down to the correct weight. _____ (! 3 hours, 19 minutes, and 2 seconds)

Use these standard potentials in answering questions 98 through 102

$$Nt^{2+}(aq) + 2e \rightleftharpoons Nt(s) \quad -0.422 \text{ volt}$$
$$NtSO_4(s) + 2e \rightleftharpoons Nt(s) + SO_4^{2-}(aq) \quad -0.715 \text{ volt}$$
$$Nt(NH_3)_4^{2+}(aq) + 2e^- \rightleftharpoons Nt(s) + 4NH_3(aq) \quad -0.922 \text{ volt}$$
$$Nt(CN)_4^{2-}(aq) + 2e^- \rightleftharpoons Nt(s) + 4CN^-(aq) \quad -1.014 \text{ volt}$$

98. What is value of the formation constant for the tetracyanonortonate(2-) ion. The reaction is:
$$Nt^{2+}(aq) + 4CN^-(aq) \rightleftharpoons Nt(CN)_4^{2-}(aq)$$
_____ (! $\approx 1.03 \times 10^{+20}$)

99. What is the equilibrium constant for the reaction
$$Nt(NH_3)_4^{2+}(aq) + 4CN^-(aq) \rightleftharpoons Nt(CN)_4^{2-}(aq) + 4NH_3(aq)$$
_____ (! $\approx 1.29 \times 10^{+3}$)

100. the equation for the chemical reaction from which the expression for the solubility product of $NtSO_4(s)$ is derived. Use this equation and the data above to calculate the solubility product of nortonium sulfate. _____ (! 1.24×10^{-10})

101. Calculate the value of the equilibrium constant, K_c, for the reaction
$$Nt(CN)_4^{2-}(aq) + SO_4^{2-}(aq) \rightleftharpoons NtSO_4(s) + 4 CN^-(aq)$$
_____ (! 7.79×10^{-11})

102. The solubility product constant for $NtCrO_4$ is 4.50×10^{-12}. Using the potentials provided in the listing above, calculate the value or the equilibrium constant, K_c, for the reaction
$$Nt(CN)_4^{2-}(aq) + CrO_4^{2-}(aq) \rightleftharpoons NtCrO_4(s) + 4 CN^-(aq)$$
_____ (! 2.15×10^{-9})

103. An electrolysis study was carried to determine the atomic weight of nortonium from a study on the compound, nortonium nitrate. Another study had established that the formula was probably $Nt(NO_3)_2$. In the present study, electrolysis was carried on an aqueous sample of nortonium nitrate, and the quantities of the electrolysis products were carefully measured. At the anode a gas was collected which, after correction for the vapor pressure of water, registered a volume of 94.25 ml when the temperature was 25.0 °C and the pressure was 748.5 torr. The mass of the nortonium which plated out on the cathode was measured as 836.2 mg. From this data, calculate a value for the atomic weight of nortonium. _____ (! 110.2)

104. An electrolysis study was carried to determine the atomic weight of nortonium from a study on the compound, nortonium chloride. Another study had established that the formula was probably $NtCl_2$. In the present study, electrolysis was carried on an aqueous sample of nortonium chloride, and the quantity of electrical energy was carefully measured. A current measuring 1.550 amperes at a voltage of 12.25 volts, was passed through the electrolysis with the aqueous nortonium chloride solution starting at 2:00:00 P.M. and ending at 2:53:30 P.M. the same day. The amount of nortonium which plated out on the cathode measured 2.848 g. From this data, calculate a value for the atomic weight of nortonium. _____ (! 110.4 or 110.5)

Chapter 20 Properties of Metals and Metal Complexes

Multiple Choice

1. Iron ore is reduced to iron by reaction with

    a. calcium carbonate
    ! b. carbon
    c. carbon monoxide
    d. carbon dioxide
    e. sulfur dioxide

2. Where are alkali elements and their compounds found in nature?

    a. primarily in caves
    b. primarily in clay soils
    c. primarily in closed lakes which have no outlet
    d. primarily in soils from desert regions
    ! e. primarily in sea water

3. Sodium metal is prepared commercially by

    a. displacement from its fused salts by magnesium or aluminum
    ! b. electrolysis
    c. reduction of sodium carbonate by lime at 600 °C
    d. reduction of sodium carbonate by carbon at 2000 °C
    e. reduction of sodium oxide by carbon at 2000 °C

4. Lithium metal is prepared commercially by

    a. displacement from its fused salts using metallic magnesium
    ! b. electrolysis of fused lithium chloride
    c. reduction of lithium chloride by boron at 2000 °C
    d. reduction of lithium carbonate by carbon at 2000 °C
    e. reduction of lithium oxide by carbon at 2000 °C

5. Which one of the following listed oxides is very water soluble and hence is not found in natural ore deposits?

    ! a. Na_2O
    b. Fe_3O_4
    c. Al_2O_3
    d. SiO_2
    e. TiO_2

6. The chief source of phosphate fertilizers which is found in nature is

    a. H_3PO_4
    b. $Ba_3(PO_4)_2$
    c. NaH_2PO_4
!   d. $Ca_3(PO_4)_2$
    e. $Fe_3(PO_4)_2$

7. The most commercially important reducing agent for recovering metals like lead and tin from their oxides which can be readily produced from minerals is

    a. sodium metal
    b. calcium metal
    c. aluminum metal
!   d. carbon, in the form of coke
    e. hydrogen gas

8. A chemical reducing agent which is commonly used to remove tarnish from silver by reduction of the silver compounds is

    a. sodium metal
    b. calcium metal
!   c. aluminum metal
    d. carbon, in the form of coke
    e. hydrogen gas

9. Which one of these metal oxides is likely to have the lowest melting point?

    a. Al_2O_3
    b. FeO
    c. CrO
    d. Cr_2O_3
!   e. CrO_3

10. Which one of these metal oxides is likely to have the lowest melting point?

    a. Mn_3O_4
    b. MnO
    c. MnO_2
    d. Mn_2O_3
!   e. Mn_2O_7

11. Which statement below about ligands that form coordination complexes with transition metals is false?

    ! a. A ligand that attaches itself to a metal ion is functioning as a Lewis acid.
    b. Neutral molecules can function as ligands and can form coordination complexes with transition metal ions.
    c. Anions can function as ligands and can form coordination complexes with transition metal ions.
    d. The ligand in a coordination complex contains a particular atom which functions as the donor atom.
    e. The bond between the ligand and the transition metal ion in a coordination complex is a coordinate covalent bond.

12. The number of possible donor atoms in the edta (ethylenediaminetetraacetate) ligand is

    a. 2
    b. 3
    c. 4
    ! d. 6
    e. 8

13. The charge on the metal ion in the coordination complex ion, $[Co(CO_3)_3]^{3-}$, is

    a. 0
    b. 2+
    c. 3-
    ! d. 3+
    e. 6-

14. A coordination compound formed from cobalt(III) sulfate and ammonia contains <u>six</u> ammonia molecules which function as ligands. The formula of the compound is properly written as

    a. $Co_2(SO_4)_3 \cdot 6NH_3$
    ! b. $[Co(NH_3)_6]_2(SO_4)_3$
    c. $Co_3SO_4(NH_3)_6$
    d. $Co_2(SO_4)_3(NH_4)_6$
    e. $Co_2[(NH_3)_6](SO_4)_3$

15. A coordination compound formed from chromium(III) chloride contains <u>five</u> ammonia molecules and one water molecule which function as ligands. The correct expression for its formula is

    ! a. $[Cr(NH_3)_5(H_2O)]Cl_3$
    b. $Cr_3Cl(NH_3)_5H_2O$
    c. $CrCl_3 \cdot 5NH_3 \cdot H_2O$
    d. $Cr(NH_3)_5Cl_3 \cdot H_2O$
    e. $[Cr(NH_3)_5]Cl_3 \cdot H_2O$

16. A compound contains a transition metal coordination complex. This coordination complex consists of one iron(III) ion with three $C_2O_4{}^{2-}$ ions attached as ligands. Which formula below correctly describes a compound that would fit the description?

   ! a. $K_3[Fe(C_2O_4)_3]$
       b. $Fe(C_2O_4)_3$
       c. $[Fe(C_2O_4)_3]Cl_3$
       d. $Fe(C_2O_4)_3](SO_4)_3$
       e. $Ca_3[Fe(C_2O_4)_3]$

17. A complex ion is formed by a Co^{3+} ion which is linked up to one carbonate ion and four ammonia molecules. Which formula below would correctly represent a salt of this complex ion?

       a. $Na_3[Co(NH_3)_4CO_3]$
       b. $Na[Co(NH_3)_4CO_3]$
       c. $[Co(NH_3)_4CO_3]CO_3$
       d. $[Co(NH_3)_4CO_3]Cl_2$
   ! e. $[Co(NH_3)_4CO_3]_2SO_4$

18. A compound contains a transition metal coordination complex. This coordination complex consists of one cobalt(III) ion with five ammonia molecules and one cyanide ion attached as ligands. Which formula below correctly describes a compound that would fit the description?

       a. $K_4[Co(NH_3)_5CN]$
       b. $K_2[Co(NH_3)_5CN]$
       c. $[Co(NH_3)_5CN](SO_4)_2$
   ! d. $[Co(NH_3)_5CN]SO_4$
       e. $[Co(NH_3)_5CN]Cl_3$

19. A coordination complex has the general formula, $Cr(NH_3)_5Cl_3$ and has a limited solubility in water. The reaction of a solution of this complex with silver nitrate solution consistently produces two millimoles of silver chloride for every millimole of the $Cr(NH_3)_5Cl_3$. Reaction with aqueous H_2SO_4 or HCl clearly shows a lack of free ammonia in the solution. Which formula below is consistent with the observed reactions?

   ! a. $[Co(NH_3)_5Cl]Cl_2$
       b. $[Co(NH_3)_5Cl_2]Cl$
       c. $[Co(NH_3)_5Cl_3]$
       d. $[CoCl_3]\cdot5NH_3$
       e. $[Co(NH_3)_3Cl_3]\cdot2NH_3$

20. The correct name for the complex ion, $[Ni(CN)_4]^{2-}$, is

       a. tetracyanonickel(II)
       b. nickel(II) tetracyanide
       c. tetracyanonickelo(II)
   ! d. tetracyanonickelate(II)
       e. tetracyanonickelite(II)

21. The correct name for the complex ion, $[Co(NH_3)_6]^{3+}$, is

      a. cobalt hexammine
      b. cobalt(III) hexamine
      c. hexamminecobaltate(III)
      d. hexaminocobaltate(III)
 ! e. hexamminecobalt(III)

22. The correct name for the complex ion, $[AuCl_4]^-$, is

      a. gold tetrachloride
      b. gold(II) tetrachloride
      c. auric tetrachloride
      d. tetrachlorogold(III)
 ! e. tetrachloroaurate(III)

23. The correct name for the compound, $[Cr(en)_2Cl_2]_2C_2O_4$, is

 ! a. dichlorobis(ethylenediamine)chromium(III) oxalate
      b. bis(ethylenediamine)dichlorochromate(III) oxalate
      c. dichlorobis(ethylenediamine)oxalatochromium(III)
      d. dichlorobis(ethylenediamine)oxalatochromate(III)
      e. bis(dichlorobis(ethylenediamine)chromium(III)) oxalate

24. The compound, $[Co(NH_3)_6][PtCl_4]$, is named

      a. cobalt(III) hexammine tetrachloroplatinate
      b. cobalt(II) hexammine tetrachloroplatinate
      c. cobalt(III) hexammine platinum tetrachloride
 ! d. hexamminecobalt(III) tetrachloroplatinate
      e. hexamminecobalt(III) platinum tetrachloride

25. The correct name of neutral coordination complex below is

$$\begin{array}{c} NH_3 \\ | \\ H_3N-Pt-Cl \\ | \\ Cl \end{array}$$

      a. *cis*-diaminodichloroplatinate(II)
      b. *cis*-diaminodichloroplatinum(II)
 ! c. *cis*-diamminedichloroplatinum(II)
      b. *trans*-diaminodichloroplatinum(II)
      c. *trans*-diamminedichloroplatinum(II)

26. The compound, $(NH_4)_3[FeF_6]$, is named

      a. ammonium hexafluoroiron(III)
 ! b. ammonium hexafluoroferrate(III)
      c. ammonium iron(III) hexafluoride
      d. hexafluoroiron(III) ammonium
      e. triammonium hexafluoroiron(III)

27. The coordination complex, $[Co(NH_3)_5(ONO)]Cl_2$, is named

      a. pentaamminenitrocobalt(III) chloride
      b. pentaamminenitritocobalt(II) chloride
      c. pentaamminenitrocobalt(II) chloride
 ! d. pentaamminenitritocobalt(III) chloride
      e. nitropentaamminecobalt(II) chloride

28. The coordination number of the chromium ion in the complex ion, $[Cr(dien)_2]^{3+}$, is

$$\text{(dien} = H_2N-CH_2-CH_2-\overset{\overset{\displaystyle H}{|}}{N}-CH_2-CH_2-NH_2)$$

      a. 1
      b. 2
      c. 3
      d. 4
 ! e. 6

29. The coordination number of the platinum ion in the complex ion, $[Pt(C_2O_4)_2]^{2-}$, is

      a. 1
      b. 2
      c. 3
 ! d. 4
      e. 6

30. The coordination number of the nickel ion in the complex ion, $[Ni(en)_3]^{2+}$, is

      a. 1
      b. 2
      c. 3
      d. 4
 ! e. 6

31. A platinum coordination complex has the formula, $[Pt(NH_3)_2BrCl]$, and exhibits a square planar geometry. How many geometric isomers of this compound should exist?

        a. 1(no isomers)
!   b. 2
        c. 3
        d. 4
        e. 5

32. A platinum coordination complex has the formula, $[Pt(NH_3)BrClI]^-$, and exhibits a square planar geometry. How many geometric isomers of this compound should exist?

        a. 1(no isomers)
        b. 2
!   c. 3
        d. 4
        e. 5

33. A coordination complex in which the ligands exhibit an octahedral geometry about the central metal ion has the formula, $[Co(NH_3)_4Cl_2]$. How many geometric isomers of this compound should exist?

        a. 1(no isomers)
!   b. 2
        c. 3
        d. 4
        e. 5

34. Which one of the following complex ions is a chiral complex?

        a. square planar $[Pt(en)_2]^{2+}$
        b. tetrahedral $[NiCl_4]^{2-}$
!   c. octahedral $[Co(en)_3]^{3+}$
        d. octahedral $[Co(NH_3)_4Cl_2]^+$
        e. square planar $[Pt(NH_3)ClBrI]^-$

35. A coordination complex in which the ligands exhibit an octahedral geometry about the central metal ion has the formula, $[Cr(en)_2Cl_2]^+$. How many geometric isomers of this compound should exist?

        a. 1(no isomers)
!   b. 2
        c. 3
        d. 4
        e. 5

36. The splitting of the 5-fold degenerate d-orbital energy level of transition metal ions by the field potential of a particular geometry gives rise to the pattern,

$$\overline{d_{xz}} \quad \overline{d_{xz}} \quad \overline{d_{xz}}$$

$$E\uparrow \quad \overline{d_{x^2-y^2}} \quad \overline{d_{z^2}}$$

Which one of the following geometries produces the splitting pattern above?

    a. linear
    b. octahedral
    c. planar triangular
    d. square planar
!   e. tetrahedral

37. The following order is observed in the spectrochemical series for the ligands listed,
$$CN^- > NO_2^- > en > NH_3 > H_2O > C_2O_4^{2-} > OH^- > F^- > Cl^- > Br^- > I^-$$
It was observed that for the two 6-coordinate cobalt complexes, CoF_6^{3-} and $Co(NH_3)_6^{3+}$, one is diamagnetic and one is paramagnetic. How many unpaired electrons are there in the paramagnetic complex ion?

    a. 1
    b. 2
    c. 3
!   d. 4
    e. 5

38. The following order is observed in the spectrochemical series for the ligands listed,
$$CN^- > NO_2^- > en > NH_3 > H_2O > C_2O_4^{2-} > OH^- > F^- > Cl^- > Br^- > I^-$$
How many unpaired electrons would you expect to find in the complex ion, $Cr(CN)_6^{3-}$ if the value of the splitting parameter is as large as it is in typical cyanide complexes?

    a. 1
    b. 2
!   c. 3
    d. 4
    e. 5

39. Many, but not all coordination complexes are colored due to absorption of light in the visible region of the spectrum. A complex ion which has its absorption maximum in the blue region of the visible spectrum would most likely appear to be

    a. blue
    b. green
    c. yellow
    d. orange
!   e. red

40. The following order is observed in the spectrochemical series for the ligands listed,
$$CN^- > NO_2^- > en > NH_3 > H_2O > C_2O_4^{2-} > OH^- > F^- > Cl^- > Br^- > I^-$$
FeF_6^{3-} and $Fe(CN)_6^{3-}$ are both negatively charged coordination complexes. Which statement below is the only one that could possibly describe the situation?

    a. FeF_6^{3-} and $Fe(CN)_6^{3-}$ are both diamagnetic.
    b. FeF_6^{3-} is diamagnetic while $Fe(CN)_6^{3-}$ is paramagnetic.
    c. FeF_6^{3-} is paramagnetic while $Fe(CN)_6^{3-}$ is diamagnetic.
!   d. Both complex ions are paramagnetic, but FeF_6^{3-} has a larger number of unpaired electrons than $Fe(CN)_6^{3-}$ hence its paramagnetism is more pronounced.
    e. Both complex ions are paramagnetic, but $Fe(CN)_6^{3-}$ has a larger number of unpaired electrons than FeF_6^{3-} hence its paramagnetism is more pronounced.

41. The following order is observed in the spectrochemical series for the ligands listed,
$$CN^- > NO_2^- > en > NH_3 > H_2O > C_2O_4^{2-} > OH^- > F^- > Cl^- > Br^- > I^-$$
$Cr(NH_3)_6^{3+}$ and $Co(NH_3)_6^{3+}$ are both negatively charged coordination complexes. Which statement below is the only one that could possibly describe the situation?

    a. $Cr(NH_3)_6^{3+}$ and $Co(NH_3)_6^{3+}$ are both diamagnetic.
    b. $Cr(NH_3)_6^{3+}$ is diamagnetic while $Co(NH_3)_6^{3+}$ is paramagnetic.
!   c. $Cr(NH_3)_6^{3+}$ is paramagnetic while $Co(NH_3)_6^{3+}$ is diamagnetic.
    d. Both complex ions are paramagnetic, but $Cr(NH_3)_6^{3+}$ has a larger number of unpaired electrons than $Co(NH_3)_6^{3+}$ hence its paramagnetism is more pronounced.
    e. Both complex ions are paramagnetic, but $Co(NH_3)_6^{3+}$ has a larger number of unpaired electrons than $Cr(NH_3)_6^{3+}$ hence its paramagnetism is more pronounced.

42. The following order is observed in the spectrochemical series for the ligands listed,
$$CN^- > NO_2^- > en > NH_3 > H_2O > C_2O_4^{2-} > OH^- > F^- > Cl^- > Br^- > I^-$$
$Cr(NH_3)_6^{3+}$ and $Ni(NH_3)_6^{2+}$ are both negatively charged coordination complexes. Which statement below is the only one that could possibly describe the situation?

    a. $Cr(NH_3)_6^{3+}$ and $Ni(NH_3)_6^{2+}$ are both diamagnetic.
    b. $Cr(NH_3)_6^{3+}$ is diamagnetic while $Ni(NH_3)_6^{2+}$ is paramagnetic.
    c. $Cr(NH_3)_6^{3+}$ is paramagnetic while $Ni(NH_3)_6^{2+}$ is diamagnetic.
!   d. Both complex ions are paramagnetic, but $Cr(NH_3)_6^{3+}$ has a larger number of unpaired electrons than $Ni(NH_3)_6^{2+}$ hence its paramagnetism is more pronounced.
    e. Both complex ions are paramagnetic, but $Ni(NH_3)_6^{2+}$ has a larger number of unpaired electrons than $Cr(NH_3)_6^{3+}$ hence its paramagnetism is more pronounced.

43. Many, but not all coordination complexes are colored due to absorption of light in the visible region of the spectrum. Which one of the following coordination complexes of transition metals is definitely *not* expected to be a colored complex?

    a. $Co(NH_3)_6^{3+}$
    b. $Cr(NH_3)_6^{2+}$
    c. $Cu(NH_3)_4^{2+}$
    d. $V(H_2O)_6^{3+}$
!   e. $Zn(NH_3)_4^{2+}$

44. Which one of the following coordination complexes would you expect to be the most stable (having the highest formation constant)?

    a. $Co(NH_3)_6^{3+}$
    b. CoF_6^{3-}
    c. $Co(en)_3^{3+}$
    d. $Co(dien)_2^{3+}$ dien = H_2N—CH_2—CH_2—NH—CH_2—CH_2—NH_2
!   e. $Co(edta)^-$ edta = ethylenediaminetetraacetate

45. The Cu^{2+} ion reacts with ammonia molecules to form $Cu(NH_3)_4^{2+}$ ions. Which statement below is true?

    a. The copper ion is functioning as a Lewis base.
    b. The ammonia molecule is functioning a an acceptor molecule.
    c. The bond between the ammonia and the copper(II) ion is an ionic bond.
!   d. The ammonia molecule is a monodentate ligand.
    e. The copper (II) ion is a 6-coordinate species in this complex ion.

46. Which one of the following species can function as a chelating ligand?

    a. NH_3
    b. NH_4^+
    c. CN^-
    d. CH_3—CH_2—CH_2—NH_2
!   e. NH_2—CH_2—CH_2—NH_2

47. Which one of the following species can function as a chelating ligand?

    a. NH_3
    b. NH_4^+
    c. CN^-
    d. CH_3—CH_2—CH_2—O—H
!   e. NH_2—CH_2—CH_2—NH—CH_3

48. Which one of these chromium complexes should be the most stable?

    a. $Co(NH_3)_6^{2+}$
    b. $Co(NH_3)_6^{3+}$
    c. $Co(H_2O)_6^{2+}$
    d. $Co(F)_6^{3-}$
!   e. $Co(en)_3^{3+}$

Fill in the Blanks

49. Here is some data for the compound Au_2O_3. $\Delta H^\circ_f = +80.8$ kJ mol^{-1}, $S^\circ = 125$ J K^{-1} mol^{-1}. For Au, $S^\circ = 47.7$ J K^{-1} mol^{-1} while for O_2, $S^\circ = 205$ J K^{-1} mol^{-1} At what temperature does this oxide of gold become unstable with respect to thermal decomposition? _____ (! It is unstable at all temperatures because ΔG for decomposition is < 0 at all temperatures.)

50. The ethylenediamine molecule, usually abbreviated as en, functions as a bidentate ligand and forms coordination complexes with platinum which have the formula: $[Pt(en)_2]^{2+}$. Based on this information, assign a coordination number to the platinum(II) ion in this coordination complex. _____ (! 4)

51. The ethylenediamine molecule, usually abbreviated as en, functions as a bidentate ligand and forms a coordination complex with cobalt which has the formula: $[Co(en)_2(H_2O)_2]^{3+}$. Based on this information, assign a coordination number *and* a charge to the cobalt ion in this coordination complex. _____ (! 6, 3)

52. The equilibrium constant expression obtained for the process
$$Cu^{2+}(aq) + 4\ NH_3(aq) \rightleftharpoons Cu(NH_3)_4^{2+}(aq)$$
is $[Cu(NH_3)_4^{2+}]/[Cu^{2+}][NH_3]^4$. This constant is called the _____ constant. (! formation)

53. Which complex ion should exhibit the larger value of the crystal field splitting parameter, $Co(NH_3)_6^{2+}$ or $Co(NH_3)_6^{3+}$? _____ (! $Co(NH_3)_6^{3+}$)

54. Which complex ion should exhibit the larger value of the crystal field splitting parameter, $Co(NH_3)_6^{3+}$ or $Rh(NH_3)_6^{3+}$? _____ (! $Rh(NH_3)_6^{3+}$)

True and False

55. Coordination complexes of a particular metal ion in which water is the ligand usually contain fewer ligands than coordination complexes of the same metal with ethylenediamine as the ligand. (! F)

56. A polydentate ligand is one which has more than one acceptor atom which can attach itself to the metal ion to form a coordination complex. (! F)

57. A polydentate ligand is one which has more than one donor atom which can attach itself to the metal ion to form a coordination complex. (! T)

58. Na^+, K^+, and Li^+, being ions of "A" group metals, have a greater tendency to form coordination complexes with ligands than Fe^{2+}, Co^{2+}, and Ni^{2+} ions. (! F)

59. Ethylenediaminetetraacetate, abbreviated edta^{4-}, is a ligand whose ability to form coordination complexes has found a wide range of useful applications. (! T)

60. Monodentate ligands form chelate complexes more readily than polydentate ligands due to the chelate effect. (! F)

372

61. Another name for the ferrocyanide, a transition metal complex ion in which the iron is in the +2 oxidation state, is hexacyanoferrite. (! F)

62. The following order is observed in the spectrochemical series for the ligands listed,
$$CN^- > NO_2^- > en > NH_3 > H_2O > C_2O_4^{2-} > OH^- > F^- > Cl^- > Br^- > I^-$$
It was observed that for the two 6-coordinate cobalt complexes, CoF_6^{3-} and $Co(NH_3)_6^{3+}$, one is diamagnetic and one is paramagnetic. Which one is the diamagnetic complex? (! $Co(NH_3)_6^{3+}$)

63. Even though silver chloride is only very very slightly soluble in water, addition of a reagent which forms complexes with silver increases this solubility. (! T)

64. The following order is observed in the spectrochemical series for the ligands listed,
$$CN^- > NO_2^- > en > NH_3 > H_2O > C_2O_4^{2-} > OH^- > F^- > Cl^- > Br^- > I^-$$
It was observed that for the two 6-coordinate cobalt complexes, $Co(NH_3)_6^{3+}$ and $Co(H_2O)_6^{2+}$, one is diamagnetic and one is paramagnetic. Which one is the paramagnetic complex? (! $Co(H_2O)_6^{2+}$)

Critical Thinking

65. Even though there are two isomers of the 4-coordinate planar complex $[Pt(NH_3)_2Cl_2]$ there are no isomers for a related complex, $[Pt(en)Cl_2]$. Suggest a reason why.

_____

_____

(! The "bite" distance of the donor atoms in the chelating ligand, ethylenediamine, is too small to coordinate to trans positions around the Pt^{2+} ion)

66. A coordination complex in which the ligands exhibit an octahedral geometry about the central metal ion has the formula, $[Cr(en)_2Cl_2]^+$. How many isomers of this complex ion (all kinds) should exist?

      a. 1(no isomers)
      b. 2
  ! c. 3
      d. 4
      e. 5

Multiple Choice

1. The metalloids are found in nature primarily

    a. in compounds where they are combined with metals
    ! b. in compounds where they are combined with nonmetals
    c. in alloys where they are combined with metals
    d. in alloys where they are combined with nonmetals
    e. in the free state as the elements themselves

2. When they are found in compounds in nature, metalloids are obtained in the elemental state from these compounds by

    a. roasting the compounds in air
    ! b. chemical reduction using carbon or hydrogen as the reducing agent
    c. chemical oxidation using hydrogen as the oxidizing agent
    d. chemical reduction using sodium or magnesium as the reducing agent
    e. chemical reduction using hydrazine or carbon monoxide as the reducing agent

3. An important use of metalloids and some of their compounds is

    a. as additives in the manufacture of special steels with specific characteristics
    b. in fabrication of coatings used in the building industry
    ! c. in semiconductors used in fabrication of electronic devices
    d. in radiation detectors
    e. in high density electromagnets used for magnetic resonance work

4. The most abundant nonmetal found in the earth's atmosphere is

    a. oxygen
    ! b. nitrogen
    c. argon
    d. helium
    e. hydrogen

5. The most abundant metalloid found in the material of the earth's crust is

    a. hydrogen
    b. oxygen
    ! c. silicon
    d. aluminum
    e. boron

6. The most abundant nonmetal found in the material of the earth's crust is

      a. hydrogen
!   b. oxygen
      c. nitrogen
      d. chlorine
      e. carbon

7. Carbon, when found in the free state in nature, is usually in the form of

!   a. graphite
      b. diamond
      c. carbon monoxide
      d. γ-carbon
      e. ^{14}C

8. The less reactive non-metallic elements of Group VIIA can be conveniently prepared from their simple ionic compounds in the laboratory by

      a. reduction with magnesium
      b. reducing using carbon as the reducing agent
      c. oxidation using hydrogen as the oxidizing agent
!   d. oxidation using MnO_2 as the oxidizing agent
      e. oxidation using carbon as the oxidizing agent

9. Chlorine is very important commercially in the manufacture of a variety of important large volume chemicals. It is obtained primarily on a large scale by

      a. reduction of particular solutes in sea water or brine using magnesium as a reducing agent
      b. oxidation of particular solutes in sea water or brine using oxygen as an oxidizing agent
!   c. electrolysis of sea water or brine
      d. oxidation of particular solutes in sea water or brine using potassium permanganate as the oxidizing agent
      e. oxidation of calcium chloride using sodium chloride as the oxidizing agent

10. Phosphorus can be obtained from calcium phosphate (which is available from natural sources containing phosphate minerals) by

      a. reduction with hydrogen
      b. reduction with sodium metal
!   c. reduction with a mixture of carbon (the reducing agent) and SiO_2 (sand)
      d. reduction with magnesium metal
      e. reduction with aluminum metal, which is readily available in large quantities

11. Which of the groups below is a list of elements which exist as diatomic molecules in their standard state?

       a. hydrogen, helium, oxygen, nitrogen, fluorine
       b. nitrogen, phosphorus, sulfur, chlorine, argon
!   c. hydrogen, nitrogen, oxygen, chlorine, bromine
       d. hydrogen, helium, krypton, radon, xenon
       e. polonium, hydrogen, nitrogen, fluorine, bromine

12. Which one of the groups below lists the species in order of **decreasing** stability?

       a. $O_3 > O_2 > O$
!   b. $O_2 > O_3 > O$
       c. $O_3 > O > O_2$
       d. $O > O_3 > O_2$
       e. $O > O_2 > O_3$

13. O_3 and O_2 are an example of

       a. allomers
!   b. allotropes
       c. isochrones
       d. isotones
       e. allochrones

14. The carbon atoms in a crystalline diamond lattice are arranged in the form of

!   a. a three dimensional lattice
       b. two dimensional layers
       c. one dimensional chains
       d. a two dimensional lattice
       e. face centered unit cells packed on one another

15. The carbon atoms in a graphite lattice are arranged in the form of

!   a. a three dimensional lattice
       b. three dimensional chains
       c. two dimensional layers
       d. one dimensional chains
       e. face centered unit cells packed on one another

16. In the diamond structure, the hybrid orbital set used by the carbon atoms to form σ-bonds is

       a. sp
       b. sp^2
!   c. sp^3
       d. sp^3d
       e. sp^3d^2

17. In the graphite structure, the hybrid orbital set used by the carbon atoms to form σ-bonds is

    a. sp
!   b. sp^2
    c. sp^3
    d. sp^3d
    e. sp^3d^2

18. Fullerenes are an allotropic form of

!   a. carbon
    b. phosphorus
    c. oxygen
    d. nitrogen
    e. fluorine

19. The hardest elements known, as measured by various physical measurement techniques, are

    a. carbon and iron
    b. nickel and iron
    c. iridium and carbon
!   d. carbon and boron
    e. carbon and osmium

20. The most stable forms of elemental sulfur are

    a. monoclinic and triclinic
    b. orthorhombic and hexagonal
!   c. orthorhombic and monoclinic
    d. monoclinic and tetragonal
    e. orthorhombic and triclinic

21. Elemental phosphorus exhibits three modifications identified by color, namely

    a. red, white and blue
    b. red, white and yellow
    c. red, yellow, and black
!   d. white, black, and red
    e. yellow, white, and black

22. A nonmetal which spontaneously ignites in air at ordinary temperatures and pressures is

    a. carbon
    b. boron
    c. arsenic
!   d. phosphorus
    e. sulfur

23. Which one of the following elements does not form a simple hydride which contains one atom of the element combined with the appropriate number of hydrogen atoms?

  a. carbon
! b. boron
  c. oxygen
  d. nitrogen
  e. fluorine

24. A gaseous nonmetallic element which is sufficiently unreactive that it can serve as an inert atmosphere in chemical reactions where oxygen or moisture must be excluded is

  a. hydrogen
! b. nitrogen
  c. fluorine
  d. chlorine

25. The Haber process is an important industrial chemical process in which the industrial product is

  a. ozone
  b. methane
  c. hydrogen chloride
  d. chlorine
! e. ammonia

26. The strongest Brønsted conjugate base among those listed below is

! a. F^-
  b. Cl^-
  c. Br^-
  d. I^-
  e. HSO_4^-

27. The strongest Brønsted conjugate base among those listed below is

  a. F^-
  b. HS^-
  c. HSe^-
  d. OH^-
! e. NH_2^-

28. Which one of the species below undergoes hydrolysis to yield a strongly basic solution?

  a. F^-
  b. HS^-
  c. NH_3
  d. OH^-
! e. O^{2-}

378

29. The chemical equation for a reaction which can be used in the laboratory preparation (as contrasted with industrial scale) of pure HCl(g) is the reaction,

   a. $NaCl(s) + HBr(l) \rightarrow NaBr(s) + HCl(g)$
   b. $NaCl(s) + HF(l) \rightarrow NaF(s) + HCl(g)$
   c. $NaCl(s) + NaH(s) \rightarrow 2\ Na(s) + HCl(g)$
   ! d. $NaCl(s) + H_3PO_4(l) \rightarrow NaH_2PO_4(s) + HCl(g)$
   e. $NaCl(s) + NH_3(g) \rightarrow NaNH_2(s) + HCl(g)$

30. The name of the ion shown to the right, is

   a. disulfate
   b. disulfite
   c. sulfosulfite
   d. thiosulfite
   ! e. thiosulfate

31. The name of the ion shown to the right, is

$$\begin{array}{ccc} O & O & {}^{2-} \\ \| & \| & \\ O-S-S-O & \\ \| & \| & \\ O & O & \end{array}$$

   a. disulfate
   b. peroxydisulfate
   c. disulfite
   d. peroxydisulfite
   ! e. dithionate

32. The reaction, $3\ NO_2(g) + H_2O \rightarrow 2\ HNO_3(aq) + NO(g)$, is an example of

   a. catenation
   ! b. disproportionation
   c. elimination
   d. substitution
   e. metathesis

33. The most important industrial chemical, in terms of quantity manufactured is

   a. ammonia
   b. chlorine
   c. hydrogen chloride
   d. nitric acid
   ! e. sulfuric acid

34. Which set of the reactants below will yield a nonmetal oxide as one of its products?

        a. Cu + dilute $H_2SO_4(aq)$
        b. Cu + dilute $HCl(aq)$
  ! c. Cu + dilute $HNO_3(aq)$
        d. Cu + dilute $H_3PO_4(aq)$
        e. Cu + dilute $HC_2H_3O_2(aq)$

35. The NO_2 molecule unites with another NO_2 molecule to form a dimer. In the Lewis structure for this dimer there are

        a. 5 σ-bonds and 0 π-bonds
        b. 5 σ-bonds and 1 π-bonds
  ! c. 5 σ-bonds and 2 π-bonds
        d. 4 σ-bonds and 2 π-bonds
        e. 4 σ-bonds and 4 π-bonds

36. Quartz is the pure, crystalline form of SiO_2. The hybridization around the silicon atom in the crystal is

        a. sp
        b. sp^2
  ! c. sp^3
        d. sp^3d
        e. sp^3d^2

37. Quartz is the pure, crystalline form of SiO_2. In quartz, each silicon atom is bonded to

        a. 1 silicon atom and 3 oxygen atoms
        b. 2 silicon atoms and 2 oxygen atoms
        c. 1 silicon atom and 1 oxygen atom
  ! d. 0 silicon atoms and 4 oxygen atoms
        e. 2 silicon atoms and 4 oxygen atoms

38. The reaction, $Cl_2(g) + 2\,OH^- \rightarrow OCl^- + Cl^- + H_2O$, is an example of

        a. simple displacement
  ! b. disproportionation
        c. elimination
        d. substitution
        e. metathesis

39. Clorox™, which contains the OCl^- ion in a basic solution,

  ! a. should be unstable but decomposes only very slowly if kept at very cold temperatures
        b. is unstable and decomposes rapidly, even at low temperatures
        c. is stable at low temperatures and remains unchanged at these temperatures
        d. is unstable even at low temperatures and decomposes at a moderate pace

40.

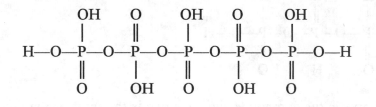

The compound shown above is

    a. pentaphosphorus acid
! b. pentaphosphoric acid
    c. hypophosphoric acid
    d. orthophosphoric acid
    e. pyrophosphoric acid

41.

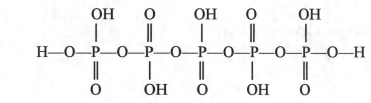

The compound shown above is

    a. a monoprotic acid
    b. a diprotic acid
    c. a pentaprotic acid
! d. a heptaprotic acid
    e. a tetraprotic acid

42.

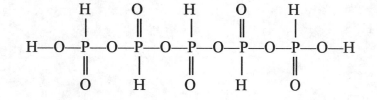

The compound shown above is

    a. a monoprotic acid
! b. a diprotic acid
    c. a pentaprotic acid
    d. a heptaprotic acid
    e. a tetraprotic acid

43.

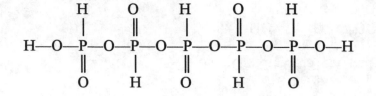

The oxidation state of the phosphorus in the compound shown above is the same as that in

    a. orthophosporic acid
! b. phosphorus acid
    c. hypophosphorus acid
    d. hypophosphoric acid
    e. hydrophosphoric acid

44.

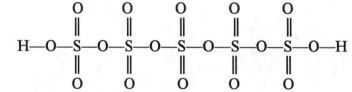

The compound shown above is

    a. pentasulfurous acid
! b. pentasulfuric acid
    c. orthosulfuric acid
    d. hyposulfuric acid
    e. pyrosulfuric acid

45.

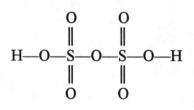

The compound shown above can be called either

    a. disulfuric acid or orthosulfuric acid
    b. disulfuric acid or oxyorthosulfuric acid
    c. orthosulfuric acid dithionic acid
! d. disulfuric acid or pyrosulfuric acid
    e. pyrosulfuric acid or dithionic acid

46.

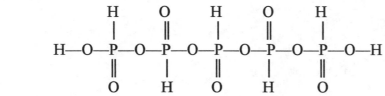

The compound shown can be called either

    a. diphosphoric acid or orthophosphoric acid
    b. diphosphorous acid or oxyorthophosphorous acid
    c. diphosphoric acid or phosphonic acid
! d. diphosphoric acid or pyrophosphoric acid
    e. diphosphoric acid or tetrahydrogen oxydiphosphate

47.

$$\text{H---O---P---O---P---O---P---O---P---O---P---O---H}$$

The oxidation number of phosphorus in the compound above is

    a. +2
! b. +3
    c. +5
    d. -3
    e. -1

48. The bottle filled with chunks of sulfur on the laboratory shelf contains this variety of sulfur:

! a. orthorhombic sulfur
    b. red sulfur
    c. γ-Sulfur
    d. plastic sulfur
    e. white sulfur

49. A student carrying a bottle of $PCl_5(s)$ to her lab from the stockroom dropped it in the hallway. The shattered contents started to give off smoky fumes with an acrid odor, so the Hazmat Team was quickly called in. What chemical substance was responsible for the fumes?

    a. $PCl_5(g)$
    b. $PCl_3(g)$
    c. $H_2PtCl_4(g)$
    d. $H_3PO_4(s)$
! e. $HCl(g)$

50. Phosphate anions can form species which can be thought of as being dimers and trimers--precursors to polymers. These larger anions contain

      a. P—P—P—P . . . chains
!   b. P—O—P—O—P—O—P—O . . . chains
      c. P—P—O—P—P—O—P—P—O . . . chains
      d. P—H—P—H—P—H—P—H . . . chains
      e. P—H—O—P—H—O—P—H—O . . . chains

51. Even though hydrofluoric acid is a monoprotic acid it forms an ion named the bifluoride ion. The formula for the bifluoride ion is

!   a. HF_2^-
      b. H_2F^+
      c. HFO^{2-}
      d. H_2FO^-
      e. $H_2F_2O^-$

52. All of the following are known oxyacids of chlorine, except

      a. $HClO_4$
      b. $HClO_2$
      c. $HClO$
!   d. $H_2Cl_2O_9$
      e. $HClO_3$

Fill in the Blanks

53. What is catenation? _____
(! ability of atoms of elements to form extended chains or rings through bonding with like atoms)

54. Ionic nitrides, containing the N^{3-} ion, are very reactive with water because they are

_____
(! the conjugate base of a very very weak Brønsted acid and react with the acid, H_2O)

55. When an ionic nitride, containing the N^{3-} ion, reacts with D_2O, the products are

_____
(! $ND_3(g)$ and OD^- ion)

True and False

56. Crystalline sulfur is the hardest non-metallic element known with the exception of diamond. (! F)

57. Nuggets which are almost pure elemental boron are usually found in the deposits left behind by retreating glaciers. (! F)

58. The element phosphorus is never found in the free state in nature. (! T)

59. Several examples of catenation involving halogen atoms are found in naturally occurring compounds. (! F)

60. Catenation of carbon atoms is the property responsible for the exceedingly large number of carbon containing compounds which are known. (! T)

Chemicals In Our World 11: Synthetic Diamonds and Diamond Coatings

61. For the process, $C(s)_{graphite} \rightarrow C(s)_{diamond}$, to occur, which condition below must be met?

     a. $\Delta G/T$ must vary with temperature for a given pressure.
     b. The pressure must be one atmosphere.
!   c. ΔG must be negative.
     d. T must be negative.
     e. $\Delta G/T$ must be positive.

62. Diamonds can be made from graphite. The equation for the process is,
$$C(s)_{graphite} \rightarrow C(s)_{diamond},$$
Analysis of the data gave $\Delta H^\circ = 1.88$ kJ mol^{-1} and $\Delta S^\circ = -3.29$ J mol^{-1} K^{-1}. These are the values for a pressure of **1.0 atm**. It is also noted that diamond is more than 1.6 times as dense as graphite. If we assume that since the physical states do not change, that ΔH and ΔS remain fairly constant from below room temperature to 3000 K and beyond if the pressure remains at 1.0 atm, what set of conditions would most greatly favor the conversion process?

     a. very high temperatures and very low pressures
     b. very high temperatures and very high pressures
     c. low temperatures and very low pressures
!   d. low temperatures and very high pressures

63. When a diamond film is formed, which one of the following statements described the situation?

     a. Carbon and hydrogen atoms form a film of CH_4 with a tetrahedral structure
     b. Carbon atoms form a film of carbon with sp^2 hybridization
     c. At high temperatures and pressures, methane and graphite unite to produce and deposit a smooth carbon film at a surface
     d. High pressures and high temperatures produce the best conditions for preparation of diamond coatings on a surface
!   e. Carbon atoms form a film in which the carbon atoms are in a tetrahedral structure

64. At the present time, the preferred method for manufacturing reasonably sized diamonds in quantity is:

    a. expose graphite to high intensity x-rays at high temperatures
    b. expose graphite to high intensity z-rays in a vacuum chamber at temperatures near absolute zero
    c. irradiate graphite in a high pressure chamber with neutrons at temperatures near absolute zero
  ! d. subject graphite to very high pressures at very high temperatures
    e. irradiate graphite with radiation from a pulsed x-ray laser in a high pressure chamber

65. All of the following are applications of diamond coated surfaces except

    a. heat sinks
    b. high frequency audio speaker (tweeter) cones
    c. scratch resistant coatings
  ! d. dental caps
    e. transistor contacts in semiconductor devices

66. In a diamond, the structure is that of a network covalent solid. The hybridization of the carbon in this diamond structure is

    a. sp
    b. sp^2
  ! c. sp^3
    d. sp^4
    e. sp^3d

67. A property, normally associated with metals, in which diamond excels over the best metals is

    a. malleability
    b. ductility
  ! c. thermal conductivity
    d. electrical conductivity
    e. elasticity

Chapter 22 Nuclear Reactions and Their Role in Chemistry

Multiple Choice

1. The scientists of the "Manhattan Project" realized that the conversion of mass to energy becomes significant only in

    a. chemiluminescent transformations
    b. exothermic reactions
    c. explosive chemical reactions
    d. spontaneous processes
    ! e. nuclear reactions

2. Which one of the following nuclides has the maximum binding energy per nucleon, that is, it lies at or near the maximum in the binding energy per nucleon (nuclear particle) curve?

    a. ^{251}Cf
    b. ^{197}Au
    ! c. ^{56}Fe
    d. ^{1}H
    e. ^{4}He

3. The nuclear particle which is partially described by the representation, $^{1}_{1}x$, is a(n)

    a. alpha particle
    b. electron
    c. neutron
    d. positron
    ! e. proton

4. The nuclear particle which is partially described by the representation, $^{0}_{+1}x$, is a(n)

    a. alpha particle
    b. electron
    c. neutron
    ! d. positron
    e. proton

5. The nuclear particle which is partially described by the representation, $^{4}_{2}x$, is a(n)

    ! a. alpha particle
    b. electron
    c. neutron
    d. positron
    e. proton

6. The nuclear particle which is partially described by the representation, $_0^1 x$, is a(n)

      a. alpha particle
      b. electron
!   c. neutron
      d. positron
      e. proton

7. The rest mass of a proton is 1.00727252 u and that of a neutron is 1.008665 u. The ^{4}He nucleus weighs 4.00150286 u. Calculate the total binding energy of the nucleus.

      a. 1.66×10^{-7} joule
      b. 2.27×10^{-12} joule
      c. 3.86×10^{-11} joule
!   d. 4.53×10^{-12} joule
      e. 4.53×10^{-10} joule

8. The rest mass of a proton is 1.00727252 u and that of a neutron is 1.008665 u. The ^{19}F nucleus weighs 18.9934659 u. Calculate the binding energy per nucleon (nuclear particle) for this nucleus.

!   a. 1.246×10^{-12} joule
      b. 2.368×10^{-11} joule
      c. 4.735×10^{-11} joule
      d. 6.230×10^{-13} joule
      e. 8.307×10^{-13} joule

9. The rest mass of a proton is 1.00727252 u and that of a neutron is 1.008665 u. The ^{75}As nucleus weighs 74.903487 u. Calculate the total binding energy of the nucleus.

      a. 1.464×10^{-7} joule
!   b. 1.045×10^{-10} joule
      c. 2.090×10^{-10} joule
      d. 6.235×10^{-12} joule
      e. 1.045×10^{-7} joule

10. The rest mass of a proton is 1.00727252 u and that of a neutron is 1.008665 u. The ^{103}Rh nucleus weighs 102.880814 u. Calculate the binding energy per nucleon (nuclear particle) for this nucleus.

      a. 2.442×10^{-12} joule
      b. 3.174×10^{-12} joule
      c. 1.375×10^{-9} joule
      d. 2.442×10^{-9} joule
!   e. 1.375×10^{-13} joule

11. The rest mass of a proton is 1.00727252 u and that of a neutron is 1.008665 u. The ^{31}P nucleus weighs 30.96553 u. Calculate the total binding energy of the nucleus.

    a. 2.662×10^{-11} joule
    b. 2.801×10^{-12} joule
!   c. 4.212×10^{-11} joule
    d. 4.191×10^{-11} joule
    e. 4.212×10^{-8} joule

12. The number of naturally occurring nuclides which are radioactive is limited and they are concentrated mostly in one region of the periodic table. Approximately how many naturally occurring radioactive nuclides are there?

    a. 10
!   b. 50
    c. 100
    d. 250
    e. 500

13. The radiation involving particles with the greatest charge of those in the set below is

!   a. alpha radiation
    b. beta radiation
    c. gamma radiation
    d. neutrons
    e. x-rays

14. The radiation with the least penetrating characteristics from the set below is

!   a. alpha radiation
    b. beta radiation
    c. gamma radiation
    d. neutrons
    e. x-rays

15. The radiation involving particles with the greatest mass of those in the set below is

!   a. alpha radiation
    b. beta radiation
    c. gamma radiation
    d. neutrons
    e. x-rays

16. The rest mass of a proton is 1.00727252 u and that of a neutron is 1.008665 u. The ^{197}Au nucleus weighs 196.92320 u. Calculate the binding energy per nucleon (nuclear particle) for this nucleus.

     a. 2.498 x 10^{-10} joule
     b. 1.227 x 10^{-12} joule
!   c. 1.268 x 10^{-12} joule
     d. 2.117 x 10^{-12} joule
     e. 3.162 x 10^{-12} joule

17. Identify the missing species in the nuclear equation given
$$^{55}_{26}Fe + ^{0}_{-1}e \rightarrow \text{????}$$

     a. $^{53}_{27}Fe$

!   b. $^{55}_{25}Mn$

     c. $^{55}_{27}Co$

     d. $^{55}_{27}Fe$

     e. $^{55}_{25}Fe$

18. Identify the missing species in the nuclear equation given
$$^{211}_{82}Pb \rightarrow \text{????} + ^{0}_{-1}e$$

     a. $^{211}_{81}Tl$

!   b. $^{211}_{83}Bi$

     c. $^{212}_{82}Pb$

     d. $^{210}_{82}Pb$

     e. $^{210}_{83}Bi$

19. When a nuclide emits a beta particle, the atomic number of the particle produced

     a. is the same as that of the original nuclide
!   b. increases by one unit
     c. decreases by one unit
     d. increases by two units
     e. decreases by two units

20. When $^{54}_{27}Co$ decays an isotope of iron is formed. What other products are also formed?

!   a. a positron and neutrino(s)
     b. a positron only
     c. beta rays and gamma rays
     d. alpha particles and gamma rays
     e. gamma rays only

21. Identify the missing species in the nuclear equation given

$$_{96}^{245}Cm \rightarrow ???? + _{2}^{4}\alpha$$

   a. $_{94}^{249}Pu$

! b. $_{94}^{241}Pu$

   c. $_{98}^{249}Cf$

   d. $_{98}^{241}Cf$

   e. $_{92}^{247}U$

22. Identify the missing species in the nuclear equation given

$$_{88}^{226}Ra \rightarrow ???? + _{2}^{4}\alpha$$

! a. $_{86}^{222}Rn$

   b. $_{90}^{226}Th$

   c. $_{90}^{230}Th$

   d. $_{86}^{230}Rn$

   e. $_{88}^{230}Ra$

23. Identify the missing species in the nuclear equation given

$$_{10}^{19}Ne \rightarrow ???? + _{-1}^{0}e$$

   a. $_{11}^{19}F$

! b. $_{11}^{19}Na$

   c. $_{9}^{19}F$

   d. $_{11}^{19}Ne$

   e. $_{9}^{19}Ne$

24. Identify the missing species in the nuclear equation given

$$_{36}^{87}Kr \rightarrow _{36}^{86}Kr + ????$$

   a. $_{1}^{0}n$

   b. $_{+1}^{0}e$

! c. $_{0}^{1}n$

   d. $_{-1}^{0}e$

   e. $_{1}^{1}p$

25. One Becquerel is equivalent to the radiation produced by

  ! a. one disintegration per second
    b. 3.7×10^{10} disintegration per second
    c. a mole of disintegration
    d. 100 rads
    e. one rem

26. This radiation source has caused quite a panic in recent years because it is the most common source of natural radiation and one of the easiest to eliminate.

  ! a. radon
    b. cosmic rays
    c. rocks and soils
    d. foods
    e. water

27. The intensity of x-ray, gamma ray, or any radiation is

    a. directly proportional to the distance from the source
    b. directly proportional to the square of the distance from the source
    c. inversely proportional to the distance from the source
  ! d. inversely proportional to the square of the distance from the source
    e. inversely proportional to the cube of the distance from the source

28. If the half-life of a radioactive element is 30.0 years, how long will it take to decay to the point where the activity is 70.0% of the original value?

    a. 5.0 years
    b. 12.2 years
  ! c. 15.4 years
    d. 30.8 years
    e. 86.1 years

29. If a radioactive sample of a newly discovered element, coronium, decays to the point where the activity is 40.0 percent of its original activity in 44.0 years, what is the half-life of the nuclide?

    a. 21.6 years
  ! b. 33.3 years
    c. 58.2 years
    d. 80.6 years
    e. 89.9 years

30. Rhenium-186 is a β-emitter with a half life of 90.0 hours. How long would it take for the activity in a sample of this nuclide to decay to exactly one-third of its original value?

        a. 121 hours
!   b. 143 hours
        c. 158 hours
        d. 180 hours
        e. 189 hours

31. Ytterbium-175 is a β-emitter with a half life of 101 hours. How long would it take for the activity in a sample of this nuclide to decay to exactly one-fifth of its original value?

        a. 215 hours
        b. 225 hours
!   c. 235 hours
        d. 250 hours
        e. 275 hours

32. Terbium-152 is a positron emitter with a half life of 18.0 hours. How long would it take for the activity in a sample of this nuclide to decay to exactly three-eighths of its original value?

        a. 32.8 hours
        b. 28.8 hours
        c. 23.6 hours
!   d. 25.5 hours
        e. 48.9 hours

33. Gadolinium-147 is a positron emitter with a half life of 35 hours. How long would it take for the activity in a sample of this nuclide to decay to exactly two-sevenths of its original value?

        a. 68 hours
!   b. 63 hours
        c. 71 hours
        d. 78 hours
        e. 106 hours

34. How many nucleons (nuclear particles) are there in the most common isotope of uranium?

        a. 234
        b. 235
        c. 236
!   d. 238
        e. 239

35. How many nucleons (nuclear particles) are there in the fissionable isotope of uranium?

   a. 234
 ! b. 235
   c. 236
   d. 238
   e. 239

36. The specific activity of a carbon sample from the bones of a mummy in a secret tomb recently discovered in Egypt is found to be at a level which is 60.0% of that of living plants. Calculate the age of the artifact. ($^{14}_{6}C$: t$_{1/2}$ = 5730 years)

   a. 3438 years
   b. 2865 years
 ! c. 4223 years
   d. 2111 years
   e. 8444 years

37. Which one of the following is *not* a device for determining radiation?

   a. Geiger counter
   b. Wilson cloud chamber
   c. scintillation counter
   d. film dosimeter
 ! e. ionometer

38. Which one of the following is a unit of nuclear disintegrations per unit time?

 ! a. the curie
   b. the rad
   c. the gray
   d. the sievert
   e. the rem

39. Which one of the following is a unit of radiation dose which is the same regardless of type of radiation?

   a. the curie
   b. the becquerel
 ! c. the rem
   d. the rad
   e. the gray

40. What is the mass number of an alpha particle?

      a. 0
      b. 1
      c. 2
      d. 3
 ! e. 4

41. Which one of the following nuclear processes does not cause a change in the atomic number of the nuclide undergoing the process?

      a. emission of α-particle
      b. emission of β-particle
 ! c. emission of a γ-ray
      d. emission of a positron
      e. capture of an electron

42. When radium-226 is transmuted by a nuclear decay to radon-222, the process involved is

 ! a. emission of α-particle
      b. emission of β-particle
      c. emission of a γ-ray
      d. emission of a positron
      e. capture of an electron

43. All isotopes of elements beyond ___ in the periodic are unstable and hence radioactive, though some have much longer half lives than others.

      a. bismuth
      b. platinum
 ! c. lead
      d. francium
      e. thallium

44. The nuclear reaction which is depicted below is an example of
$$_{78}^{197}Pt \rightarrow _{79}^{197}Au + ????$$

      a. emission of α-particle
 ! b. emission of β-particle
      c. emission of a γ-ray
      d. emission of a positron
      e. capture of an electron

45. The nuclear reaction which is depicted below is an example of
$$^{200}_{81}Tl \rightarrow ^{200}_{80}Hg + ????$$

    a. emission of α-particle
    b. emission of β-particle
    c. emission of a γ-ray
!   d. emission of a positron
    e. capture of an electron

46. Carbon-14 is generated in the atmosphere by the nuclear reaction,
$$^{14}_{7}N + ^{1}_{0}n \rightarrow ^{14}_{6}C + ????$$
The missing species is

    a. an α-particle
    b. a β-particle
    c. a γ-ray
    d. a positron
!   e. a proton

47. The two steps in the reaction which takes place in breeder reactors is
$$^{238}_{92}U + ^{1}_{0}n \rightarrow XXXX + ^{0}_{-1}e$$
$$XXXX \rightarrow YYYY + ^{0}_{-1}e$$
The missing species are

    a. ^{239}Np and ^{239}Am
    b. ^{239}Np and ^{241}Pu
!   c. ^{239}Np and ^{239}Pu
    d. ^{239}U and ^{239}Np
    e. ^{237}Np and ^{237}Pu

48. The radiocarbon dating method can be used to determine the age of

    a. carbonate rocks
    b. silicate rocks
!   c. art canvases
    d. bronze beakers
    e. Roman coins

49. Fission reactors are restrained from going supercritical through

    a. use of liquid metal coolants
    b. use of heavy water coolant
!   c. use of control rods which absorb neutrons
    d. use of liquid nitrogen to maintain correct reaction rate
    e. proper reactor design

50. The following are all applications of radioactivity except one. Which one?

   a. tracer analysis
   b. neutron activation
   c. carbon-14 dating
   d. potassium-14 dating
   ! e. electron impact activation

51. Reactor "meltdowns" like the one at Chernobyl in the Ukraine are caused by

   a. supercritical masses of fissile nuclides accumulating near the bottom of the reactor
   ! b. failure of the cooling system which distributes the heat generated in the reactor core
   c. decomposition of heavy water coolant D_2O into H_2O and neutrons which very large thermal energies
   d. slow accumulation of critical masses of impurities at particular sites in the fuel rods, caused by improper design
   e. inhomogeneities in the containment magnetic fields caused by small temperature fluctuations in the field winding coils

52. The last step in the series of steps by which radium-226 is transmuted into lead-206 by nuclear decay involves the emission of an α-particle. What is the nuclear symbol for the precursor nuclide?
   _____ (! $^{210}_{84}Po$)

True and False

53. Tritium is an isotope of hydrogen which is radioactive. (! T)

54. The mass of a nucleus is exactly equal to the weights of all the protons and neutrons which are in that nucleus, taken separately. (! F)

55. The emission of a positron produces the same effect as replacement of a proton by a neutron. (! T)

56. When radiation passes through gaseous matter, ionization results. (! T)

57. Neutrinos have very high penetrating power. (! T)

58 Fission reactions used for generation of electrical energy employ capsules containing supercritical masses of fissile nuclear material. (! F)

Fill in the Blanks

59. A neutral particle with the mass of an electron is known as a _____ (! neutrino)

60. The energy that an electron receives when accelerated through a potential difference of one volt is one _____ (! electron volt)

61. The energy which holds the nucleons (nuclear particles) in the nucleus together is called _____ (! binding energy)

62. The force which holds the nucleons (nuclear particles) in the nucleus together is called _____ (! nuclear strong force)

63. The change of one nuclide into another is termed _____ (! transmutation)

64. A nucleus which results from the combination of a particle and nucleus is termed a _____ (! compound nucleus)

65. The nucleus of a deuterium atom is called a _____ (! deuteron)

66. A _____ measures radiation by detecting the resultant ionization (! Geiger counter)

67. A _____ will detect radiation by way of flashes of light which are emitted when particles strike (! scintillation counter)

68. A common unit of absorbed radiation dose is the _____ (! the rad or the gray)

69. The formula of the pertechnetate ion, a species widely used in nuclear medicine to locate brain tumor location through trace analysis, is: _____ (! TcO_4^-)

Critical Thinking

70. Radium 226, which undergoes a first order nuclear decay process to yield ^{222}Rn, has a half life of 1620 years. A 24.45 milligram sample of ^{226}Ra was placed in a time capsule on January 1, 1932 with instructions to open the capsule and weigh it again on July 1, 2276. How many milligrams of the radium should there be in the capsule at that time?

      a. 21.85 milligrams
!   b. 21.10 milligrams
      c. 19.25 milligrams
      d. 20.14 milligrams
      e. 21.65 milligrams

Critical Thinking, Level 2

71. Nuclide X, which has an isotopic mass of 209.9829 u and a half-life of 138 days, decays by alpha emission to form the stable nuclide lead-206. A sample being studied gave off enough gaseous material in 240 hours to exert a gas pressure of 86.0 torr in a gas measuring system with a volume of 2.500 milliliters when the temperature was 26.5 °C. What was the mass of nuclide X when the study commenced? _____ (! 3.45 mg)

Chapter 23 Organic Compounds and Biochemicals

Multiple Choice

1. Which one of the compounds whose condensed structural formulas are given below is butane?

    a. CH_3CH_3
    b. $CH_3CH_2CH_3$
    ! c. $CH_3CH_2CH_2CH_3$
    d. $CH_3CH_2CH_2CH_2CH_3$
    e. $CH_3CH_2CH_2CH_2CH_2CH_3$

2. Which one of the compounds whose condensed structural formulas are given below is *n*-pentane?

    a. CH_3CH_3
    b. $CH_3CH_2CH_3$
    c. $CH_3CH_2CH_2CH_3$
    ! d. $CH_3CH_2CH_2CH_2CH_3$
    e. $CH_3CH_2CH_2CH_2CH_2CH_3$

3. How many isomers of butane, C_4H_{10}, can be drawn?

    a. 1 (no isomers)
    ! b. 2
    c. 3
    d. 4
    e. 5

4. How many isomers of pentane, C_5H_{12}, can be drawn?

    a. 1 (no isomers)
    b. 2
    ! c. 3
    d. 4
    e. 5

5. CH_3—CH_2—O—H and CH_3—O—CH_3 are a pair of compounds which are

    a. allotropes
    b. allomers
    c. isochrones
    ! d. isomers
    e. allotones

6. Which one of the groups below goes by the name, *n*-propyl?

    a. CH_3—CH_2—
    b. CH_2—CH—
! c. CH_3—CH_2—CH_2—
    d. CH_2—CH—CH_2—
    e. CH_3—CH—CH—

7. The functional group, —O—H, is found in which one of these types of organic compounds?

    a. alkanes
    b. alkenes
    c. amines
! d. alcohols
    e. ethers

8. Functional groups containing nitrogen at the active site are found in

    a. alkenes
    b. alcohols
! c. amines
    d. carboxylic acids
    e. ethers

9. Functional groups containing the C=O group or linkage are found in

    a. alkenes
! b. ketones
    c. amines
    d. alcohols
    e. ethers

10. One of the compounds listed below is an organic base and functions as a proton acceptor. Identify this organic base.

    a. CH_3—CH_2—CH_2—O—H
    b. CH_3—CH=CH_2
    c. H_3C—C—CH_3
            $\|$
            O

    d. CH_3—CH_2—C—O—H
                 $\|$
                O

! e. CH_3—CH_2—NH_2

11. Based on the properties of the attached functional group, which one of the compounds below would you expect to interact most strongly with water, thus making it the most soluble of the group below?

       a. CH_3—CH_2—Cl
       b. CH_3—CH_2—F
       c. CH_3—CH_2—I
       d. CH_3—CH_2—S—H
!   e. CH_3—CH_2—O—H

12. Based on the properties of the attached functional group, which one of the compounds below would you expect to interact most strongly with water, thus making it the most soluble of the group below?

       a. CH_3—CH_2—H
!   b. CH_3—CH_2—NH_2
       c. CH_3—O—CH_3
       d. CH_3—CH_2—I
       e. CH_3—CH_2—S—H

13. Which one of the following compounds is not an unsaturated compound?

       a. H_2C=CH_2
       b. CH_3—CH=CH_2
       c. H_2C=CH—Cl
!   d. CH_3—CH_2—O—H
       e. H_2C=CH—O—H

14. Various hydrocarbons are separated from the crude oil mixture by

       a. filtration
       b. chromatography
       c. precipitation
!   d. distillation
       e. centrifugation

15. The alkane hydrocarbon whose skeleton is shown immediately below, is regarded as a derivative of

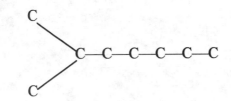

       a. butane
       b. hexane
!   c. heptane
       d. octane
       e. pentane

16. The alkane hydrocarbon whose skeleton is shown immediately below, is regarded as a derivative of

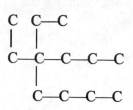

    a. dodecane
    b. decane
    c. heptane
    d. pentane
! e. octane

17. The hydrocarbon fragment, —CH_3, which has one position open (unfilled) is named

    a. methide
    b. methonium
    c. methal
! d. methyl
    e. trihydrocarbide

18. The hydrocarbon fragment shown below is properly named

$$H_3C-CH-CH_3$$
$$|$$

    a. propyl
    b. propide
    c. propanium
! d. isopropyl
    e. propanyl

19. The name for the compound, $CH_3-CH=CH-CH_3$, is

    a. butene-2
    b. butene-3
! c. 2-butene
    d. 2-butyne
    e. 2-butyl

20. If two of the hydrogen atoms in *n*-butane are replaced by two chlorine atoms to form dichlorobutane, how many different possible dichlorobutanes will there be?

    a. 1
    b. 2
    c. 3
    d. 4
    ! e. 6

21. Draw a structural formula for cyclohexane, a cyclic saturated hydrocarbon (C_6H_{12}). How many σ-bonds are there in cyclohexane?

    a. 12
    b. 16
    c. 17
    ! d. 18
    e. 20

22. Draw a structural formula for benzene. How many σ-bonds are there in a benzene molecule?

    a. 6
    ! b. 12
    c. 14
    d. 18
    e. 20

23. Draw a structural formula for cyclohexane, a cyclic saturated hydrocarbon (C_6H_{12}). How many π-bonds are there in a cyclohexane molecule?

    ! a. 0
    b. 2
    c. 3
    d. 4
    e. 6

24. Draw a structural formula for benzene. How many π-bonds are there in a benzene molecule?

    a. 0
    b. 2
    ! c. 3
    d. 4
    e. 6

25. The general structural formula for an ether can be expressed as

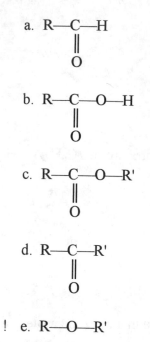

a. R—C—H
      ‖
      O

b. R—C—O—H
      ‖
      O

c. R—C—O—R'
      ‖
      O

d. R—C—R'
      ‖
      O

! e. R—O—R'

26. Which one of the compounds below has the general structural formula for an alcohol?

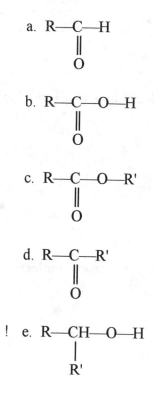

a. R—C—H
      ‖
      O

b. R—C—O—H
      ‖
      O

c. R—C—O—R'
      ‖
      O

d. R—C—R'
      ‖
      O

! e. R—CH—O—H
       |
       R'

27. Which one of the following is a product of the oxidation of CH_3—CH_2—CH_2—O—H?

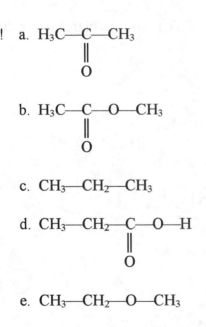

    a. H_3C—C—CH_3 ($\parallel$ O)

    b. H_3C—C—O—CH_3 ($\parallel$ O)

    c. CH_3—CH_2—CH_3

! d. CH_3—CH_2—C—O—H ($\parallel$ O)

    e. CH_3—CH_2—O—CH_3

28. Which one of the species below is a product of the oxidation of CH_3—CH—CH_3 (with O—H on the middle carbon)

! a. H_3C—C—CH_3 ($\parallel$ O)

    b. H_3C—C—O—CH_3 ($\parallel$ O)

    c. CH_3—CH_2—CH_3

    d. CH_3—CH_2—C—O—H ($\parallel$ O)

    e. CH_3—CH_2—O—CH_3

29. When CH_3—CH=CH_2 is treated with chlorine, a compound is formed in which the Cl_2 adds across the double bond. How many σ-bonds are there in the product of this addition reaction?

    a. 7
    b. 8
    c. 9
! d. 10
    e. 11

30. When CH_3—CH=CH_2 is reacted with water in the presence of a catalytic amount of acid, a new compound is formed. Which one of the set below might be the product of this reaction?

    a. CH_3—CH—CH_2

    b. CH_3—C—CH—O—H
              |
         H—O—H

! c. CH_3—CH—CH_3
              |
       H—O

    d. H_3C—C—CH_3
            ‖
           O

    e. CH_3—CH_2—C—H
                ‖
              O

31. The reaction of $(CH_3)_2CH_2$—CH_2—O—H with concentrated HBr using controlled heating yields which one of the products below?

    a. CH_3—CH_2—CH_2—Br
! b. $(CH_3)_2CH_2$—CH_2—Br
    c. $(CH_3)_2CH_2$—CH_2—O—Br
    d. $(CH_3)_2CH_2$—$CH_4^+ Br^-$
    e. $(CH_3)_2CH_2$—CH_3

32. The compound, trimethylamine is a _____ and has the formula _____

    a. base, $(CH_3NH_2)_3$
    b. base, $(CH_3NH)_2$
    c. base, $(CH_3)_3NH_2$
! d. base, $(CH_3)_3N$
    e. base, $(CH_3)_3(NH_2)_2$

33. Dodecylamine, $CH_3(CH_2)_{10}CH_2NH_2$, is absolutely insoluble in water. Yet, it can be converted to a water soluble form. Which of the species below represents the water soluble form of this compound?

    a. $CH_3(CH_2)_{10}CH_2NH_2$—O—H
    b. $CH_3(CH_2)_{10}CH_2NH_2$—Cl
    c. $CH_3(CH_2)_{10}CH_2NH$—CH_3
! d. $CH_3(CH_2)_{10}CH_2NH_3^+ Cl^-$
    e. $CH_3(CH_2)_{10}CH_2NH_2$—O—CH_3

34. The compound below is classified as which type of compound?

$$H_3C-C-CH_3$$
$$\overset{\|}{O}$$

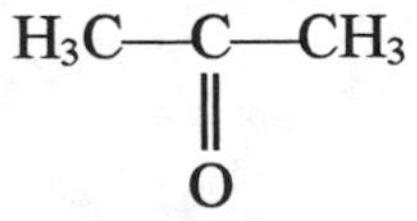

   a. aldehyde
! b. ketone
   c. acid
   d. ester
   e. amine

35. The compound below is classified as which type of compound?

$$H_3C-C-NH_2$$
$$\overset{\|}{O}$$

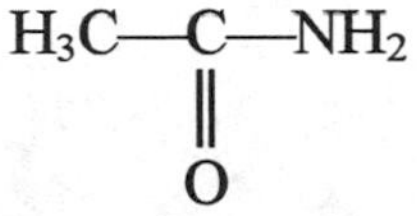

   a. aldehyde
   b. amine
   c. ester
! d. amide
   e. amino acid

36. The compound below is classified as which type of compound?
$$H_3C-CH_2-CH_2-C-O-H$$
$$\overset{\|}{O}$$

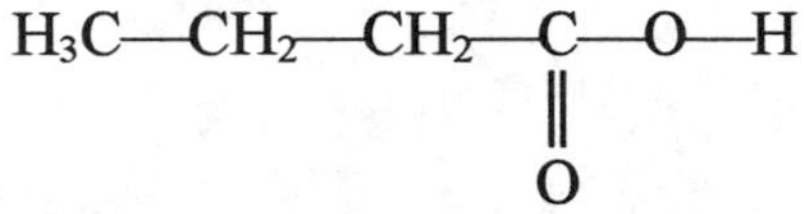

   a. ketone
   b. aldehyde
   c. ester
! d. acid
   e. amide

37. The compound below is correctly named as

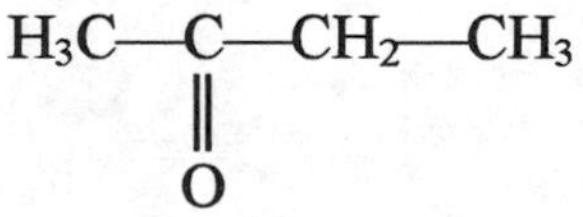

$$H_3C-C-CH_2-CH_3$$
$$\overset{\|}{O}$$

   a. butanamine
   b. butanamide
   c. butanketone
! d. 2-butanone
   e. 2-butanal

38. The compound below is correctly named

$$H_3C—CH_2—CH_2—CH_2—\overset{\displaystyle O}{\underset{\|}{C}}—H$$

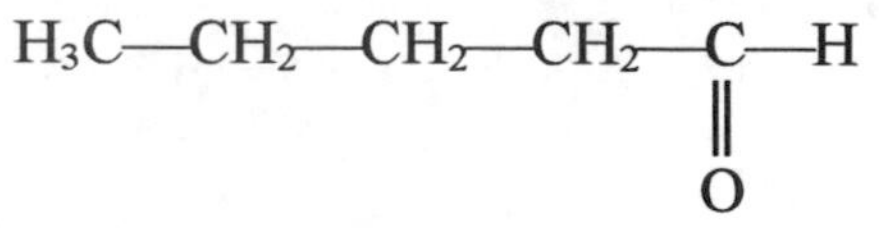

   a. pentaketone
   b. pentaldehyde
 ! c. pentanal
   d. pentanone
   e. pentanoic acid

39. The compound below is correctly named

$$H_3C—CH_2—CH_2—CH_2—\overset{\displaystyle O}{\underset{\|}{C}}—NH_2$$

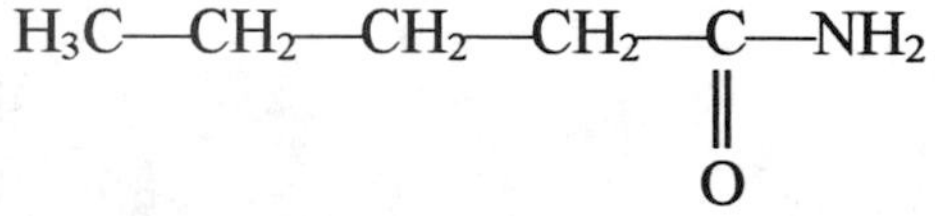

   a. pentanamine
   b. pentamine
   c. 1-pentanamide
 ! d. pentanamide
   e. pentaketoneamine

40. The ester which is prepared by heating 1-pentanol with acetic acid in the presence of an acidic catalyst is named

   a. acetic pentanoate
   b. pentanoic acetate
 ! c. 1-pentyl acetate
   d. acetyl 1-pentanoate
   e. acetyl pentanol

41. Linear polyethylene is a straight chain polymer. The repeating unit in linear polyethylene is

   a. —CH_2=CH_2—
   b. —CH—CH—
   c. —CH=CH—
   d. —C≡C—
 ! e. —CH_2—CH_2—

408

42. Which one of the following sets contains the proper compounds from which an addition copolymer can be formulated?

    a. $H_2C=CH_2$ and $H_2C=CH_2$
    b. $F_2C=CF_2$ and $F_2C=CF_2$
    c. $C_6H_5CH=CCl_2$ and $H_2N-(CH_2)_6-NH_2$
! d. $C_6H_5CH=CCl_2$ and $H_2C=CHCl$
    e. $C_6H_5CH=CCl_2$ and $H-O-\underset{\underset{O}{\|}}{C}-(CH_2)_4-\underset{\underset{O}{\|}}{C}-O-H$

43. Which one of the following sets contains the proper compounds from which a condensation polymer can be formulated?

    a. $H_2N-(CH_2)_6-NH_2$ and $H_2C=CCl_2$
    b. $H_2C=CHCl$ and $F_2C=CF_2$
    c. $C_6H_5-CH=CCl_2$ and $H_2N-(CH_2)_6-NH_2$
    d. $C_6H_5-CH=CCl_2$ and $H_2C=CH-Cl$
! e. $H_2N-(CH_2)_6-NH_2$ and $H-O-\underset{\underset{O}{\|}}{C}-(CH_2)_4-\underset{\underset{O}{\|}}{C}-O-H$

44. The basic repeating unit in the rubber made from naturally occurring material is

! a. $-CH_2-\underset{\underset{CH_3}{|}}{C}=CH-CH_2-$

    b. $-H_2C-CH_2-$

    c. $-\underset{\underset{CH_3}{|}}{HC}-CH_2-$

    d. $-\underset{\underset{H_3C}{|}}{HC}-\underset{\underset{CH_3}{|}}{CH}-$

    e. $-\underset{\underset{C_6H_5}{|}}{HC}-CH_2-$

45. The basic repeating unit in polystyrene is

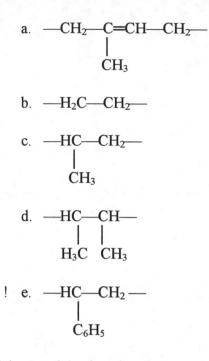

   a. —CH$_2$—C=CH—CH$_2$—
                |
                CH$_3$

   b. —H$_2$C—CH$_2$—

   c. —HC—CH$_2$—
           |
          CH$_3$

   d. —HC—CH—
          | |
       H$_3$C CH$_3$

! e. —HC—CH$_2$—
          |
        C$_6$H$_5$

46. Which one of the functional groups below is not usually found in carbohydrates?

    a. aldehyde
! b. amide
    c. ether
    d. hydroxy
    e. ketone

47. Lipids, by definition, are naturally occurring compounds which

    a. contain ester groups
    b. contain cholesterol
    c. contain fatty acids as structural units
! d. are water insoluble but soluble in nonpolar solvents
    e. are unsaturated

48. Triglycerides are compounds which contain (combined)

    a. fatty acids and choline
! b. fatty acids and glycerin
    c. fatty acids and phospholipids
    d. cholesterol and other steroids
    e. lecithin and choline

49. The chemical bond which links glycerin to a fatty acid is an example of what type of linkage?

   a. ether
   b. peptide
 ! c. ester
   d. ionic
   e. hydrogen bond

50. When lard is hydrolyzed, the products are

   a. amino acids
   b. alcohols and lipids
   c. glycerin and lipids
   d. carbohydrates
 ! e. glycerin and fatty acids

51. DNA is a(n)

   a. enzyme
 ! b. nucleic acid
   c. protein
   d. peptide
   e. steroid

52. Which one of the following compounds is not a lipid?

   a. andosterone
 ! b. glucose
   c. cholesterol
   d. testosterone
   e. triglycerides

Fill in the Blanks

53. The sheer number of organic compounds, greater than all other kinds put together, is made possible by the ability of _____ to _____ (! carbon, form long chains and still bond to other atoms)

54. The hydrocarbon group formed by removal of one hydrogen from methane is called _____ (! methyl)

55. _____ are the major source of hydrocarbon compounds. (! fossil fuels)

56. The amide formed when formic acid is heated with ammonia and the product is separated from the reaction mixture is _____ (name and formula). (! formamide, $H-\overset{\displaystyle \|}{\underset{\displaystyle O}{C}}-NH_2$)

411

57. The name of the alkane hydrocarbon whose skeleton is shown below is _____

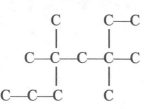

(! 3,3,5,5-tetramethyloctane)

58. When the ester, isopropyl butanoate is hydrolyzed in the presence of catalytic amounts of a strong base, two compounds are obtained. Their names are _____ and _____.
(! isopropyl alcohol (2-propanol) and butanoic acid)

59. In a copolymer, there are _____ kinds of repeating units. (! two)

True and False

60. A reactive group, called a functional group, which is attached to the hydrocarbon portion of the molecule, influences or determines the kind of reactions a molecule undergoes. (! T)

61. Hydrocarbons can be either gases, liquids or solids. (! T)

Critical Thinking

62. A carbonyl compound with 6 carbons was hydrogenated in a high pressure apparatus at 300 °C using a hydrogenation catalyst. The product had the formula,

$$CH_3—CH_2—CH_2—CH_2—CH_3$$
$$|$$
$$O—H$$

The original carbonyl compound was therefore _____ (! 3-pentanone)

63. An ester with 6 carbons was hydrolyzed in the presence of catalytic amounts of a base to yield two compounds, one of which was a 4 carbon acid with a branched chain. What is the name of the *other* product of the reaction? _____ (! ethanol)

64. A very important compound, used as a fertilizer, can be prepared by the reaction of
H—O—C—O—H with ammonia under the proper conditions. This important compound is a(n)
$$||$$
$$O$$

   ! a. amide
   b. ammonium salt
   c. acid salt
   d. amine
   e. ketone

412

Supplementary Chapter 1 Simple Molecules and Ions of Nonmetals: Part I

Multiple Choice

1.   The chemical elements of which the matter in the universe is composed are

  !   a. primarily hydrogen and helium (> 99%)
       b. primarily nitrogen and oxygen, with hydrogen and helium present in a lesser amount
       c. primarily calcium, magnesium and carbon in planetary rocks and stellar interiors
       d. primarily ferrous metals like iron, cobalt, and nickel
       e. probably primarily some unknown and maybe even hitherto undiscovered elements when
            all the matter in the millions of galaxies and universes which exist in the cosmos are
            considered

2.   In the earth's environmental region (atmosphere, crust) the largest percent of *all* the atoms in
     existence are found as

       a. nitrogen atoms
  !   b. oxygen atoms
       c. hydrogen atoms
       d. calcium atoms
       e. carbon atoms

3.   The boiling point of hydrogen, H_2, is about

       a. -272 °C
  !   b. -252 °C
       c. -200 °C
       d. -100 °C
       e. - 30 °C

4.   The XYZ corporation is one of the largest producers of hydrogen gas in the Western region. Based
     on your knowledge of the methodology being used currently in the industry, which method listed
     below are they probably using?

       a. electrolysis of water
       b. reaction of sodium with water
       c. reaction of metals with acid
       d. isolation from natural gas
  !   e. reaction of hydrocarbons with steam

5. A two person chemistry team from XYZ corporation are doing a laboratory demonstration at an eighth grade class in a local school, in which they are going to prepare some hydrogen gas, then observe and demonstrate some properties of hydrogen. What is the common method used in the field for generating small amounts of the gas?

     !   a. reaction of zinc metal with a strong acid, like hydrochloric acid
         b. reaction of zinc metal with hot water
         c. reaction of zinc metal with concentrated sodium hydroxide solution
         d. reaction of zinc metal with superheated steam
         e. reaction of zinc metal with alcohol

6. Sally Mae, a graduate student, needs to carry out an NMR measurement on the compound she just synthesized. Of the available solvents she decides to use D_2O to dissolve her compound. D_2O, also known as "heavy water", contains two deuterium atoms, where deuterium is the second most abundant isotope of hydrogen. How many nuclear particles are there in each deuterium atom?

         a. 1
     !   b. 2
         c. 2.5
         d. 3
         e. 4.

7. The molecular weight of D_2O is most nearly, in g/mole,

         a. 16
         b. 17
     !   c. 18
         d. 19
         e. 20

8. Concerning tritium, the radioactive isotope of hydrogen, how many nuclear particles are there in its nucleus?

         a. 1
         b. 2
         c. 2.5
     !   d. 3
         e. 4

9. Ionic hydrides react with water to liberate $H_2(g)$. In turn, these ionic hydrides are formed when metals of groups IA and IIA are reacted with

         a. superheated steam
     !   b. hydrogen gas
         c. strong acids
         d. weak acids
         e. water

10. The electronic configuration of the hydride ion is the same as that of

    a. hydrogen
! b. helium
    c. lithium
    d. deuterium
    e. tritium

11. All of the following are properties of the hydride ion except

    a. strong base
    b. reducing agent
    c. reactive towards water
    d. reacts with acids to produce H_2 gas
! e. proton donor

12. Which one of the following hydrides is the one which reacts *violently* with water? (a good point to remember when stressing the point that all chemical fires aren't best handled with water)

    a. NH_3, a nitrogen hydride
    b. H_2S, a sulfur hydride
    c. SiH_4, a silicon hydride
    d. CH_4, a carbon hydride
! e. NaH, a sodium hydride

13. Hydrogenated oils are being used in place of animal fats for health reasons in the food industry. Which of the following is one of the effects that hydrogenation has on a property of vegetable oil?

    a. lowers its fat content
    b. increases the number of double bonds
! c. increases the melting point
    d. gives it a yellow color
    e. converts it to soap

14. The air that we breathe every day is composed mainly of nitrogen and oxygen. What is the percent (V/V) concentration of oxygen in air?

! a. 21
    b. 78
    c. 1
    d. 50
    e. 25

15. A tank of pure oxygen such as one used in a laboratory was probably obtained from industrial sources, where it was made by

  a. heating potassium chlorate
  b. electrolysis of water
  ! c. distillation of liquid air
  d. pyrolysis of superheated steam
  e. passing superheated steam of heated metal oxides

16. Dave is preparing his pre-lab for next week's lab experiment. In this experiment, he will be heating a mixture of potassium chlorate and manganese dioxide. What would be one of the chief products of this reaction?

  a. potassium permanganate
  ! b. potassium chloride
  c. potassium hypochlorite
  d. manganese chlorate
  e. manganese chloride

17. Professor Morris will be doing a lecture demonstration for his class--the preparation of ozone. Which method will he be most likely to use.

  a. heating O_2 to a high temperature
  b. distilling liquid air
  c. heating chlorate salts
  ! d. passing an electric discharge through O_2
  e. electrolysis of water

18. The oxide ion reacts rapidly with water to form

  a. ozone
  b. oxygen
  ! c. hydroxide ion
  d. peroxide ion
  e. hydrogen peroxide

19. Really heavy water could be prepared if we use the heaviest isotope of oxygen with the non-radioactive heavy isotope of hydrogen. This would be "heavier" than regular water. How many percent heavier would these molecules be?

  a. 10 %
  b. 20 %
  ! c. 22 %
  d. 25 %
  e. 33 %

20. The major use of the oxygen produced by manufacturing processes worldwide is for

    a. waste water treatment
    b. manufacture of hydrogen peroxide
    c. rocket fuel, in the form of liquid oxygen
  ! d. production of steel and other metals
    e. preparation of oxygen based bleaches as an environmentally preferred alternative to to chlorine based bleaches

21. Ozone is a modification of oxygen. It is called

    a. an isotope of oxygen
    b. an isomer of oxygen
  ! c. an allotrope of oxygen
    d. an enantiomer of oxygen
    e. an allomer of oxygen

22. An element which forms more compounds with more elements than any other is

    a. fluorine
    b. chlorine
    c. sodium
  ! d. oxygen
    e. carbon

23. The refractory oxides are binary oxides with elements from

    a. Group IA
  ! b. Group IIA
    c. Group VIA
    d. Group IB
    e. Group VIB

24. An amphoteric oxide is one (in) which

    a. can be employed as either a cathode or an anode
    b. can function as an oxidizing agent or a reducing agent
  ! c. can neutralize either an acid or a base
    d. can exist as more than one isomer
    e. the other element can form more than one compound with oxygen, and these different compounds have the other element in different oxidation states.

25. When a given transition metal forms several oxides having different oxidation states, it is observed that

    a. the higher the oxidation state, the more amphoteric the oxide
    b. the lower the oxidation state, the more amphoteric the oxide
! c. the higher the oxidation state, the more acidic the oxide
    d. the higher the oxidation state, the more basic the oxide
    e. the higher the oxidation state, the more powerful the oxide

26. Which statement about H_2O_2 is definitely not true?

    a. It has a higher boiling point than water.
    b. It has a higher density than water.
    c. It has a higher molecular weight than water.
! d. It has a higher chemical stability than water.
    e. It has a higher basicity than water.

27. Chemically, hydrogen peroxide is well recognized as

    a. a strong reducing agent
! b. a strong oxidizing agent
    c. a strong acid
    d. a strong base
    e. a good coordinating ligand

28. Alkali metals of group IA react with oxygen. Which statement below is true about the reaction?

    a. The metals, M, always react with O_2 to form compounds with the general formula M_2O.
    b. The metals, M, always react with O_2 to form compounds with the general formula MO.
    c. The metals, M, always react with O_2 to form compounds with the general formula MO_2.
    d. The metals, M, react with O_2 to form varied products, depending on the metal, with the generic formulas MO and M_2O.
! e. The metals, M, react with O_2 to form varied products, depending on the metal, with the generic formulas MO, MO_2 and M_2O.

29. Nitrogen gas is an extremely important industrial chemical, and some 30 million tons are produced for use yearly. How is nitrogen for industrial use produced?

    a. electrolysis of concentrated ammonia solution
    b. the reaction, $4LiNH_2 + 4CaO \rightarrow 4LiOH + 4CaH + 2N_2$
! c. reaction of hydrocarbons with ammonia gas
    d. passing ammonia gas over iron shavings at 650 °C
    e. the fractional distillation of liquid air

30. The workers in a custodial services business use commercial strength ammonia solutions as a cleaning agent to clean the floors of residential structures. How is this ammonia manufactured in the first place?

   ! a. reacting H_2 with N_2 in the presence of a catalyst
      b. reduction of NO_2 with sodium or hydrogen peroxide
      c. heating ammonium salts
      d. extraction from ammonium compounds in the soil
      e. treating ammonium salts with strong base

31. Ammonia is a very important derivative compound of nitrogen and, in terms of quantity manufactured, is one of the top 10 industrial chemicals. The major use of ammonia is

      a. manufacture of nitric acid
   ! b. manufacture of chemical fertilizers
      c. manufacture of industrial cleaning chemicals
      d. as a refrigerant in the refrigeration industry
      e. in the manufacture of nylon

32. Sodium amide, a product of the reaction of ammonia with sodium, is used chiefly as a

      a. reducing agent
      b. source of ammonium
      c. cleaning agent
      d. bleach
   ! e. strong base

33. When NH_4Cl is heated above 500 °C it sublimes. The actual products are

      a. $NH_3 + Cl_2$
   ! b. $NH_3 + HCl$
      c. $H_2 + NH_2Cl$
      d. $N_2 + HCl$
      e. $NH_3 + H_2 + Cl_2$

34. Amy just started working for Maids-R-Us. She missed one of the training sessions, the one on safety--mixtures to avoid, so Amy didn't know that a dangerous and toxic substance can be produced when her detergent containing chlorine bleach is mixed with ammonia. This dangerous substance is

      a. NO_2
      b. N_2O
   ! c. N_2H_4
      d. NH_4Cl
      e. NO

35. The oxidation number of nitrogen in ionic metal nitrides is

> ! a. -3
> b. -2
> c. 0
> d. +1
> e. +2

36. The correct name for the compound, NaN_3 is

> a. sodium nitride
> ! b. sodium azide
> c. sodium nitrazide
> d. sodium nitrazine
> e. sodium trinitride

37. The correct name for the compound, Na_3N is

> ! a. sodium nitride
> b. sodium azide
> c. sodium nitrazide
> d. sodium nitrazine
> e. sodium trinitride

38. The XYZ Corporation is going to raze its old abandoned offices to make way for a new building which will accommodate their needs based on their five year plan. Which of the following compounds would the demolition crew be most likely to use in their explosives to implode the old structure and cause it to collapse?

> a. NaN_3
> ! b. $Pb(N_3)_2$
> c. Mg_3N_2
> d. $Na^+NH_2^-$
> e. Na_3N

39. What chemical substance is manufactured using the Ostwald process?

> a. hydrogen peroxide
> b. hydrazine
> c. ammonium nitrate
> ! d. nitric acid
> e. dynamite

40. The person who invented the process for manufacturing dynamite is

      a. Fritz Haber
      b. Wilhelm Ostwald
!   c. Alfred Nobel
      d. Carl Wilhelm Scheele
      e. Antoine Laurent Lavoisier

41. Nitric acid is one of the top 20 chemicals manufactured worldwide. Its principal use is in

      a. the manufacture of nitroglycerin
      b. the manufacture of nitrites for the food industry
      c. the manufacture of gunpowder
      d. the plastics recycling industry
!   e. the manufacture of ammonium nitrate for the fertilizer industry

42. One major difference in properties of hydrochloric acid and those of nitric acid resides in the fact that

      a. $HCl(aq)$ contains a spectator ion while $HNO_3(aq)$ contains no spectator ion.
      b. $HCl(aq)$ is an oxidizing acid while $HNO_3(aq)$ is a non-oxidizing acid.
!   c. $HCl(aq)$ is a non-oxidizing acid while $HNO_3(aq)$ is an oxidizing acid.
      d. $HCl(aq)$ is a halo acid while $HNO_3(aq)$ is an oxo acid.
      e. $HCl(aq)$ does not expand when heated, while $HNO_3(aq)$ expands when heated.

43. Kellie, an undergraduate student, complains to her TA that the brown coloration in the old bottle of concentrated nitric acid means that it is "spoiled". Her teaching assistant explains that the brown coloration in an old bottle of concentrated nitric acid is most likely due to

      a. NO
!   b. NO_2
      c. N_2O
      d. HNO_2
      e. N_2O_5

44. Different oxides of nitrogen in which the oxidation state of the nitrogen is different are known. Which of the following are known (observed) oxidation states for nitrogen oxides?

      a. +1, +3, +4, +5
      b. +2, +4, +5
      c. +1, +3, +5
!   d. +1, +2, +3, +4, +5
      e. +2, +3, +5

45. The nitrogen oxide used as an anesthetic has the formula,

    a. NO
!   b. N_2O
    c. N_2O_3
    d. N_2O_4
    e. N_2O_5

46. The nitrogen compound which is used in airbag devices in the personal automobile industry is

    a. $NaNH_4$
!   b. NaN_3
    c. $NaNO_2$
    d. $NaNH_2$
    e. NH_4OCl

47. Which one of the following compounds contains nitrogen in a positive rather than a negative oxidation state?

    a. $NaNH_2$
    b. NH_3
    c. N_2H_4
    d. NH_2OH
!   e. N_2O

48. Which one of the following is not a form of elemental carbon?

    a. coke
    b. charcoal
    c. graphite
    d. fullerenes
!   e. kevlar

49. A particular water filter manufacturer claims its product will absorb impurities from water. Victor learned from the salesman that the filter contains powdered charcoal. The absorbent properties of this powdered charcoal are due mainly to

    a. chemical reactivity of the charcoal
    b. polar nature of the surface of the charcoal
!   c. the high surface area of the charcoal in this form
    d. the porous structure of the charcoal
    e. the basic (to litmus) properties of the charcoal

50. An oxide of carbon which is used as a fuel in industrial plants is

   ! a. CO
     b. CO_2
     c. C_2O_3
     d. C_2O_4
     e. CO_3^{2-}

51. A combustible fuel mixture used commercially which goes by the name "water gas" is

     a. C*(powder)* + $H_2(g)$
     b. C*(powder)* + $H_2O(g)$
     c. $CO(g)$ + $H_2O(g)$
   ! d. $CO(g)$ + $H_2(g)$
     e. $CO_2(g)$ + $H_2(g)$

52. An important chemical which is used industrially as an inexpensive base is obtained by the thermal decomposition of a carbonate compound or a bicarbonate compound. The chemical is

   ! a. CaO (lime)
     b. $CO(NH_2)_2$ (urea)
     c. $Ca(HCO_3)_2$ (calcium bicarbonate)
     d. $H_2C_2O_4$ (oxalic acid)
     e. $HC_2H_3O_2$ (acetic acid)

53. Which one of the following is *not* one of the major industrial uses of carbon dioxide?

     a. production of carbonated beverages
     b. production of solid refrigerants
     c. production of the gaseous component in fire containment equipment
     d. supercritical extraction of caffeine from coffee, an non-contaminating technique
   ! e. reducing agent in metallurgy of iron

54. Which one of the following is **not** a gas at ordinary temperatures and pressures?

     a. CO
     b. CO_2
     c. HCN
     d. H_2S
   ! e. CS_2

55. Some carbide compounds behave as though they are salts, containing a cation and an anion. Calcium carbide, CaC_2, behaves as though it contains the C_2^{2-} ion, a diatomic species. The Lewis structure for the carbide ion reveals

        a. 1 σ-bond, 1 π-bond and 6 non-bonded valence electrons
        b. 2 σ-bonds, 1 π-bond and 4 non-bonded valence electrons
  ! c. 1 σ-bond, 2 π-bonds and 4 non-bonded valence electrons
        d. 1 σ-bond, 3 π-bonds and 2 non-bonded valence electrons
        e. 1 σ-bond, no π-bonds and 8 non-bonded valence electrons

56. Calcium carbide, CaC_2, behaves as though it contains the C_2^{2-} ion, a diatomic species. The Lewis structure for the carbide ion reveals that it has the same electronic configuration as

        a. the N_2^{2+} ion
        b. the O_2^{2+} ion
        c. the O_2^{2-} ion
        d. the N_2^{2-} ion
  ! e. the N_2 molecule

57. Joe Jackson has been a welder for 15 years, and his son Bill knows a few things about acetylene gas, including where he obtains it. One day at a demonstration lecture in his high school chemistry class Bill was completely amazed when the visiting scientist from the local university generated acetylene gas by mixing some gray rocks with water. What chemical substance was the gray rocks composed of?

        a. calcium carbonate
        b. silicon carbide
  ! c. calcium carbide
        d. magnetite
        e. boron carbide

58. Joe Jackson has been a welder for 15 years, and his son Bill knows a few things about acetylene gas. After doing a demonstration on generating acetylene by mixing water with some gray rocks, the visiting scientist did a second demonstration where he mixed water with some magnesium carbide and generated a combustible gas. Bill didn't think it was acetylene--it didn't smell right and it didn't burn the same way acetylene does. What chemical substance was the gas which is generated from reacting magnesium carbide with water?

        a. hydrogen
        b. carbon monoxide
  ! c. methane
        d. ethylene
        e. propane

59. A covalent network carbide compound which has structural features and a hardness comparable to that of diamond is

       a. boron carbide
       b. calcium carbide
       c. magnesium carbide
  ! d. silicon carbide
       e. antimony carbide

Fill in the Blanks

60. What is the correct name for the compound: BaO_2? _____ (! barium peroxide)

61. In an important intermediate step in the Ostwald process, air is used to convert the $NO(g)$ produced by the catalytic reaction into _____ (! $NO_2(g)$)

62. When considered as a pair of complementary processes, the net effect of the Haber process and the Ostwald processes combined is to convert _____, _____, and _____ into nitric acid. (! natural gas, air, and water)

63. Urea, a very important fertilizer, is made by the reaction of _____ with _____ (! CO_2 with NH_3)

64. Hydrogen cyanide can be readily produced by the reaction of a cyanide salt with _____. (! a strong acid)

True and False

65. Ammonium salts of strong acids, like NH_4Cl, NH_4I and $(NH_4)_2SO_4$ dissolve in water to give solutions which are basic to litmus paper. (! F)

66. The percent of oxygen in the air is slowly decreasing due to the greenhouse effect. (! F)

67. The percent of oxygen in the air is slowly decreasing due to excessive combustion of hydrocarbon fossil fuels. (! F)

68. The physical and chemical properties of O_3 and O_2 are very similar, as might be suspected from their common components. (! F)

69. O_3 is a better reducing agent than O_2. (! F)

70. Ozone is a dangerous component of polluted atmospheres, to the point where it is subject of special and individual attention in weather reporting and forecasting. (! T)

71. All metals which form oxides form oxides which are basic anhydrides. (! F)

72. Transition metal oxides with the metal in a high oxidation states, like CrO_3, Mn_2O_7 and V_2O_5, are acidic oxides rather than basic oxides. (! T)

73. Ammonia solutions are highly ionized to form primarily a mixture of NH_4^+ and OH^-. Very little un-ionized ammonia remains in solution. (! F)

74. An important intermediate step in the Ostwald process is the conversion of NO_2 to NO_3 using the oxygen in the air stream. (! F)

75. Carbon dioxide and carbon disulfide are both stable, non-combustible substances. (! F)

Critical Thinking

76. From the equation for the self ionization of liquid ammonia we deduce several important things when we compare it to the related equation in the water solvent system. From these comparisons, which compound below should be the strongest base than can exist in $NH_3(l)$?

 a. KOH
 b. KCl
 c. NH_4Cl
 ! d. KNH_2
 e. $Ag(NH_3)_2^+$

77. From the equation for the self ionization of liquid ammonia we deduce several important things when we compare it to the related equation in the water solvent system. From these comparisons, which compound below should be the strongest acid than can exist in $NH_3(l)$?

 a. KOH
 b. KCl
 ! c. NH_4Cl
 d. KNH_2
 e. $Ag(NH_3)_2^+$

77. From the equation for the self ionization of liquid $HC_2H_3O_2$ we deduce several important things when we compare it to the related equation in the water solvent system. From these comparisons, which compound below should be the strongest base than can exist in $HC_2H_3O_2(l)$?

 a. KOH
 b. KCl
 ! c. $KC_2H_3O_2$
 d. NH_4Cl
 e. NH_4HSO_4

78. The ionic nitrides which dissolve in liquid ammonia immediately react with that solvent. What equation below describes the true situation? (Observe the notation used for ammonia solutions in contrast to that used for aqueous solutions)

a. N^{3-} *(amm)* + $NH_3(l)$ → $N_2(g)$ + $3H^-$ *(amm)*

! b. N^{3-} *(amm)* + $2 NH_3(l)$ → $3 NH_2^-$ *(amm)*

c. N^{3-} *(amm)* + $2 NH_3(l)$ → NH_4^+ *(amm)* + NH_2^- *(amm)* + $\frac{1}{2} N_2(g)$

d. N^{3-} *(amm)* + $3 NH_3(l)$ → $2 N_2(g)$ + $9 H^+$ *(amm)*

e. N^{3-} *(amm)* + $2 NH_3(l)$ → $3/2 N_2(g)$ + $3 H_2(g)$

Supplementary Chapter 2 Simple Molecules and Ions of Nonmetals: Part II

Multiple Choice

1. Roger, a chemistry student, has just read about another method by which hydrogen sulfide can be produced. It involves the reaction of a metal sulfide. Just for the record, when a metal sulfide is roasted in air, the products are

    a. a metal oxide and hydrogen sulfide
! b. a metal oxide and sulfur dioxide
    c. metal sulfate and hydrogen sulfide
    d. metal sulfite and hydrogen sulfide
    e. metal and sulfur dioxide

2. Some samples taken from sulfur deposits deep in a mine shaft in a sub-Sahara country were analyzed and their isotopic composition was recorded. The data:

isotope	mass, amu	% abundance
^{32}S	31.97207	94.996
^{33}S	32.97146	00.762
^{34}S	33.96786	04.226
^{36}S	35.96709	0.0016

Calculate the average atomic weight of the sulfur from this cave.

    a. 32.062
! b. 32.065
    c. 32.066
    d. 32.892
    e. 33.720

3. Large amounts of sulfuric acid are produced in the United States. The principal use of the sulfuric acid is in

    a. the manufacture of nitric acid
    b. the manufacture of plastics
! c. the manufacture of fertilizers
    d. the manufacture of paper in the paper and pulp industry
    e. the manufacture of steel

4. The bottle filled with chunks of sulfur on the laboratory shelf contains this allotrope of sulfur:

! a. orthorhombic
    b. monoclinic sulfur
    c. β-sulfur
    d. plastic sulfur
    e. red sulfur

5. Sulfuric acid has several properties which gives it an advantage over other strong acids for industrial uses and also for laboratory use. Which one on the following listed set is *not* one of these advantages?

        a. cost
        b. can be prepared readily in nearly pure form (> 98% pure)
        c. is chemically stable, and does not decompose easily
        d. is not volatile, hence doesn't produce corrosive vapors under ordinary handling conditions
!   e. is chemically non-reactive with most metals and hence can be shipped in regular metal containers

6. Yahata Chemicals Ltd., like most of the producers in the chemical industry, uses sulfur dioxide chiefly for production of

        a. sulfur
!   b. sulfuric acid
        c. sodium sulfate
        d. hydrogen sulfide
        e. sodium sulfide

7. Which one of the following is not true about H_2SO_3?

!   a. It forms sulfuric acid upon warming.
        b. It is actually hydrated SO_2.
        c. It produces SO_2 when heated to 150 °C.
        d. It produces sulfite ion when treated with excess strong base.
        e. The actual molecule has never been detected in H_2O.

8. In big cities where acid rain and pollution are problems serious efforts have been made to remove SO_2 from vent gases. Which one of these compounds will do it?

        a. $CaSO_4$
        b. $CaCl_2$
!   c. $Ca(OH)_2$
        d. $NaOH$
        e. Na_2SO_3

9. The local pharmacist has been asked to order sodium bisulfite. However, on his premade order form there is no listing for sodium bisulfite. So he instead circles this equivalent:

        a. sodium sulfite
        b. sodium sulfide
        c. sodium bisulfate
        d. sodium thiosulfate
!   e. sodium metabisulfite

10. Misawa Chemicals Corporation is an industrial giant that uses large quantities of sodium sulfite. For what purpose is most of the sodium sulfite which is produced annually used?

      a. reduction of ores
  ! b. manufacture of paper pulp
      c. manufacture of soap
      d. plastics manufacturing industry
      e. food preparation and preservation industry

11. The oxidation number of sulfur in SO_3 is

      a. 2
      b. 3
      c. 4
  ! d. 6
      e. 8

12. Sulfur trioxide is present in the output stream of waste gases from a certain industrial process. In compliance with certain regulations, sulfur trioxide is being neutralized by reaction with an excess of sodium carbonate. The products are CO_2 and

      a. sodium bicarbonate
      b. sodium bisulfite
      c. sodium bisulfate
      d. sodium hydrogen sulfate
  ! e. sodium sulfate

13. Which of the following is a useful catalyst for facilitating the reaction,
$$SO_2 + O_2 \rightarrow SO_3?$$

      a. iron
      b. platinum
      c. tetraarsenic heptasulfide
      d. bismuth oxides
  ! e. vanadium pentoxide

14. A landscaping and lawn care company advertises that it uses "superphosphate" to fertilize lawns and gardens. Customers might be interested to know that "superphosphate" is made by treating which one of the following substance with sulfuric acid:

  ! a. phosphate rock
      b. gypsum
      c. limestone
      d. bauxite
      e. silicate rock

15. A student in Dr. James' research group ran out of a drying chemical, called drierite, late Friday evening. The research associate in the group suggested they could purchase some Epsom salts at the pharmacy section of the local drug store and use that. What is this chemical name of this substance that can substitute so readily for drierite?

      a. hydrated lime
      b. sodium bicarbonate
!   c. hydrated magnesium sulfate
      d. hydrated phosphate of lime
      e. sodium carbonate decahydrate

16. When the drying chemical, drierite, is exhausted it can be regenerated by

      a. treating it with a dehydrating agent like sulfuric acid
!   b. heating it for a prolonged time at temperatures above 500 °C
      c. pumping out the compound using a very good vacuum pump
      d. drying it out in direct sunlight at temperatures above 70 °C
      e. actually, drierite cannot be regenerated

17. In the fiber and fabric industry, which one of the following compounds can be used to remove excess chlorine from bleached fabric?

      a. sodium nitrate
      b. sodium sulfate
      c. sodium bisulfate
!   d. sodium thiosulfate
      e. sodium carbonate

18. The photographic process uses a chemical, known as "hypo", to remove unexposed silver halide from the film. The chemical name for "hypo" is

      a. sodium sulfite
      b. sodium sulfate
!   c. sodium thiosulfate
      d. sodium hyposulfite
      e. sodium thiosulfite

19. Though H_2S is used in general chemistry laboratory as an analytical reagent, handling large quantities of this substance is undesirable. H_2S can be and is preferably generated in the reaction solution mixture by using

      a. sodium sulfide
!   b. thioacetamide
      c. disulfur dichloride
      d. ammonium thiosulfate
      e. sodium persulfide

20. When phosphorus was first discovered, its discoverer obtained it by distilling residues obtained from

     a. milk
! b. urine
     c. wine barrel sediments
     d. cow manure
     e. wood shavings

21. The known allotropes of phosphorus are

     a. P_2 and P_4
     b. monoclinic phosphorus and orthorhombic phosphorus
     c. white phosphorus and gray phosphorus
! d. white phosphorus and red amorphous phosphorus
     e. triclinic phosphorus and monoclinic phosphorus

22. Elemental phosphorous is manufactured on an industrial scale by reducing calcium phosphate with

! a. carbon
     b. iron
     c. zinc
     d. hydrogen
     e. superheated steam

23. Phosphine, the phosphorus analog of ammonia, can be prepared easily by the reaction of

     a. $H_3PO_4 + H_2$
     b. $H_3PO_3 + H_2$
     c. $Na_3PO_4 + H_2$
! d. $Ca_3P_2 + H_2O$
     e. $NaN_3 + H_3PO_3$

24. The reaction of P_4O_{10}, an oxide of phosphorus, with water produces,

     a. H_3PO_4 only
     b. HPO_3 only
     c. H_3PO_4 and HPO_3
     d. H_3PO_4 and $H_4P_2O_7$
! e. H_3PO_4, HPO_3 and $H_4P_2O_7$

25. $H_4P_2O_7$ is named

     a. tetraphosphoric acid
     b. metaphosphoric acid
     c. orthophosphoric acid
! d. pyrophosphoric acid
     e. paraphosphoric acid

26. A student carrying a bottle of $PCl_5(s)$ to her lab from the stockroom dropped it in the hallway. The shattered contents started to give off smoky fumes with an acrid odor, so the Hazmat Team was quickly called in. What chemical substance was responsible for the fumes?

     a. $PCl_5(g)$
     b. $PCl_3(g)$
     c. $H_2PtCl_4(g)$
     d. $H_3PO_4(s)$
 ! e. $HCl(g)$

27. The formula for hypophosphoric acid is H_3PO_2. Hypophosphoric acid is now known to be

 ! a. a monoprotic acid
     b. a diprotic acid
     c. a triprotic acid
     d. an amphoteric substance
     e. a substance which actually does not exhibit acid properties($K_a < 10^{-10}$).

28. Phosphate anions can form species which can be thought of as being dimers and trimers--precursors to polymers. These larger anions contain

     a. P—P—P—P ... chains
 ! b. P—O—P—O—P—O—P—O ... chains
     c. P—P—O—P—P—O—P—P—O ... chains
     d. P—H—P—H—P—H—P—H ... chains
     e. P—H—O—P—H—O—P—H—O ... chains

29. Which one of the compounds listed below, as the product of an acid base neutralization, is actually a fictitious compound because the anion the formula describes within is fictitious, or incorrect?

     a. Na_3PO_4
     b. Na_2HPO_4
 ! c. Na_3PO_3
     d. Na_2HPO_3
     e. NaH_2PO_3

30. Gallium arsenide is an important arsenic compound and is used in

 ! a. light emitting diodes
     b. bone structure replacement
     c. cardiac pacemakers
     d. 10-year batteries in implanted devices
     e. food preservatives

31. Phosphorus acid, H_3PO_3 is

    a. a monoprotic acid
    ! b. a diprotic acid
    c. a triprotic acid
    d. an amphoteric substance
    e. a substance which actually does not exhibit acid properties($K_a < 10^{-12}$).

32. Which one of the oxides of Group V, shown below, is amphoteric?

    a. N_2O_5
    ! b. Bi_4O_6
    c. P_4O_6
    d. As_4O_6
    e. Sb_4O_6

33. In its normal physical state, fluorine is

    a. a green liquid
    b. a colorless liquid
    c. a pale green gas
    ! d. a pale yellow gas
    e. a colorless gas

34. Which one of the following materials is unsuitable for containers to be used for shipping liquid hydrogen fluoride?

    a. alloy steel
    b. wax lined metal containers
    c. polyethylene
    d. teflon (polyperfluoroethylene)
    ! e. glass

35. Fluorine can be manufactured from fluorine containing compounds on a commercial scale by

    a. oxidation using atomic oxygen
    b. oxidation using ozone at high pressures
    ! c. electrolytic reduction of fused fluorine compounds
    d. electrolytic reduction of aqueous solutions of fluorine compounds
    e. treatment of fluoride salts, like NaF or KF, with chlorine gas at high temperatures

36. Fluoride ions are added to drinking water to provide a source of fluorine to (for)

    a. control of bacterial organisms in drinking water
    b. favor enhanced production of disease resistant antibodies in mammalian blood
    ! c. development of an acid resistant modification of tooth enamel
    d. development of a fluoride coating in the mouth which poisons bacteria
    e. neutralization of acids produced in the mouth by bacterial metabolism

434

37. Even though hydrofluoric acid is a monoprotic acid it forms an ion named the bifluoride ion. The formula for the bifluoride ion is

! a. HF_2^-
b. H_2F^+
c. HFO^{2-}
d. H_2FO^-
e. $H_2F_2O^-$

38. In its normal physical state, chlorine is

a. a green liquid
b. a colorless liquid
! c. a pale green gas
d. a pale yellow gas
e. a colorless gas

39. The physical appearance of the element bromine at ordinary temperatures and pressures is

a. a pale green gas
b. a pale yellow liquid
c. a deep green liquid
d. a deep purple liquid
! e. a deep red liquid

40. The major use of the chlorine manufactured in the United States is for

a. manufacture of chlorine bleaches
b. manufacture of perchloric acid and hydrogen chloride and hydrochloric acid
! c. manufacture of organochlorine products like PVC (polyvinyl chloride) plastics
d. disinfection of municipal water supplies
e. manufacture of steel

41. Hydrochloric acid is a major strong inorganic acid. It is primarily used in industry for

a. preparation of AgCl for photographic film
b. production of hydrogen by reaction with zinc metal
! c. removal of oxide films from metals in metallurgy and related industries
d. neutralization of alkaline wastes in water treatment plants
e. chlorination of water to remove harmful organisms

42. All of the following are known oxyacids of chlorine, except

a. $HClO_4$
b. $HClO_2$
c. $HClO$
! d. $H_2Cl_2O_9$
e. $HClO_3$

43. Chlorine, one of the top 10 manufactured chemicals in the United States in terms of quantity, is produced industrially primarily by

    a. electrolysis of fused NaCl
! b. electrolysis of brine (aqueous NaCl)
    c. thermal decomposition of sodium hypochlorite (NaOCl)
    d. oxidation of saline solutions by ozone
    e. oxidation of saline solutions by charcoal-activated oxygen

44. Hydrogen chloride is produced commercially by a variety of methods. Which scheme shown below is **not** a method by which hydrogen chloride is produced commercially?

    a. direct union of the elements, $H_2(g) + Cl_2(g) \longrightarrow 2 HCl(g)$
    b. metathesis, $NaCl(s) + H_2SO_4(l) \xrightarrow{heat} HCl(g) + NaHSO_4(s)$
    c. by product of organic reaction, $Cl_2(g) + RH \longrightarrow RCl + HCl(g)$
! d. displacement reaction, $HBr(g) + Cl_2(g) \longrightarrow HCl(g) + BrCl(g)$
    e. preparation of vinyl chloride for polyvinyl chloride plastics using the reaction,
$$H_2C{=}CH_2 + Cl_2(g) \longrightarrow HCl(g) + H_2C{=}CH{-}Cl$$

45. Bromine is manufactured in industry by which one of the following procedures?

    a. oxidation of NaBr with ozone
    b. oxidation of HBr with oxygen ($2HBr + \frac{1}{2} O_2 \rightarrow H_2O + Br_2$)
    c. reaction of bromide salts with nitric acid
! d. reaction of bromide containing brines with chlorine gas
    e. reaction of bromide containing brines with fluorine gas

46. Periodic acid comes in several modifications, whose common relation can be verified by checking the oxidation number of the iodine. Which one of the following is **not** a modification of periodic acid?

! a. $H_4I_2O_7$
    b. HIO_4
    c. $H_4I_2O_9$
    d. H_5IO_6
    e. H_3IO_5

47. Which one of the following sets does **not** list the species in the correct order for the property listed immediately before it?

    a. acid strength: $HF(aq) < HCl(aq) < HBr(aq) < HI(aq)$
    b. ionic radius: $F^- < Cl^- < Br^- < I^-$
! c. difficulty of oxidation: $F^- < Cl^- < Br^- < I^-$
    d. enthalpy of hydration: $F^- < Cl^- < Br^- < I^-$
    e. ease of reduction: $F_2 < Cl_2 < Br_2 < I_2$

48. Helium has some remarkable or outstanding properties. Which one of the following is **not** one of these remarkable properties?

    a. becomes a superfluid (loses all viscosity) at very low temperatures
    b. has lowest boiling point of any known substance
    c. cannot be changed to a solid at atmospheric pressure (no solid state exists at 1 atmosphere pressure at *any* temperature)
    d. has no triple point on its phase diagram
  ! e. becomes a superconductor at a few hundredths of a degree above absolute zero

49. Which set below from among the "noble gases" actually do form compounds?

    a. He Ne Ar
    b. He Ne Ar Kr
    c. Ne Ar Kr Xe
    d. Ar Kr Xe
  ! e. Kr Xe

50. The first compound of a "noble gas" ever synthesized was a compound of which element?

    a. He
    b. Ne
    c. Ar
    d. Kr
  ! e. Xe

Fill in the Blanks

51. The most common mineral family containing phosphorus is the _____ family of minerals.
(! calcium phosphate, or apatite)

True and False

52. Sulfur occurs in nature both in the free state (elemental sulfur) as well as in compounds. (! T)

53. Natural gas wells contain considerable quantities of SO_2 in addition to methane and helium.
(! F)

54. Even though the chemical behavior of the various isotopes of sulfur is the same, some bacteria which degrade sulfur containing compounds seem to have a slight preference for the molecules with a particular isotope of sulfur. (! T)

55. "Superphosphate of lime" is the name listed on a bag of chemical fertilizer. Does this mean the phosphate content is higher than that of ordinary phosphates? _____ (! No)

56. The final step in the manufacture of sulfuric acid is the reaction,
$$SO_3(g) + H_2O(l) \rightarrow H_2SO_4(l)$$
which is carried out using vanadium(V) oxide as a catalyst. (! F)

57. To dry a precipitate separated by filtration at room temperature in a desiccator a chemist might use P_4O_{10}. When this substance reacts with the water vapor distilling off the precipitate to saturate the air space in the desiccator, the product is $H_4P_2O_7$. (! T)

58. The acidity of the oxides of the elements of group V increase as we proceed from N_2O_5 down to Bi_4O_{10}. (! F)

59. Fluorine is so reactive that is *never* found in the free state (F_2) in nature. (! T)

Critical Thinking

The data presented here applies to questions 60 to 64 immediately below. The symbols A, B, C, and D represent the first four halogen elements. The series of reactions presented always proceed in the forward direction.
$$A_2(unk) + 2C^-(aq) \rightarrow C_2(unk) + 2A^-(aq)$$
$$B_2(unk) + 2D^-(aq) \rightarrow D_2(unk) + 2B^-(aq)$$
$$B_2(unk) + 2C^-(aq) \rightarrow C_2(unk) + 2B^-(aq)$$
$$D_2(unk) + 2C^-(aq) \rightarrow C_2(unk) + 2D^-(aq)$$

60. Will A_2 oxidize D^- to produce D_2? (! There is insufficient information presented to determine this)

61. Which one of the species is fluorine?

    a. A
    b. B
    c. C
    d. D
  ! e. There is insufficient information presented to determine this.

62. Which one of the species is bromine?

    a. A
    b. B
    c. C
    d. D
  ! e. There is insufficient information presented to determine this.

63. The physical state at ordinary temperatures and pressures of the species described as C_2 in the data above is _____. (! solid)

64. The physical state at ordinary temperatures and pressures of the species described as B_2 in the data above is _____. (! gas, because it is either fluorine or chlorine)

Special Topic 2.1 Working with Concentrated Sulfuric Acid

65. When concentrated sulfuric acid is added to an equal volume of water, one immediate result is

! a. an extreme amount of heat is generated
b. the temperature of the solution falls
c. a solid is formed which slowly dissolves
d. sulfur dioxide gas is produced
e. the water reduces the sulfuric acid to H_2S gas

66. In terms of quantity by mass produced for manufacturing and other uses, the largest volume industrial chemical in the United States is

a. ammonia
b. nitric acid
c. sodium carbonate
d. chlorine
! e. sulfuric acid

Supplementary Chapter 3 The Properties and Chemistry of Metals

Multiple Choice

1. The first step of the process by which magnesium is obtained from magnesium compounds which are dissolved in sea water is by treatment of the water with

    a. ammonia solution
    ! b. lime
    c. potassium hydroxide
    d. sodium carbonate
    e. sodium hydroxide

2. The first chemical step in the treatment of sulfide compounds of metal which are found in ores is called

    a. electrolyzing
    b. liming
    c. milling
    d. reducing
    ! e. roasting

3. Iron ore is reduced to iron by reaction with

    a. calcium carbonate
    ! b. carbon
    c. carbon monoxide
    d. carbon dioxide
    e. sulfur dioxide

4. Which one of the following techniques or chemical substances is not commonly used to reduce metal oxides to metals?

    a. carbon
    b. carbon monoxide
    c. electrolysis
    d. H_2 gas
    ! e. S

5. In the blast furnace silica, an objectionable impurity, is removed as

    a. iron silicate
    b. silicon
    c. silicon dioxide
    ! d. slag, formed by reaction of silica (acidic oxide) with lime (basic oxide)
    e. sodium silicate

6. Commercially, aluminum is obtained from the purified aluminum oxide (after pretreatment) by

    a. electrolysis of aqueous $Al_2(SO_4)_3$
    b. electrolysis of aqueous $KAl(SO_4)_2$
!   c. electrolysis of a fused mixture of Al_2O_3 and Na_3AlF_6(cryolite)
    d. reduction with coke at high temperatures
    e. reduction with sodium metal

7. Copper is usually refined by

    a. distillation
!   b. electrolysis
    c. lithification
    d. the oxygen lance
    e. smelting

8. Where are alkali elements and their compounds found in nature?

    a. primarily in caves
    b. primarily in clay soils
    c. primarily in closed lakes which have no outlet
    d. primarily in soils from desert regions
!   e. primarily in sea water

9. Which alkali element is very important in biochemical systems of plants?

    a. Cs
!   b. K
    c. Li
    d. Na
    e. Rb

10. The element below having the lowest melting point, consistent with the group periodic properties?

    a. Al
    b. Ca
    c. Cr
    d. Fe
!   e. K

11. Sodium metal is prepared commercially by

    a. electrolysis of aqueous sodium chloride
!   b. electrolysis of fused sodium chloride
    c. reduction of sodium carbonate by lime at 600 °C
    d. reduction of sodium carbonate by carbon at 2000 °C
    e. reduction of sodium oxide by carbon at 2000 °C

12. Lithium metal is prepared commercially by

    a. electrolysis of aqueous lithium chloride
    ! b. electrolysis of fused lithium chloride
    c. reduction of lithium chloride by boron at 2000 °C
    d. reduction of lithium carbonate by carbon at 2000 °C
    e. reduction of lithium oxide by carbon at 2000 °C

13. K, Cs and Rb are often obtained from their compounds by the same general method, which is

    a. a displacement reaction using elemental sodium
    b. a reduction using the reaction of hot coke with the metal carbonate
    c. a reduction using the reaction of finely powdered aluminum with the metal carbonate
    d. electrolysis of an aqueous solution of a soluble salt of the metal
    ! e. electrolysis of the fused chloride salt of the metal

14. Which one of the alkali metals will "burn" in a nitrogen atmosphere as it combines with the nitrogen exothermically?

    a. Cs
    b. K
    ! c. Li
    d. Na
    e. Rb

15. Sodium hydroxide is a very important commercial chemical, ranking in the top 10 in quantity manufactured annually. Sodium hydroxide is produced commercially by

    ! a. electrolysis of an unstirred solution of brine (aqueous sodium chloride)
    b. electrolysis of molten sodium chloride
    c. heating sodium carbonate above 1500 °C to decompose it and yield an intermediate which is converted to sodium hydroxide by the action of water
    d. reaction of sodium metal with water
    e. reaction of sodium oxide with water

16. Sodium carbonate is an important chemical in the chemical industry. Which statement below about sodium carbonate is *not* true?

    a. Sodium carbonate can be manufactured by a process known as the Solvay process.
    b. Sodium carbonate can be obtained directly from a mineral called trona.
    ! c. Sodium carbonate can be obtained by heating a mix of limestone and sodium chloride.
    d. Sodium carbonate is an important industrial base (in the acid-base sense).
    e. A form of sodium carbonate was widely utilized and is still known as "washing soda".

17. Alkali metal salts impart color to flames when they are strongly heated in an open non-luminous flame. The color produced by sodium salts is

     a. blue
     b. green
     c. orange
     d. red
 ! e. yellow

18. Alkali metal salts impart color to flames when they are strongly heated in an open non-luminous flame. The color produced by lithium salts is

     a. blue
     b. green
     c. orange
 ! d. red
     e. yellow

19. Which one of the alkali metals is known for its ability to form *covalent* organometallic compounds with hydrocarbon alkyl groups?

     a. Cs
     b. K
 ! c. Li
     d. Na
     e. Rb

20. Even though the more active metals are expected to react with water, some of them in fact are not attacked by cold water even though hot water or steam react with all of them rapidly. Which one of these active metals listed below displays this property?

     a. Ba
     b. Ca
     c. K
 ! d. Mg
     e. Na

21. Which Group IIA element forms oxides which are amphoteric in behavior?

     a. Ba
 ! b. Be
     c. Ca
     d. Mg
     e. Sr

22. The most industrially important calcium compound is

    a. calcium bicarbonate
    b. calcium carbonate (also occurs in limestone)
    c. calcium chloride
 ! d. calcium oxide (known as lime)
    e. calcium sulfate (also occurs in gypsum)

23. An important aluminum compound which is the matrix for several types of gemstones is

 ! a. α-Al_2O_3
    b. γ-Al_2O_3
    c. $Al_2(SO_4)_3$
    d. $Al(OH)_3$
    e. $KAl(SO_4)_2 \cdot 12H_2O$

24. An important use of $Al_2(SO_3)_3 \cdot 18H_2O$, also known as alum, is

    a. as an abrasive in "sandpaper"
    b. in cosmetics
    c. as a gemstone matrix
    d. reaction with coke to produce aluminum metal
 ! e. in municipal and other water treatment plants

25. Chrome yellow, a pigment formerly used in paints, is

    a. As_2S_3
    b. CdS
    c. Na_2CrO_4
 ! d. $PbCrO_4$
    e. PbS

26. The most abundant metallic element in the earth's crust is

 ! a. aluminum
    b. iron
    c. potassium
    d. silicon
    e. sodium

27. Which one of the oxides below is not amphoteric?

    a. Al_2O_3
 ! b. Fe_2O_3
    c. PbO
    d. SnO
    e. ZnO

444

28. A *metallic* element used in the free (elemental) state in preparation of solid propellants for the large vehicles used in the space program in the United States is

 ! a. aluminum
   b. cadmium
   c. lithium
   d. potassium
   e. sodium

29. A major component of many gemstones is

 ! a. Al_2O_3
   b. $CaSiO_3$
   c. K_2CrO_4
   d. $NaAl(SO_4)_2·12H_2O$
   e. $ZnCO_3$

30. Which type of substance would be most strongly attracted by a magnetic field?

 ! a. a solid ferromagnetic metal or alloy
   b. a solid paramagnetic metal or alloy
   c. a solid diamagnetic metal or alloy
   d. a molten ferromagnetic metal or alloy
   e. a molten paramagnetic metal or alloy

31. Which type of substance would be least strongly attracted by a magnetic field?

   a. a solid ferromagnetic metal or alloy
   b. a solid paramagnetic metal or alloy
 ! c. a solid diamagnetic metal or alloy
   d. a molten ferromagnetic metal or alloy
   e. a molten paramagnetic metal or alloy

32. The principal use for vanadium is

   a. as a catalyst in the oxidation of SO_2 to SO_3 in the manufacture of sulfuric acid
 ! b. manufacture of special steel alloys and cast iron
   c. in paint pigments, because it forms intensely colored chemically stable compounds
   d. in corrosion resistant coatings for metals used in construction of bridges over salt water
   e. as a component of material for special non-sparking hammers which can be safely used in construction in areas with combustible gases.

33. All of the following are industrial uses to which chromium is put except

    a. preparation of decorative or protective coatings on metals, usually deposited on the surfaces by electrolysis
    b. as a component in stainless steel alloys
    c. in heater elements for toasters, irons and such
    d. in paint pigments which contain chromate ion and other chromium ions
    ! e. water treatment chemicals

34. Vanadium forms an oxycation, which is very uncommon for elements in that region of the periodic table. The oxidation state of vanadium in the vanadyl cation is

    a. +2
    b. +3
    c. +4
    ! d. +5
    e. +6

35. The chemical reaction,
$$3 \, MnO_4^{2+}(aq) + 4 \, H^+(aq) \rightarrow 2 \, MnO_4^-(aq) + MnO_2(s) + 2 \, H_2O$$
is an example of

    a. acid base neutralization
    ! b. disproportionation
    c. double displacement
    d. protonation
    e. single displacement

36. Which statement below about iron and its compounds is *not* true?

    a. FeO is a known oxide of iron.
    b. Fe_2O_3 is a known oxide of iron.
    c. Fe_3O_4 is a known oxide of iron.
    d. Solutions of Fe^{3+} salts are acidic due to cation hydrolysis.
    ! e. Compounds with iron in the +5 oxidation are very important in chemistry of iron.

37. Nickel is a versatile and useful metal. Which one of the following is *not* true about nickel?

    a. It is used in anti-corrosion coatings.
    b. It is used in manufacture of high impact steel.
    c. It is used in manufacture of stainless steel.
    d. It is used in manufacture of monel metal, a corrosion resistant alloy with very high strength.
    ! e. It is the second most abundant metallic element in the earth's crust.

38. Which one of the following metals will *not* react with and dissolve in non-oxidizing acids?

      a. Co
!   b. Cu
      c. Fe
      d. Mn
      e. Ni

39. Which one of the following elements has been found existing in natural sources in the free (elemental) state?

      a. Co
      b. Cr
!   c. Cu
      d. Fe
      e. Ni

40. Even though they are transition elements, some oxidation states are very rare if existent at all. Which one of the following a either a very uncommon or a non existent oxidation state?

!   a. Au(II)
      b. Co(II)
      c. Cu(II)
      d. Fe(II)
      e. Ni(II)

41. Which metallic element has the highest thermal and electrical conductivity of all known metallic elements?

      a. copper
      b. gold
      c. iron
      d. nickel
!   e. silver

42. Which group of elements is most resistant to chemical acids, as a group?

      a. the Ca - Ba - Sr group
      b. the Cr - Mo - W group
!   c. the Cu - Ag - Au group
      d. the Fe - Ru - Os group
      e. the Zn - Cd - Hg group

43. Which group of elements is least resistant to chemical acids, as a group?

    ! a. the Ca - Ba - Sr group
       b. the Cr - Mo - W group
       c. the Cu - Ag - Au group
       d. the Fe - Ru - Os group
       e. the Zn - Cd - Hg group

44. Which reagent below does *not* react with metallic copper to any significant extent?

       a. cold dilute (1M) nitric acid
       b. hot dilute (6M) nitric acid
       c. hot concentrated (15M) nitric acid
    ! d. cold dilute (6M) sulfuric acid
       e. hot concentrated (18M) sulfuric acid

45. Which reagent below does *not* react with metallic copper to any significant extent?

       a. cold dilute (1M) nitric acid
       b. hot dilute (6M) nitric acid
       c. hot concentrated (15M) nitric acid
    ! d. hot concentrated (12M) hydrochloric acid
       e. hot concentrated (18M) sulfuric acid

46. Which one of the following reagents will react with metallic silver?

    ! a. cold dilute (3M) nitric acid
       b. cold dilute (3M) acetic acid
       c. cold dilute (3M) hydrochloric acid
       d. cold dilute (3M) sulfuric acid
       e. cold dilute (3M) ammonia

47. A metal which dissolves in 3M HCl(aq), 3M H$_2$SO$_4$(aq), 3M HNO$_3$(aq), and 3M NaOH(aq) is

       a. Cd
       b. Co
       c. Fe
       d. Hg
    ! e. Zn

48. A metal which dissolves in 3M HCl(aq), 3M H$_2$SO$_4$(aq), 3M HNO$_3$(aq), and 3M NaOH(aq) is

    ! a. Al
       b. Ag
       c. Cd
       d. Co
       e. Fe

49. A metal oxide which, in a finely divided state, will *not* dissolve in 3M HCl(*aq*), 3M H$_2$SO$_4$(*aq*), 3M HNO$_3$(*aq*), or 3M NaOH(*aq*) is

      a. aluminum oxide
! b. iron (III) oxide
      c. lead (II) oxide
      d. tin (II) oxide
      e. zinc oxide

50. All these elements or their compounds are used in the manufacture of commercial electrical batteries except

      a. Ag
! b. Cr
      c. Hg
      d. Ni
      e. Zn

51. All these elements or their compounds are used in the manufacture of commercial electrical batteries except

      a. Cd
      b. Hg
      c. Mn
      d. Pb
! e. Sn

52. Which element below is not attacked by (does not react with) any of the following reagents:
6M HNO$_3$ 15M (conc) HNO$_3$ 18M (conc) H$_2$SO$_4$ 12M (conc) HCl   6M HF

      a. cadmium
! b. gold
      c. iron
      d. mercury
      e. silver

53. An element used in the preparation of galvanized steel or iron is

      a. Cd
      b. Cr
      c. Co
      d. Ni
! e. Zn

54. A metal with a property such that structures made of this metal crumble and disintegrate when temperatures hover around 0 °C for extended periods (weeks and months).

      a. aluminum
      b. copper
      c. lead
  ! d. tin
      e. zinc

Fill in the Blanks

55. The rock, sand, and other unwanted material present in an ore when it is mined are collectively referred to as _____ (! gangue)

56. The thermite process involves the reaction of iron(III) oxide with _____ (! aluminum)

57. A compound of barium which can be safely ingested (and excreted), leading to its use in internal medicine even though soluble barium is a toxic element _____ (! barium sulfate)

58. An alloy with a very low melting point which is used in the switching element in sprinkler systems is _____ (! Wood's metal)

59. A qualitative test for the presence of Fe^{3+} ions in solution (which is sensitive enough for use in water quality testing) is the reaction of the Fe^{3+} ions with the _____ ion. (! SCN$^-$)

True and False

60. Beryllium, though it is in Group II of the periodic table, is different in many ways from the remaining members of the group. (! T)

61. $SnCl_4$ has a melting point of -33 °C and a boiling point of 114 °C. These suggest that $SnCl_4$ is a covalent compound with discrete molecules and just average intermolecular forces. (! T)

62. Even though atomic radii tend to show a regular increase within a group or family as the atomic number increases, post lanthanide elements do not appear to follow this pattern closely. (! T)

63. The ability to display several different oxidation states is much more pronounced among metallic members of transition elements than among non-transition metals. (! T)

64. The most common oxidation states of chromium in its compounds are the +2, +4, and +5 states. (! F)

Critical Thinking

65. Which one of the following compounds does *not* belong to the class of compounds called "alums"?

      a. $NaAl(SO_4)_2 \cdot 12H_2O$
      b. $KCr(SO_4)_2 \cdot 12H_2O$
      c. $NH_4Fe(SO_4)_2 \cdot 12H_2O$
      d. $KV(SO_4)_2 \cdot 12H_2O$
 ! e. $NH_4Zn(SO_4)_2 \cdot 12H_2O$

66. Which one of the following is not a property of some post lanthanide transition metals which is linked to the "lanthanide contraction"?

      a. high mass density of the neutral element in the solid state
      b. high resistance to oxidation of the neutral element
      c. comparative chemical inertness
      d. higher than expected ionization energies
 ! e. formation of oxides which are much more stable than those in the previous row

NOTES

NOTES

NOTES

NOTES

NOTES

NOTES

NOTES